W9-BTI-693

THE USE OF MATHEMATICS IN ECONOMICS

The use of MATHEMATICS IN ECONOMICS

RUSSIAN EDITION EDITED BY

V. S. NEMCHINOV

CONTRIBUTORS

O. LANGE A. L. LUR'E

L. V. KANTOROVICH

V. S. NEMCHINOV

V. V. NOVOZHILOV

ENGLISH EDITION EDITED BY

A. NOVE

OLIVER & BOYD

EDINBURGH & LONDON

OLIVER AND BOYD LTD

Tweeddale Court
Edinburgh 1

39a Welbeck Street
London W.1

First English Edition .. 1964

Printed in Great Britain by
ROBERT CUNNINGHAM & SONS LTD, ALVA

Contents

Introduction

A. Nove

This volume was published in Moscow in 1959, and has since been followed by another on the same theme. At the time of its original publication it represented or symbolised an important turning-point in Soviet economic thought. To appreciate its significance it is therefore necessary to refer briefly to the development of Soviet economics in the last two decades.

In the Stalin period, economics in the USSR suffered greatly from the prevailing atmosphere. Because economic policy was an integral part of politics, and economic theory was closely bound up with the fundamentals of Marxist-Leninist ideology, it was very difficult indeed to express original views on economics while Stalin was alive. It is true that original thinking did not cease. The fact that both Kantorovich and Novozhilov developed under Stalin the ideas which they elaborate in the present volume, and were able to publish some of them, proves that Stalin's long reign was not a complete intellectual desert, even for economists. However, Kantorovich's pioneering work in the field of linear programming, published as early as 1939, was ignored by Soviet economists and planners, and Novozhilov's arguments, published in 1946, met with a hostile reception from orthodox critics.

Soviet planners struggled with the tasks of producing and distributing goods, of co-ordinating the operations of industries and enterprises and of devising patterns of investment; but they had virtually no theory to guide them; and no theory of planning emerged from their activities. Investment and production decisions were based very largely on a system of 'material balances'. Thus it was known from experience that a ton of steel required given quantities of iron ore, coking coal and other inputs. If the required inputs were available, or could be produced by existing capacity, appropriate allocation decisions were taken by the planning organs; otherwise, investment decisions were taken so that the required inputs would be available when needed. Since new capacity could be of several different kinds, choices had to be made between investment variants, and some theoretical discussion on this topic did develop while Stalin was still alive, but this was unsatisfactory and inconclusive.

Yet Soviet theory and practice could have drawn upon two relevant sets of experience. The first was wholly Russian: in the 'twenties, when planning was still in an experimental stage, much work was done on devising 'balances of the national economy'; this was interrupted by the elimination, during the 'thirties, of most of the economists concerned. The second was Leontief's input-output technique, which may have been inspired by his own Russian upbringing (he was a student at Leningrad in the early 'twenties), and which provided the planners with valuable mathematical tools if they would consider using them. None of this was done until well after Stalin's death. One reason was that both sources were 'tainted'; Leontief's ideas were 'bourgeois'; and this, at a time when Stalin's policies were to cut Russia off from foreign influences, put them out of court.

There were other reasons too. One, never formulated as such in Russia itself, was that strictly economic criteria have only very limited application in the midst of crash programmes designed to build up heavy industry in the shortest possible time. This type of operation, carried out by methods reminiscent of a war economy, is genuinely hard to reconcile with an economic theory in which choices are related to economic effectiveness, and particularly so because the typical administrative arrangements of a war economy —allocation of materials, priorities, strict price controls and so on—distort the measurement of economic advantage and of costs of alternatives. This is, of course, not a defence of irrationality; no doubt much avoidable inefficiency existed, and still exists, in the USSR. The point is rather that arguments for subordinating arbitrariness to economic criteria obtain a better hearing when the period of crash-programme industrialisation passes and the problems of normal functioning of a largely modernised economy loom larger. No doubt this, and not only Stalin's death, explains the recent resurgence of Soviet economic thought.

Another reason still survives, still acts as an obstacle to the modernisation of Soviet economics. This is the particular form in which Marxian theory was adopted, or adapted, in the USSR. One should not assume, as some western critics do, that Marxian economics is inherently inconsistent with reality, that the 'vulgar-Marxist' simplifications of the late-Stalin period are the essence of the theory. Novozhilov, for instance, would certainly argue that his theories are consistent with Marxism; are indeed the correct application of Marxian theory to the circumstances of the Soviet Union. But certain Marxian propositions did help to block progress. Many of the arguments of Novozhilov and his colleagues in the present book are designed to overcome or circumvent objections based upon what they regard as a misunderstanding or misapplication of Marxism. There is indeed in Marxism a 'traditional' dislike for anything connected with marginalism, or diminishing returns, or a value theory which stresses subjective valuations as distinct from the labour content of the goods in question. Value was taken to be equal to the average amount of socially necessary labour devoted to production; and, despite the chance of so interpreting the words 'socially necessary' as to admit degrees of utility, the official theorists virtually ignored the relative degree to which labour devoted to this or that sphere actually satisfied the wants of individuals or of society. Nor did the concept of scarcity enter into their pattern of thinking, save in the administrative-planning sense familiar in our war-time economics, the sense rendered by the phrase 'in short supply'. Consequently the official theorists could not use the concept of opportunity cost, the idea that the use of labour or other scarce factors for one purpose involves forgoing their use for another. This idea, which is elementary to a western economist, is central to Novozhilov's (and others') position, but it has to be argued in a rather circuitous way, and this explains why Novozhilov spends so many pages and devises clumsy-looking concepts ('feedback costs'—*zatraty obratnoi svyazi*—and so on) to put an argument which a western economist could explain to an average student much more simply and shortly. Novozhilov also uses a Russian word for scarcity (*defitsitnost*) which could stand both for the *relative* scarcity familiar to the western economist and for the physical-shortage sense familiar to the planner. The ambiguity is, we may be sure, deliberate, and is part of the process of gradually persuading the more orthodox economists to look reality in the face.

For quite plainly opportunity cost is a reality in the USSR as elsewhere. It does indeed matter whether a given expenditure of labour (or of any other reproducible factor, which can be expressed as labour, present or past, to conform to Marxian principles) satisfies needs at minimum real cost. And it is a fact that mathematical techniques do, of their nature, involve a kind of marginalism, and are inconsistent with valuations based on the average labour content of this or that product. Unless these things are taken into account, the economic policies of the Soviet government cannot be effectively carried out. Therefore, the 'new wave' of Soviet economists can, and do, regard themselves as men desirous of making the system work better.

The practice of Soviet pricing has had little in common with orthodox or any other theory. Omitting farm prices, which raise quite special problems, the general principle has been one of fixing prices of producers' goods (i.e. of goods sold by one productive enterprise to another) at cost plus a profit margin of a few per cent. For this purpose, cost consists of wages, material inputs, depreciation (amortisation) and a few very small items, which include interest on short-term credits. Interest on basic capital was and is almost wholly absent; state enterprises are deemed to be convenient units for administering the state's capital assets. Rent is virtually zero. Costs so computed at enterprise level are known in Russian as *sebestoimost'*, literally 'own-cost'. This word will be rendered as 'prime cost' in this book, although of course it is not strictly prime cost, (it includes depreciation, for instance). Prices, then, were supposed to be based on average prime cost of producing the given commodity, plus a profit margin expressed as a percentage of this cost. Note the word 'average'; it implied that the relatively high-cost producers were operating at a loss, a situation familiar in the nationalised British coal industry, for instance. In practice, however, prices departed substantially from this cost-plus principle. Some basic industries (e.g. coal, timber) had for years to sell their products below average cost and received a subsidy. Others were allowed to make very high profits. Some prices were increased to discourage consumption of particularly scarce materials, others were influenced by prices of close substitutes, still others seem to have no logical explanation at all. There was confusion in both theory and practice, and much of the post-Stalin debate on the 'law of value' (of which more in a moment) was related to the task of finding a theoretical basis for a fundamental revision of the price system. It should be noted that all prices of inputs and output of state enterprises are fixed by state agencies and may not, as a rule, be varied by the enterprises concerned.

Because of inadequacies in pricing, as well as of the role of politically-determined priorities, profits (or losses) were not and could not be sufficient guides for deciding the allocation of resources or the pattern of production. To a limited extent they could be used as a guide to the efficiency with which enterprise directors used resources entrusted to them; thus if an enterprise's planned costs were 100 roubles, then, if costs proved to be 95 roubles, the enterprise could be rewarded, both by way of bonuses and by allowing the retention of most of the 'over-plan' profits. (The profit of state enterprises belongs in principle to the state and is a major source of budgetary revenues.) However, the basic task of enterprises is not to maximise profits but to fulfil output plans, and also cost-reduction plans, labour-productivity plans and some other tasks decided by higher authority. Success under these various heads earns bonuses for the management. Various problems arise in defining output for this purpose: if it is 'gross output' in money terms, then there is advantage in increasing inputs of materials; if it is in tons, then managers choose heavier variants, and so on.

The Russian compound-word *khozrashchyot* literally means 'commercial accounting'—the enterprise has some financial autonomy, covers its costs out of revenues and has some incentive to make profits. However, in a wider sense it also represents the totality of incentives which operate at enterprise level. Novozhilov in particular generally uses it in this sense. The problem which troubles Soviet economists in this connexion is that material stimuli, whether in terms of profit or bonuses for various kinds of plan fulfilment, are frequently inconsistent with the needs of the economy as a whole.

We have referred so far to prices of producers' goods. The same general principles apply to the prices ex factory of consumers' goods. Retail prices, however, include a large and variable element of turnover tax. Retail prices are also fixed by the government. Consumers' goods are not rationed and so must to some extent reflect the supply and demand situation (though queues and waiting-lists exist). Since direct taxation is of minor importance it follows that there is a large gap between total personal incomes and the total prime-cost (*sebestoimost'*) of consumers' goods and services. Only part of this gap is covered by the profit margin of enterprises. The rest consists principally of turnover taxes, which form the principal source of budgetary revenues and which are levied almost entirely on consumers' goods (the only significant exceptions to this being oil, electricity and gas).

Thus wholesale (factory) prices are based on average prime-cost plus profit margin, while retail prices are fixed on quite different principles and include a large and variable element of turnover tax. Some Soviet economists have criticised this as being in conflict with 'the law of value'. To explain the debate on this law, which has some bearing on the discussions in the present book, it is necessary briefly to refer to some of the elementary terminology of Marxian economics and to its possible meanings in the context of Soviet institutions.

Marx held that the 'value' of any commodity is composed of three elements: the means of production used up in its production (i.e. the products of past labour, or 'constant capital' in his terminology), the current expenditure of labour, represented by the wages bill ('variable capital'), and 'surplus value'. (For a clear exposition of this method of presentation and its use in analysing economic growth the reader is referred to Dr Lange's contribution to this volume.) Under Soviet conditions, the first two elements in 'value' can in principle be measured in money terms: raw materials, depreciation of basic capital, wages—in fact prime-cost (*sebestoimost'*) in the definition used here. Values are held to relate to material goods at their point of final use, i.e. they include value added in transportation and in wholesale and retail trade. But logically total value must include 'surplus value'. In the USSR this is called the 'surplus product', or sometimes 'product for society', i.e. that part of the value of the product of labour (labour being the source of all value) which the labour force does not receive in wages and salaries. This sum under Soviet conditions consists principally of two items: turnover tax and profits.

But if this is so, then prices of consumers' goods include a much larger share of the surplus product (i.e. bear a much larger share of the burden of the state's overheads) than do producers' goods, which are largely free of turnover tax. Some economists consider this to be wrong in principle. But this particular debate merged in a much more general and fundamental one: what should be the role of prices in the Soviet economy, on what principles and by what criteria should prices be determined? It was widely understood that rational decision-making by planners and effective decentralisation were both deeply influenced by the prices used in calculations and in the process of choice between alternatives. The 'law of value' became a basis for discussions about objective price-criteria. It was first necessary to clear the ground of ideological obstacles left over from the Stalin era; in particular,

Stalin's own last work sought to exempt producers' goods circulating within the state sector of the economy from the operations of this law.

Having established that the 'law of value' applies throughout the Soviet economy, Soviet economists debated vigorously among themselves concerning the meaning of the term 'value' and how to calculate the surplus product. One group, of whom Strumilin was a leader, proposed to 'share out' the total surplus product in proportion to the wages bill in each branch of material production, and add the resulting sum to average prime cost (*sebestoimost'*). A second group also based itself on prime cost, but argued that the share of the surplus product should be calculated in proportion to fixed and working capital. This would be in conformity with Marx's view (in Volume III of *Das Kapital*) that prices in capitalist markets fluctuate around a magnitude which allows an equal return to all the advanced capital, which implies a departure from the simple labour-theory, since the 'organic structure of capital' varies in different sectors. Such a price would correspond, in the Marxian language, not to value (*Wert*) but to 'production price' (*Produktionspreis*).[1] These and other schools disagreed among themselves, but were united in criticising existing pricing policies.

However, pricing policies and value theories based on these 'average-prime-cost-plus' approaches are of little relevance to the problem of using prices as a guide to choice, at any level. Clearly, choice between alternatives involves considerations of relative scarcity, and of the degree to which this or that commodity or plan variant corresponds to requirements. Neither prime costs as such, nor prime costs plus an amount derived arithmetically from the relative wages bills or capital assets, can express the true usefulness of output or its real cost in terms of inputs. Programming techniques provide a possible means of identifying economically rational solutions to many problems of choice between alternative ways of arriving at the goals desired by the central authorities. These techniques unavoidably involve a different approach to pricing, an approach based not on 'cost plus' but on scarcity relationships in respect of the postulated goals, which considers opportunity costs, concepts which are of their nature of a 'marginalist' character. Experiments in the use of computers and linear programming methods in planning have indeed been made on a large scale in the USSR in recent years, and a leading part in developing these new ideas has been played by Academician V. S. Nemchinov, the editor of the present volume. The ideas of Kantorovich and Novozhilov have been given renewed publicity; a number of able young mathematical economists are coming forward. A flood of publications on this subject has been appearing.

The tasks of Soviet economists in this field are of several different kinds. They must, firstly, find a theoretical basis for this new approach, must reconcile it with orthodox theory and must show that the commonly held

[1] Novozhilov in his contribution to this book uses the term in a somewhat different sense from that used by other supporters of this concept.

views about Marxian economics (in east and west alike) is mistaken. One way of doing this is to express in the new 'language' the traditional Marxist model of a static and growing economy, a task which Dr Lange performs in this book. Secondly, they seek to demonstrate the ways in which the use of mathematical techniques in planning will help to overcome weaknesses which exist in the system, notably in respect of an economically rational and effective deployment of resources. Thirdly, there is the need to improve and refine the techniques themselves, and to teach the Soviet economists and planners. These various approaches will be found in the present volume, though the refinements figure mainly in the second volume, published in 1961.

In the context of Soviet controversies, it is useful for a protagonist to be able to argue that ideas and techniques are of Soviet or Russian origin. This helps to explain why Nemchinov in his contribution emphasises the pioneering roles of Kantorovich and Novozhilov, mentions the Russian education of W. Leontief, and refers also to the important studies (on Walrasian lines) of the little-known Russian economist Dmitriev who died in 1913.

A few words are needed to explain certain terminological usages, which come naturally to Marxian economists but which may well puzzle readers brought up in quite a different tradition.

National income is the sum of the values of material products. Personal services, army, civil service, teaching, etc., are excluded; the rewards of the service-providers are a result of redistributing the (material) national income. In the USSR national income is computed by using the final selling prices of products, and therefore includes turnover tax.

The material product is produced by two branches: *department I* producers' goods, and *department II* consumers' goods. The products of department I are in turn divided between goods used for the production of more producers' goods (or to replace worn-out producers' goods), and those which go into the making of consumers' goods.

The Marxian growth model, discussed by Dr Lange, makes common use of the terms 'simple reproduction' (in the original German *einfache Reproduktion*) and 'expanded reproduction' (*erweiterte Reproduktion*). The first of these presupposes that used-up means of production are merely replaced, the second that means of production are added to, making an increase in output possible.

'*Live labour*' refers to labour currently used in the given stage of the production process, as distinct from '*past labour*' which is embodied in capital assets and materials. It is sometimes the practice to refer to the latter as 'embodied labour'. It should also be noted that 'expenditure of labour' or 'input of labour', is generally intended to express *all* expenditure, or *all* inputs, since the philosophy of the labour theory of value involves the assumption that all expenditure and all inputs in the last analysis consist of labour.

As already explained above, the terms '*product for society*' and '*surplus product*' are synonymous, both being the equivalent in a Soviet-type economy of Marx's 'surplus value'. Such terms should not be confused with 'social labour', which merely refers to productive activities by the labour force in society.

The '*gross* (or total) *social product*' is the sum of all the gross values of the output of all productive enterprises. For example, the gross value of the output of the iron ore industry is counted as such, is then counted again in the value of the steel industry, and again (along with the steel) in the output of the automobile industry, and so forth.

'*Gross industrial output*' in its Soviet meaning is the value of the production of an enterprise, industry or industries inclusive of all inputs. Output plans are frequently expressed in such terms.

Capital investments have much the same meaning in east and west. A significant institutional difference needs to be mentioned, however. The bulk of investments in the state sector of the economy are financed by non-interest-bearing non-returnable grants. Therefore, under existing arrangements, they affect future costs only through depreciation charges. This is relevant to the comparisons of the rate of return on alternative investment projects. Some economists have advocated making a notional capital charge in choosing between alternative projects, and this underlies the method of calculating 'recoupment periods' which is part of the recommended official methodology. The logic of this is examined by Novozhilov in his contribution.

The term *value* (the German *Wert*, in Russian *Stoimost'*) always refers to value in its Marxian sense. However, the precise content of the term is in dispute, as may be seen in the efforts of Kantorovich to find 'objectively determined valuations' which would seem to replace 'values', and of Novozhilov to deny the possibility of deriving the values of particular commodities from their own production costs in isolation from the economy as a whole.

Some western readers may be tempted to neglect the work of the Soviet economists in this field because of the unfamiliar phraseology, or they may lose patience with the intricacies of the battle with the 'vulgar-Marxist' critics of the new approach. Such readers would be well advised to take the Soviet work seriously. The USSR has inherited a first-class mathematical tradition, which is being increasingly harnessed to the task of meeting the challenge posed by problems of rational economic planning. There is also to be found in the Marxian approach a concern for economic dynamics. The growth-models of *Das Kapital*, however artificial or over-simplified, do contain a necessary insight into the connexion between growth and the composition of industrial output, and it could also be argued that the distinction between productive and unproductive activities is a useful one when the growth-effectiveness of resource allocation is considered. Consequently, if Soviet economists can free themselves from dogmatic *vulgar-Marxismus* inherited from the Stalin epoch, and if they can utilise the analytical tools to the development of which they have themselves contributed much, we should expect major contributions from them in the field of mathematical economics.

The present volume is a beginning, and some of its contents reflect the need to clear the ground. Subsequent progress may be rapid, at least in the theoretical field. The application of these techniques to the actual planning and administration of the Soviet economy is impeded by a number of obstacles, but here too we must expect to see some fascinating new experiments. For experiments there must be: the 'traditional' methods are not adequate to the tasks which now face the Soviet economy.

If the science of economics is to do its job its methods will have to be improved; it will have to study real life, become an exact science in the full sense of the word, make extensive use of the latest computing techniques; it must become a searchlight in national economic planning.

From A. N. Nesmeyanov's speech at the Twenty-first Congress of the CPSU

Preface

V. S. Nemchinov

The immense problems of planning and running a socialist economy cannot be fully solved unless the technical and mathematical basis of planning is seriously developed and consolidated. This is a necessity imposed by the vast scale of the Soviet economy and the complexity of the technical and economic problems entailed in planning it.

The country's national economic plans cover an immense number of economic units, both on the production and on the consumer side, which are interconnected in a variety of ways. Up-to-date computing techniques, including the latest high-speed electronic computers, are essential to such planning, yet their use is seriously hampered by the very poor state of Soviet economics in regard to work on the application of mathematical techniques to planning, economics and the organisation of production.

Soviet economists long held the mistaken notion that mathematics could not be used in planning a socialist economy because the problems involved in compiling and carrying out the plan were too complex and multifarious. This was to ignore the great importance of investigating the laws of socialist economics not simply in qualitative terms but also in terms of quantitatixe interconnexions and ratios.

Not that mathematics is in itself a sufficient, still less a decisive factor in the complicated economic problems of socialism involved in the general trend of Soviet economic growth. It would be a gross mistake to use bourgeois notions of 'mathematical economics', which misinterpret the inner laws governing the capitalist mode of production and are purely apologetic in character, in planning a socialist economy.

As an 'instrumental' science, on the other hand, mathematics can in our hands become an excellent and serviceable tool with which to help build communism. There is plenty of scope in a socialist economy for its use in calculating balances for the economy as a whole, in analysing the relationships between different branches of the economy, and especially in working out optimum plans for the use of available resources and production reserves. The problem of optimum planning is bound up with solving such extremal problems as, for example, how to combine maximum output with minimum expenditure of ores or other raw materials; how to transport loads from a large number of production points to a large number of consumer points at minimum cost; and so on. Problems of this kind can be solved only mathematically; but in planning, a great many of them arise.

Considering the great importance of applying mathematical methods to economic research, the Praesidium of the Soviet Academy of Sciences decided to set up an independent research unit under its Siberian Division, to work on this group of problems. One of this unit's tasks is to produce monographs and symposia on the present state of the application of mathematics to economic research.

This book contains papers by Soviet economists and mathematicians and by experts from some of the other socialist countries on aspects of this question. Some have been published before[1] but the editors believed that they could well be reprinted, partly because of their undoubted theoretical and practical value and partly because the original editions are now bibliographical rarities. The publishers also intend to assert the priority of Soviet scholars in the formulation and solution of a number of scientific problems involved in applying mathematics to economic research.

In the main, however, the book consists of new works by Soviet authors on the use of mathematics in investigating economic processes in a planned socialist economy, and contains certain propositions put forward as a basis for discussion.

V. S. Nemchinov's paper on the development of mathematical techniques of economic analysis is of great interest and shows where it is reasonable to draw the line in using these methods. L. V. Kantorovich contributes a paper specially written for this symposium, in which he crystallises and expands the most important of the ideas he has expounded in a number of earlier works. V. V. Novozhilov has produced an original, if largely controversial, discussion of important problems of national economy.

G. Sh. Rubinstein's investigation of *Numerical methods of Solving Linear Programming Problems*[2] reviews and explains the mathematical basis of various methods of solving extremal problems.

[1] L. V. Kantorovich's paper on *Mathematical Methods of Organising and Planning Production*, first published in 1939, was the first paper on linear programming to appear anywhere in the world. Certain chapters of Novozhilov's *Cost-Benefit Comparisons in a Socialist Economy* appeared as separate papers in 1941 and 1946.

[2] This paper is not included in the present English edition.

Papers by A. L. Lur'e and M. A. Yakovleva[1] deal with the transportation problem. Lur'e expounds his 'circular differences method' and suggests a practical technique for solving transportation problems by means of a series of tables without examining the actual configuration of the transportation network.

Yakovleva's contribution[1] describes a procedure for using electronic computers to solve transportation problems.

The papers by O. Lange (Poland) and B. Kreko[1] (Hungary) are authorised translations. Lange attempts a mathematical interpretation of Marx's systems of reproduction which enables these to be expanded into an input-output model with a large number of the interconnexions between different branches of the national economy. The essay is not without defects from the standpoint of Marxist methodology, but is none the less of undoubted value in giving Soviet economists and statisticians a more detailed idea of the procedure for calculating input and output balances.

B. Kreko's paper[1] is a summary of his Budapest lectures on linear programming. These lectures provide an elementary introduction to the subject, the essence of which is the search for optimum solutions to a certain class of extremal problems. As no elementary textbooks on linear programming have been published in the Soviet Union this paper should be of interest to the Soviet reader.

All quotations from works originally published in languages other than Russian, with the exception of English, have been translated from the Russian. On occasion, where the point of the quotation is the use of a particular term, the original is given in a footnote.

The publishers hope that this symposium will make some contribution in helping Soviet economists to solve the problems posed by the demands of a rapidly growing socialist economy.

[1] This paper is not included in the present English edition.

The Use of Mathematical Methods in Economics

V. S. Nemchinov

1. The founders of Marxism-Leninism attached great importance to the economic applications of mathematics. Marx's interest in mathematics and the use of mathematical analysis in investigating economic phenomena appears in his well-known *Mathematical Notebooks* and in his letters. On 31 May 1873 he writes to Engels, 'You know those tables showing the movement of prices, discounts and the like, with their fluctuations over a year or some other period? I have often tried to work out the irregular curves for these *up and downs* (*sic*) for the purpose of analysing crises, believing (and I still believe this would be possible if one had sufficiently reliable information) that the main laws of crises could be mathematically deduced from this.'[1]

Marx saw in mathematics a serious and very valuable tool of economic analysis. In particular, he cast his formula for expanded production as an algebraic equation in the case of simple reproduction and as a mathematical inequality in the case of expanded reproduction.

N. G. Chernyshevskii, the great economist whose thought dominated the minds of nineteenth-century Russian revolutionary democrats, commented on Mill's *Principles of Political Economy* in these terms: 'We already have many examples to illustrate the methods political economy uses in solving its problems. These methods are mathematical. It could not be otherwise, for science deals in quantities which can be counted and measured and are intelligible only through measurement and computation.'[2]

Marx and Lenin thought highly of Chernyshevskii's economic works and the power of his creative intelligence.

In recent years, however, Soviet economists have shown a fairly strong prejudice against using mathematical methods in economics. The reason is that bourgeois economic schools—for example, the Austrian 'marginal utility' school and the Anglo-American econometrics school—have tried to justify

[1] K. Marx and F. Engels, *Collected Works*, Vol. xxiv, p. 414 (Russian edition).

[2] N. G. Chernyshevskii, *Selected Economic Works*, Vol. iii, pt. 1, p. 81, Gospolitizdat, 1948.

their pseudo-scientific apologetic concepts by substituting purely mathematical methods in place of socio-economic analysis. That the misuse of mathematics in economic research has been exposed, however, is no reason why Soviet economists should reject all use of mathematics in economics.

Mathematics is known to be like a grindstone. You cannot get flour by grinding chaff but, on the other hand, you cannot get edible flour from wheat without first grinding it. Mathematical techniques are a powerful aid to analysis, to be properly used in conjunction with the qualitative and quantitative study of economics. Their auxiliary, functional character does not in the least reduce their enormous importance in economic research.

There is not the slightest reason why the misuse of mathematics by bourgeois economic schools should lead Marxist economists to repudiate the use of mathematics in economics. This is a case where economists on the socialist side of the fence must be guided entirely by Lenin's view: 'We must not close our eyes to bourgeois science; we must follow it and use it, but with a critical attitude and without budging from our own complete and definite *Weltanschauung*.'[1] Yet sometimes we refuse to use the positive aspects of bourgeois science and this is what we have done, for example, in regard to the Anglo-American works on balances of input and output.

This type of research was very extensively developed in other countries during and just after the war, under the name of 'input-output analysis'. Originating in Soviet statistical and planning practice during the mid-twenties, it spread to other countries only later; but when production cost and output accounting penetrated to us from abroad in the form of 'input-output analysis', certain Soviet economists started to reject this method out of hand, without taking the trouble to distinguish between the bourgeois distortions of the ways in which it was being used and its very necessary and useful role under socialism.

2. The requirements of a planned economy during the early years of socialist construction generated a variety of research projects on economic balances of the 'balance sheet' type. Above all, a start was made in drawing up the natural quantitative balances of grain products and fuel. In 1924, by decision of the Soviet Government, the Central Statistics Board started to compile the balance sheet for the nation's economy in the year 1923-4. In 1925 the Board's Director, P. I. Popov, published a report on the preliminary results of this work in the journal *Ekonomicheskaya zhizn*' (No. 72). The journal *Planovoe khozyaistvo* replied with a review of this report containing the following comment: 'The main novelty here, as compared with conventional economic and statistical surveys such as the American and British censuses, lies in the attempt to produce figures covering not only production but also distribution of the social product so as to give a general picture of the reproduction process in the form of a *tableau économique*.'[2]

[1] V. I. Lenin, *Collected Works*, Vol. 3, p. 559 (Russian edition).
[2] *Planovoe khozyaistvo*, 1925, No. 12, p. 254.

In 1926 the Central Statistics Board issued a long monograph[1] giving the material balances in regard to 28 agricultural, 2 forestry and 8 manufactured products widely consumed in the country. The most valuable feature of this work was the tables showing capital, the production-distribution balance of the social product, national income and a 'chessboard' balance sheet of productive consumption.

The production and use of the social product balance was broken down into 4 branches and 37 separate products in agriculture, 3 branches in the extractive industry and 11 branches in manufacturing. Building and publishing were also distinguished as independent branches. The end products, raw materials and material, fuel and equipment used in production were shown in separate lines for all branches of production.

All four of these categories of production goods add up to the productive consumption. If we exclude equipment from the productive consumption, we are left with the costs of material (without deductions for amortisation). To determine the national income the authors of the balance sheet added amortisation deductions to costs of material and subtracted the turnover inside the productive sphere (productive consumption).

In a paper entitled *The expanded reproduction ratio*[2] I gave the first Soviet table for 'balance of outlay and output, 1923-4' based on the Central Statistics Board publications, where the relevant figures appeared in the 'balance of production and distribution of the social product' and 'national income' tables.

By a careful analysis of the entire volume on 'Balance of the National Economy for 1923-4' one could extract from it an improved and more comprehensive version of the original table of the 'Balance of Input and Output' (see Table 1).

The first publication of the Soviet national economic balance sheet contains in particular a table of 'consumption of industrial products' where the intra-industrial turnover between individual branches of industry is given in the form of a 'chessboard' Table. The figures are reproduced in Table 1, lines 6-20 and columns 7-21.

The interbranch connexions with agriculture (items 2-5 and columns 1-5 and 7-21, Table 1) are taken from the 'gross and net production' table.

Analysing the intra-industrial turnover figures, F. G. Dubovikov, one of the authors of the balance sheet, wrote of a 'chain connexion between the individual branches of the national economy' and pointed out that 'analysis of this chain connexion shows how tight it is in regard to productive consumption and sources from which industrial consumers obtain material from producing enterprises'. He believed that 'it is equally important to establish the connexion and interdependence between individual groups of industries in the

1 'Balance sheet of the national economy of the USSR for 1923-4', *Transactions of the USSR Central Statistics Board*, Vol. 29, Moscow, 1926.

2 *Voprosy ekonomiki*, 1958, No. 10.

TABLE

Input and Output

(in millions

Item No.	Branch of Production	Intra-industrial			
		Crops and Pastures	Livestock	Forestry	Fishing and Hunting
	1	2	3	4	5
2	Agriculture, meadows and pastures	575·8	1,699·2		
3	Livestock		483·7		
4	Forestry	36·4	26·1		
5	Fishing and Hunting				
6	Total for agriculture	612·2	2,209·0		
7	Mineral extraction and primary processing				
8	Mineral fuels	9·8	2·2	0·1	
9	Other branches of extractive industry				
10	Mineral processing				
11	Metal working	0·3	0·1		
12	Wood working	14·9	2·2	1·4	
14	Chemicals	2·3			
15	Food		158·2		
16	Processing of solid animal products	23·2	4·9	0·7	
17	Textiles	15·8			
18	Paper				
19	All forms of printing				
20	Power and water supply				
21	Arts and applied sciences				
22	Total for industry	66·3	167·6	2·2	
23	Publishing				
24	Building				
26	Trade	561·8	305	466·1	19·7
27	Transport	152·6	26·4	65·2	1·5
28	Total for productive consumption	1,392·9	2,708·0	533·5	21·2
29	Net production				
30	External (import)				
31	Stocks at beginning of year				
32	Balance				
33	Total for items 29-32				
34	Grand total				
35	Capital investment means of production)				
36	Cost (in thousands of man-days): (*a*) manufacturing and rail transport (*b*) small-scale industry and agriculture	5,392,000			

[1] The chervonts was a 10-rouble note, first issued

1

Balance for the USSR 1923-4

of chervontsi[1])

Turnover (Productive Consumption)

Total for agriculture	Mineral extraction and primary processing	Mineral fuels	Other branches of extractive industry	Mineral processing	Metal working	Wood working
6	7	8	9	10	11	12
2,275·0				0·1		
483·7						
62·5	0·7	7·2	2·9	12·2	7·8	82·6
2,821·2	0·7	7·2	2·9	12·3	7·8	82·6
	2·0			9·3	0·8	
12·1	0·4	204·0	3·3	9·6	65·6	0·8
			2·3		31·2	
				1·8	3·5	
0·4		0·3	0·1	0·4	263·3	4·1
18·5	0·1		0·5	0·6	15·9	42·3
2·3		2·8	1·6	3·0	2·5	1·0
158·2						
28·8					0·2	0·1
15·8		0·1	0·2	0·2	0·1	
		3·0	0·3	0·4	7·0	0·7
236·1	2·5	210·2	8·3	25·3	390·1	49·0
1,352·8	16·1	15·3	45·0	48·5	138·6	53·3
245·7	10·2	148·1	20·6	6·9	12·5	22·1
4,655·8	29·5	380·8	76·8	93·0	549·0	207·0
5,864·9	56·8	350·2	58·1	63·6	338·7	142·5
86·0	3·6	7·8	13·2	0·6	16·5	2·9
118·7	5·3	210·7	86·2	14·3	236·3	47·8
(−46·9)	(+19·0)	(+12·6)	(+15·4)	(+0·2)	(+74·2)	(−2·0)
6,022·7	84·7	581·3	172·9	78·7	665·7	191·2
10,678·5	114·2	962·1	249·7	171·7	1,214·7	398·2
733·0	0·1	3·8		0·2	57·6	0·6
		124,879·1			70,485·6	17,543·0
5,392,000		12,032·0			60,729·4	91,742·0

in 1922. It was withdrawn from circulation in 1947.

TABLE

Item No.	Branch of Production	Intra-industrial			
		Chemicals	Food	Processing of solid animal products	Textiles
	13	14	15	16	17
2	Agriculture, meadows and pastures	0·1	1,973·6		80·8
3	Livestock	6·3	45·6	137·5	85·0
4	Forestry	4·3	32·3	13·7	25·4
5	Fishing and Hunting		22·0	2·0	
6	Total for agriculture	10·7	2,073·5	153·2	191·2
7	Mineral extraction and primary processing	2·3		0·2	
8	Mineral fuels	14·0	19·2	3·2	25·3
9	Other branches of extractive industry	3·3	3·6	1·3	0·3
10	Mineral processing	0·4	0·2	0·6	1·0
11	Metal working	0·4	3·6	3·3	3·5
12	Wood working	1·0	4·0	3·0	2·1
14	Chemicals	22·3	1·7	9·3	25·7
15	Food	9·9	262·6	0·8	0·9
16	Processing of solid animal products	6·3	0·1	177·3	34·2
17	Textiles	18·8		11·0	722·9
18	Paper	0·4	12·1		0·1
19	All forms of printing	0·1			
20	Power and water supply	0·9	5·5	2·4	9·2
21	Arts and applied sciences				
22	Total for industry	80·1	312·6	212·4	825·2
23	Publishing				
24	Building				
26	Trade	76·6	405·6	149·1	334·6
27	Transport	22·6	101·3	18·4	38·3
28	Total for productive consumption	190·0	2,893·0	533·1	1,389·3
29	Net production	126·3	663·2	277·3	598·5
30	External (import)	37·4	32·8	5·9	149·1
31	Reserves at beginning of year	85·9	66·7	28·8	273·3
32	Balance	(+12·6)	(+157·1)	(+0·1)	(+1·2)
33	Total for items 29-32	262·2	919·8	312·1	1,022·1
34	Grand total	452·2	3,812·8	845·2	2,411·4
35	Capital investment (means of production)	0·7	6·0	1·6	27·7
36	Cost (in thousands of man-days):				
	(*a*) manufacturing and rail transport	15,692·1	35,607·7	8,963·1	122,339·8
	(*b*) small-scale industry and agriculture	1,287·7	85,834·4	14,639·6	190,887·4

1 (*Continued*)

Turnover (Productive Consumption)

Paper	Printing	Power and water supply	Arts and applied sciences	Total for industry	Publishing	Building
18	19	20	21	22	23	24
				2,054·6		6·0
				274·4		
1·2	0·4	4·2	0·3	195·2		139·4
				24·0		
1·2	0·4	4·2	0·3	2,548·2		145·4
0·6				15·2		64·6
2·7	0·8	55·8	0·1	404·8		
0·2	0·1		0·6	42·9		
			0·1	7·6		94·4
	0·2	0·2	3·6	283·0		71·8
			0·4	69·9		54·6
2·0	1·2	0·6	0·2	73·9		19·5
0·3				274·5		7·6
	0·2		0·1	218·5		
6·6	0·4		1·5	761·8		0·5
15·5	20·3			48·4		3·6
0·1	1·8			2·0		
3·1	0·9	8·4	0·1	41·9		
			1·2	1·2		
31·1	25·9	65·0	7·9	2,245·6		316·6
15·5	0·6		7·6	1,306·4	25·6	
2·6				403·6	3·5	
50·4	26·9	69·2	15·8	6,503·8	29·1	462·0
37·5	41·4	69·1	9·0	2,832·2		391·3
13·8			10·9	294·5	1·2	
19·3				1,074·6		
(+1·5)	—	(−7·3)	(+7·9)	(+292·5)	(+70·9)	—
72·1	41·4	61·8	27·8	4,493·8	72·1	391·3
122·5	68·3	131·0	43·6	10,997·6	101·2	853·3
	0·9					
7,376·1	14,340·0	7,330·2	1,187·7			
176·7	1,518·4		3,195·7			

TABLE

Item No.	Branch of Production	Intra-industrial Turnover			
		Trade	Transport	Total for productive consumption	Capital investment
	25	26	27	28	29
2	Agriculture, meadows and pastures			4,335·6	
3	Livestock			758·1	301·6
4	Forestry	1·0	43·2	441·3	
5	Fishing and Hunting			24·0	
6	Total for agriculture	1·0	43·2	5,559·0	301·6
7	Mineral extraction and primary processing		8·0	87·8	0·2
8	Mineral fuels	0·2	125·9	543·0	
9	Other branches of extractive industry		7·3	50·2	
10	Mineral processing	5·9	6·3	114·2	2·4
11	Metal working		64·5	419·7	482·9
12	Wood working	32·1	27·6	202·7	52·4
14	Chemicals		3·5	99·2	15·1
15	Food		1·2	441·5	
16	Processing of solid animal products			247·3	8·2
17	Textiles	37·4	11·8	827·3	2·0
18	Paper	5·4	1·6	59·0	
19	All forms of printing	59·7	1·6	63·3	
20	Power and water supply	3·5		45·4	
21	Arts and applied sciences			1·2	8·5
22	Total for industry	144·2	259·3	3,201·8	571·7
23	Publishing				
24	Building				381·8
26	Trade			2,684·8	
27	Transport			652·8	
28	Total for productive consumption	145·2	302·5	12,098·4	1,255·1
29	Net production	2,400·7	554·2	12,043·3	
30	External (import)			381·7	
31	Reserves at beginning of year		83·3	1,276·6	
32	Balance	(+138·9)	(−217·7)	(+237·7)	
33	Total for items 29-32	2,539·6	419·8	13,939·3	
34	Grand total	2,684·8	722·3	26,037·7	
35	Capital investment (means of production)		88·0		
36	Cost (in thousands of man-days):				
	(*a*) manufacturing and rail transport		20,200·0		
	(*b*) small-scale industry and agriculture				

1 (*Continued*)

Final Demand for Social Product					
Stocks at end of year	Individual consump-tion	State consump-tion	External (export)	Total for unproductive consumption	Grand total
30	31	32	33	34	35
66·5	1,421·7	22·7	236·0	1,746·9	6,082·5
	2,205·8	15·9	24·8	2,548·1	3,306·2
20·1	557·5	22·0	24·5	624·1	1,065·4
	148·4		52·0	200·4	224·4
86·6	4,333·4	60·6	337·3	5,119·5	10,678 5
4·9		20·4	0·9	26·4	114·2
271·6	74·9	25·7	46·9	419·1	962·1
82·0	71·6	30·9	15·0	199·5	249·7
14·1	34·2	5·5	1·3	57·5	171·7
237·8	54·1	14·9	5·3	795·0	1,214·7
37·7	49·8	10·8	44·8	195·5	398·2
104·0	203·5	25·9	4·5	353·0	452·2
46·7	3,233·0	26·8	64·8	3,371·3	3,812·8
43·3	532·0	12·2	2·2	597·9	845·2
426·6	1,103·0	46·8	5·7	1,584·1	2,411·4
15·3	42·1	6·0	0·1	63·5	122·5
	1·7	3·3		5·0	68·3
	78·8	6·8		85·6	131·0
8·8	20·2	4·4	0·5	42·4	43·6
1,292·8	5,498·9	240·4	192·0	7,795·8	10,997·6
63·6	17·7	19·5	0·4	101·2	101·2
	471·5			853·3	853·3
					2,684·8
69·5				69·5	722·3
1,512·5	10,321·5	320·5	529·7	13,939·3	26,037·7

national economy and to discover and elucidate the overall turnover of material values'.

The idea of an input-output balance, then, was explicit in the first balance sheet of the Soviet national economy and was directly contained in it, as can be seen from Table 1, where the only additional figures supplied by us are those in brackets, indicating discrepancies. All the other figures are taken directly from tables in the original.

The only modification we have allowed by way of modernising this table is the introduction of a 'capital investment' column summarising productive consumption in instruments of labour and giving the construction production figures. The turnover of objects of labour appears in the lines and columns of an inner quadrant in the 'chessboard' table of inputs and outputs, entitled 'productive consumption' in Table 1.

The production-consumption balance sheet for 1923-4 puts 'instruments of production' on separate lines and provides for the treatment of construction as a separate branch. As a result it contains not only a chessboard balance of production costs and output but also a statement of the productive equipment and construction balance (capital investment).

This balance, extracted from the overall balance table, is shown in Table 2. Characteristically, this first balance sheet of productive equipment and construction to appear in the world remained unnoticed for a very long time and gave rise to hardly any imitations or supplementary research. Yet capital investment is one of the most difficult aspects of input-output research, particularly when one is constructing a dynamic model of the national economy. Capital investment is a most important accelerator of the process of economic growth. Moreover, the problem of accumulation in the national economy cannot be examined in concrete terms unless one first constructs a balance sheet for capital investments (productive equipment and construction).

Capital investment is preparation for the future. Society's capital investment demand is determined by the social necessity of providing new jobs for the growing generation and by the current labour requirements of the economy and the need to improve the labour conditions.

In 1928 there appeared an article by M. Barengol'ts under the title *The Capacity of the Soviet Industrial Market* containing a chessboard balance sheet for 11 branches of Soviet industry over the three years 1922-3, 1923-4 and 1924-5. The branches distinguished were: (1) mineral extraction and processing; (2) fuel; (3) other extractive industries; (4) metallurgy; (5) the metal working industry; (6) the wood working industry; (7) chemicals; (8) the food industry; (9) tanning; (10) textiles; (11) other branches of industry.

In addition the industries were consolidated into groups: (*a*) extractive (branches 1, 2 and 3), (*b*) metal (branches 4 and 5) and (*c*) all eleven branches taken together.

TABLE 2

Balance of the Instruments of Production and Building in the USSR 1923-4
(in millions of chervontsi)

Production and Other Sources	Distribution									
	Productive Consumption—Productive Capital Investment				Non-productive Consumption (Capital Investment)	Export	Stocks		Instruments of Production (Total)	Building (Total)
	Agriculture	Industry	Transport	Trade			Production	Circulation		
	A. Buildings and installations									
Building in enterprises:										
Agriculture	115·4	4·3	—	—	25·2	—	—	—	—	145·4
Industry	114·1	70·1	—	—	132·4	—	—	—	—	316·6
Total for buildings and installations	229·5	74·9	—	—	157·6	—	—	—	—	462·0
	B. Instruments of production									
Production in enterprises:										
Agriculture	300·0	—	—	—	1·8	—	—	—	301·8	
Industry	231·4	99·1	88·0	2·0	106·7	0·2	38·4	5·6	571·4	
Buildings	201·6	95·5	—	15·0	69·7	—	—	—	381·8	
Total for means of production	733·0	194·6	88·0	17·0	178·2	0·2	38·4	5·6	1,255·0	
Import	0·7	48·7				Total capital investment				(1,717·0)
Transport and trade costs	0·2	35·7				Total national income				11,965·0
Initial stocks	—	67·3				Percentage of national income				(14·7)
	733·9	346·3								

In this article Barengol'ts also formulated with great clarity the concepts of technical coefficients: 'In the absence of a technical "revolution" in the sphere of production, coefficients of intra-industrial turnover in relation to the so-called "gross turnover" yield in real life—given the appropriate correction for price changes, and in terms of value—perfectly stable dynamic indices both for determining overall demand and intra-industrial turnover and for establishing the actual interconnexion between particular branches of industry.'[1] Barengol'ts also computed intra-industrial demand coefficients as percentages of gross production.

When Leontief[2] compiled his American input-output table of production, he already had before him the Soviet examples mentioned above. His own contribution was threefold: (1) he was the first to combine two tables, one showing the balance of production and the other showing how the social product and national income were distributed; (2) he increased the number of branches in the national economy, shown in the 'chessboard' table of objects of labour (intermediate products), to 41 (46 positions); (3) he gave a mathematical interpretation of the balance sheet by constructing equations relating input and output, as Walras[3] and Dmitriev[4] had in their day suggested.

These equations include a term a_{ik} representing the direct input of a product i entailed in producing a product k. Given a_{ik} and using the equations, one can determine the coefficients of total inputs in two ways: (*a*) by proceeding from a calculation per unit of output entering into final demand (b_{ik})—public consumption, material consumption of the non-productive sphere, investments in fixed and working capital, export; (*b*) by proceeding from a calculation per unit of gross output (c_{ik}). Both procedures give practically the same value for total inputs.

The special scientific importance of Leontief's work lies in his use of the 'chessboard' table to determine not only the direct input of labour and capital in a given branch of production but also the input of other branches of the economy into that branch, so that one can determine the total input of labour, total capital investment, total input of power and so forth. These indices are based on Leontief's input and output coefficients.[5]

Leontief is the author of the method known as 'input-output analysis' by which the connexions between different branches within a system of production are analysed by reference to the top left-hand square of a table showing

[1] *Planovoe khozyaistvo*, 1928, No. 7, p. 329.

[2] W. Leontief. Well-known American bourgeois economist who took a degree at the University of Leningrad in the mid-1920's and was later the author of a method based on principles similar to those of the first Soviet balance sheet for the national economy.

[3] L. Walras, *Eléments d'économie politique pure ou théorie de la richesse sociale*, Paris 1874.

[4] V. K. Dmitriev, *Economic Essays*, St. Petersburg, 1904.

[5] W. Leontief, 'Factor proportions and structure of American trade', *Review of Economics and Statistics*, 1956, No. 4.

inputs and outputs. When the remaining squares in such a table (top right —social end product, bottom left—national income elements, bottom right —elements of income redistribution) are reduced to a minimum, we have an 'input-output analysis' table. Such a table, however, still represents only a part of the input-output balance.

3. The input-output balance is closely bound up with the subject of programming for the optimum use of resources as applied to the over-all economic accounts.

Optimum programming is an auxiliary technique in a system of planning for the economy as a whole, which can be used to advantage in solving a variety of technical-economic problems. It presupposes extensive use of mathematical techniques in the calculations required to find the optimum version of a plan for using existing productive resources in such a way as to obtain the desired end result (for example results indicated in the plan targets: quantity, prime cost and the product-mix of the output).

The technique of programming is widely used in technical-economic and statistical-economic calculations. Its successful use depends on combining premises and knowledge both of mathematical and technical sciences and of economics and statistics. Programming methods are very intensively applied in those overlapping fields of knowledge where problems in engineering and in economics, in mathematics and in statistics, are closely intertwined. Left to themselves, without the help of economists and statisticians, representatives of the technical or mathematical sciences cannot use the linear programming technique fully and to best advantage. The same is true of economists and statisticians, who would not be able to develop this technique independently, without the help of engineers and mathematicians. These are features peculiar to programming which, of course, give it a special character. It is not a universal technique and can be applied only to a strictly defined, although a fairly wide class of, problems typical of the border area, we mentioned above, between the economic, technical, and mathematical sciences.

Programming was invented in 1939 at the Leningrad University Institute of Mathematics and Engineering as a technique for solving certain production problems entailed in the construction of optimum plans for machine loads, the laying out of sheet materials and timber cutting, where targets involving a range of products had to be met. Public knowledge of this technique dates from the appearance of Professor L. V. Kantorovich's *Mathematical Methods of Organising and Planning Production.* Kantorovich called it the 'resolving multiplier method'.

Later, and almost independently of this work, a similar method began to be widely developed in the United States and Britain, under a variety of names—factors of production and of resource-utilisation programming, interdependent factor programming and so forth. More recently, the appellation 'linear programming' has become attached to this technique in foreign literature. The term does not fully reflect the most important features of the technique—papers have recently appeared, for example, on quadratic programming. It therefore seems best to keep the more accurate term, 'optimum programming'.

The same applies to the term 'resolving multipliers'. Their application is very important but they are nevertheless neither a decisive nor a unique feature of optimum programming. The term 'resolving multiplier method' emphasises the mathematical basis of the method, whereas the term 'optimum programming' brings out the significance of this method for production and its role in solving technical-economic problems.

Many problems in production planning can be solved by this method, particularly in selecting the optimum version of a plan: the load on available capacities of production plants and machinery; the disposition of means of transport (aircraft, for example) for the conveyance of various types of freight and passengers from particular starting points to particular destinations; the distribution of goods in shops in such a way as to achieve the required variety; the cutting of metal, wood, hides and so forth; the combined utilisation of valuable raw material components (for example ferrous and non-ferrous metal ore ingredients); the distribution of orders among factories and so forth.

Optimum programming is a method of solving a number of economic problems when definite and, in particular, limited productive resources are to be used to achieve a fully predetermined planned result of economic activity (for example the production of a definite quantity and variety of goods) and the problem is to combine this result with the best possible qualitative indices (for example the highest possible level of productivity or the lowest possible cost of production or the least possible input of factors in limited supply such as raw materials, power and so forth). These indices are taken as criteria for assessing each feasible version of the plan and determining which is the optimum version.

The term 'optimum' or 'rational' as applied to the solution of a programming problem accordingly has no absolute meaning but only a relative one, valid only from a given, definite point of view introduced into the problem when we fix criteria for assessing plans.

Optimum programming ensures practically useful results, for by its very nature it fully corresponds to the character of the technical and economic processes and phenomena under study. From the mathematical and statistical points of view, the technique of optimum programming is applicable to phenomena which are quantitatively expressed in the form of magnitudes having a positive value and forming in their entirety an *aggregate* of different magnitudes, i.e. some system of factors which may be variously labelled and measured in a variety of units.

An investigator faced with a problem in optimum programming will invariably have to deal with a definite number and variety of production capacities and products and a variety of combinations of magnitudes. Programming is therefore always concerned with interdependent magnitudes or factors and the problem is solved by taking into account not one, but several interdependent factors.

The technique of programming is applied to those problems which must be solved in order to achieve the optimum result when targets are precisely defined and the limitations of available resources (productive capacity, raw materials, available labour resources and so forth) are fully known in advance. The conditions of the problem usually include some system of interrelated factors, a statement of resources and a knowledge of the conditions limiting the way in which these can be used. The problem becomes capable of solution once definite valuations are introduced both for the interrelated factors and for the expected results. A result obtained on the basis of programming has a relative character and is optimum only in terms of the criteria on which both the individual factors and the result itself were based.

Accordingly there are three aspects to any problem solved by optimum programming:

1. the presence of a system of interrelated factors,
2. a strict criterion of 'optimality',
3. a precise formulation of the conditions limiting the use of available resources.

From the many possible versions that combination of factors is selected which satisfies all the conditions introduced into the problem and provides the minimum or maximum value or valuation of the given plan in terms of the chosen criterion of 'optimality'. The solution is reached by using a definite mathematical procedure which amounts to the method of successive approximations (iterations).

The initial data are reduced to a definite system and arranged in the order most convenient for rapidly finding the optimum version of the plan. The demands made on programming are best met by arranging the initial data in the form of an appropriate matrix of numbers. If, for example, the problem concerns the optimum use of available productive capacity, a matrix of machine loads is compiled and one then starts to fill in the figures for the load capacities of those machines which will give the maximum output of products. Consequently, the equipment load matrix will in this case begin to be filled in with figures for those machines and products which will give the best possible output of products and these machines will be loaded first.

Optimum programming techniques are widely used in solving extremal problems and in calculations connected with the national economy. One of the pioneers here is Professor V. V. Novozhilov, who published his first papers on these subjects in 1939, 1941 and 1946. Kantorovich's and Novozhilov's pre-war papers on optimum programming are thus, in some sense, precursors both of 'input-output analysis' and of linear programming, techniques regarded as achievements of economic science abroad.

4. The application of mathematics to economic investigations is particularly useful in determining overall inputs of labour and capital investments, power inputs and so forth. At each stage of production there are direct labour inputs, fixed and working capital and so forth. In determining overall inputs one takes into account not only such direct inputs but also inputs at previous stages of production. In steel smelting, for example, there are, in addition to the relevant direct labour inputs, the inputs of pig iron and fuel, which in turn involve labour inputs. In its turn, pig iron production involves not only labour inputs but also consumption of iron ore and coke, which again cannot be produced without corresponding labour inputs. Consequently all production is bound up with the input of some previous, related product, over and above its own direct inputs. In other words, any extended reproduction of any particular product entails, in addition to direct inputs, all kinds of indirect inputs as well.

The sum of direct and indirect inputs gives the overall inputs. Overall inputs can be determined even by elementary accounting methods. Our estimates of the overall labour inputs of various agricultural products is a case in point.[1]

Elementary accounting methods, however, do not provide the necessary accuracy and completeness. Overall input is better determined by solving a system of simultaneous linear equations. A number of the problems involved cannot be solved at all by elementary procedures. By way of illustration we shall take an example borrowed from the British economist and statistician Barna.[2]

We construct a matrix for essential input in the clothing industry:

TABLE 3

Input in the Clothing Industry

Type of input and stages of production	Cotton	Yarn	Cloth	Garments
Cotton	−1	1·2		
Yarn		−1	1·1	0·1
Cloth			−1	4
Garments				−1
Labour	0·5	0·2	0·3	0·4

The table shows input as positive and output as negative quantities. To produce 1 unit of clothing, 4 units of cloth, 0·1 unit of yarn and 0·4 unit of labour are required; the production of 1 unit of cloth calls for 1·1 unit of

[1] V. S. NEMCHINOV, 'The application of normative statistics to the study of labour productivity in agriculture', in *Uchenye zapiski po statistiki*, Vol. II, Moscow, 1956; and 'The measurement of growth factors in agricultural labour productivity', in *Vestnik sel' skokhozyaistvennoi nauki*, 1958, No. 5.

[2] T. BARNA, 'The independence of the British economy', *Journal of the Royal Statistical Society*, series A, Vol. CXV, part 1, 1952.

yarn and 0·3 unit of labour, the production of 1 unit of yarn calls for 1·2 unit of cotton and 0·2 unit of labour and the production of the cotton raw material calls for 0·5 unit of labour.

Let us assume that 1 unit of clothing (the final product) is produced and that all the other goods are only intermediate products (zero output of final product). As a result of four types of production (cotton, yarn, cloth, garments) 1 unit of clothing is produced. We now determine the total input of producing this final product by elementary procedures.

TABLE 4

Total Input in Clothing Production

Type of input and stages of production	Cotton	Yarn	Cloth	Garments	Net output
Cotton	−5·4	5·4			0
Yarn		−4·5	4·4	0·1	0
Cloth			−4	4	0
Garments				−1	1
Labour	2·7	0·9	1·2	0·4	−5·2

It follows that for each unit of clothing it is necessary to produce 5·4 units of cotton, 4·5 units of yarn and 4 units of cloth and to have 5·2 units of labour. These full labour inputs are distributed among the four kinds of production: the direct costs of producing a garment are 0·4 of a labour unit and in addition we have to count the labour inputs in producing the cloth (1·2), yarn (0·9) and cotton (2·7).

In this example the output at later stages is not used in the form of inputs at earlier stages of production. All the material input coefficients are set above and to the right of the diagonal. Here there is no place for 'feedback'. All the input coefficients characterise only the production circuit within the given production vertical (the clothing production vertical). The only link between the four productive branches is a technological one along the intermediate product consumption line (raw materials and semi-manufactured products). As there is no feedback, arithmetical solution is possible.

In real economic activity, however, there are not only technological links along the production vertical but also economic links along the production horizontals. These economic links come into existence because the output of the products at successive stages of production can be used as production inputs at previous stages of production. Any intermediate product, moreover,

TABLE 5

Input Coefficients in Machine Production

Type of input and stage of production	Coal (c)	Steel (s)	Machines (m)
Coal	−1	2	0·2
Steel	0·1	−1	0·5
Machines	0·1	0·3	−1
Labour	0·5	0·3	1

can be a final product. This gives rise to feedback and the productive connexions acquire an economic rather than a technological character. To illustrate this we give a second example also taken from Barna (Table 5).

In this case there is a 'feedback' and the total labour inputs can be computed only by solving a system of equations:

$$c-2s-0{\cdot}2m = 0 \text{ (coal output);}$$
$$-0{\cdot}1c+s-0{\cdot}5m = 0 \text{ (steel output);}$$
$$0{\cdot}1c+0{\cdot}3s+m = 1 \text{ (machine output).}$$

The coal and steel output is regarded as the output only of intermediate products (0 final product), that of the machines as the output of final products.

After solving these equations we have:

TABLE 6

Indirect Consumption and Total Input in Machine Production

Type of input and stage of production	Coal	Steel	Machines	Output of final product
Coal	−2·31	2	0·31	0
Steel	0·23	−1	0·77	0
Machines	0·23	0·3	−1·53	1
Labour	1·15	0·3	1·53	−2·98

Because of the feedback the output of one unit of machines in the form of final product calls for: first, the production of 1·53 unit of machinery, including 0·23 for coal extraction and 0·3 for steel production, and secondly for the production of 2·31 units of coal, including 2 units for steel smelting and 0·31 directly for the machinery production, and finally, for the production of one unit of steel, including 0·77 for the production of the machines themselves and 0·23 for coal extraction.

For the production of one unit of machinery, 2·98 units of labour are required, including 1·15 for coal extraction, 0·3 for steel smelting and 1·53 for manufacturing the machines themselves.

One could similarly determine the total wages bill per unit of product. All that is necessary is to substitute specific total wage norms for labour input in the last line. If we want to determine total capital investment input, the last line will have to show the specific capital investment norms per unit of production. If we want to determine the total power or fuel input, the last line will have to be expressed in units of power or fuel (specific consumption norms) and so forth.

The material costs of the intermediate products (raw materials, fuel, semi-manufactured goods and so forth) can be expressed in natural units or in value (money) expenditures for the various kinds of means of production expended per unit of the given products. The output of each of these kinds of product can also be expressed in value (money) units.

In real economic life productive interconnexions (exchange of intermediate products within industry) are a good deal more complicated. Outside the Soviet Union, therefore, an inside quadrant (top left) of the input-output table is generally used in calculating total costs. This quadrant, of course, is in the form of a 'chessboard' table. Such a table may contain tens, hundreds or even thousands of homonymous rows and columns showing the flow of goods and products back and forth within industry. On the basis of such a table one computes the input (or output) coefficients and these are then used to determine total input. With modern electronic computers a system of hundreds or thousands of equations in an input-output table can be rapidly solved.

When we were considering the Barna examples we indicated the importance of 'feedback' in real economic life.

As we mentioned, feedback (which occurs when a product produced at later stages of production enters into earlier stages of the production vertical as an element in the costs of production) has not only a technological but primarily an economic significance. It establishes a system of interaction among the later and earlier links in the productive process. Feedback means first, that a given product of industry is an essential requirement of the industry proper either directly at the final stage of the production vertical or indirectly at earlier stages of production. Feedback can, on the other hand, mean that better but limited conditions of labour utilisation influence the costs of producing other products and leads, for example, to an increase in every kind of input (outlay) for the production of these and other products.[1]

Lastly, feedback can appear in evaluating the socially necessary expenditure of labour, power and capital investments, if the conditions of production of any single product change.

Marx had this in mind: 'Although the value of a commodity is determined by the quantity of labour contained in it, this quantity is itself determined by social conditions. If the time socially necessary for the production of a commodity alters—and a given amount of cotton, for example, represents a larger amount of labour if conditions are unfavourable than if they are favourable—this exerts a *reverse action* (my italics—V.N.) on the old commodity, which always plays the part of a particular representative of its kind, its value always being measured by the socially necessary labour, that is only by the labour necessary under the social conditions existing at the time.'[2]

Marx gives other instances, in *Capital*, of reverse action, connected with the introduction of new and improved machinery, altered conditions of production and so forth.

Economic problems involving feedback can be solved only by modern mathematical analysis and with the aid of electronic computers. In particular, modern mathematics and up-to-date computing aids make it possible to determine the socially necessary expenditure of labour and the social cost

[1] This case is specially examined in V. V. Novozhilov's paper (see p. 117 of the present volume).

[2] KARL MARX, *Kapital*, Vol. I, pp. 216-17 (Russian edition), Gospolitizdat, 1955. (The excerpt is translated from the Russian.)

of producing various products and articles with sufficient accuracy for practical purposes. They also enable us to solve a number of other very important problems arising in our planned socialist economy.

5. Many of the calculations involved in planning are made a great deal easier by the auxiliary use of mathematical techniques. National economic planning is based on complicated and extensive economic calculations. Mathematics and, in particular, matrix algebra is being used to great advantage in improving the entire system of these calculations, particularly when electronic computers are used. The value of mathematical aids is well illustrated if we take as an example the compilation of a material supplies plan and of materials balances.

A change under any one head in the material supplies plan relating to one product entails amendments under many heads in other material supplies plans, since the production of one article is closely bound up and dependent on the production of a variety of other articles. Some products of labour are intermediate in the production of others and in their turn involve counter requirements in the production of all kinds of raw materials, production materials, power and fuel.

The overlapping system of interrelated connexions arising therefrom can be illustrated with a numerical example which we have taken from Martin Natterodt's *Planning Calculation Techniques and Problems*, which sets out the experience of the German Democratic Republic.

Let four final products, A, B, C, D, be produced.

There are two variants of the output plan.

TABLE 7

Product	A	B	C	D
Variant				
1	4	80	4	34
2	12	96	5	34

To produce these end products, all kinds of primary and production materials (raw materials, fuel and so forth) will be required in addition to the intermediate products E and F. We shall denote these materials by the small letters g, h and i.

Let us assume the following norms for the consumption of intermediate products and production materials.

TABLE 8

Final and Intermediate Products	Production Materials and Intermediate Products								
	A	B	C	D	E	F	g	h	i
A		2		5		1		2	
B			1	2			1		1
C					3			2	1
D					2	1			
E						5	2	1	
F								3	1

Proceeding from these norms we have to determine the combined material input norms, bearing in mind the interconnexions entailed in production. These combined norms differ from total input only in that they are compiled on the basis of a given combination of final products, in our case *A*, *B*, *C*, *D*, whereas the total costs relate to the entire system of national economy and all the final and intermediate products. The more we extend the combination of given products the closer do we approach to determining total costs.

We now compute the material supplies, using the norms matrices. We construct a table for computing the combined norms, indicating the matrix columns to which the combined norms are transferred (see Table 9). We then construct the direct and inverted material input matrices, denoting the former by R (see Table 10) and the latter by R^{-1} (see Table 11). In this case the inverted matrix serves as a check.

We shall now explain how the combined material input norms and the matrices R and R^{-1} are constructed. The combined norms table (Table 9) starts with a table of norms (that is Table 8 is included in its entirety). Next, the combined material input norms for the production of *A*, *B*, *C* and *D* are calculated separately for each product.

Let us take product *A* in order to show the procedure for this calculation. In the first column on the left we write *A*—the final product for which the combined costs are being calculated. In the same column we write *B*, *C*, *D*, *E*, *F*—all of them final and intermediate products needed to produce *A*. In the second column on the left, alongside *A*, we write the figure 1. This means that the calculation refers to 1 unit of product A. From the table of norms with which Table 9 begins it is clear that 2 units of *B* are expended in producing *A*. We write down 2 on the same line as *A* under column *B* and again in the second column on the left alongside *B*. We then consider product *C*. This is not directly expended in producing *A*; but to produce 1 unit of product *B* we need a unit of *C* and since to produce *A* we need $2B$ it follows that indirectly $2C$ are also expended. We write 2 on the same line as *B* under column *C* and again in the second column from the left alongside *C*. Now we pass on to product *D*. Of this product 5 units are expended directly in the production of *A* and 2 units indirectly, via product *B*. We write down 5 on the same line as *A* in column *D* and 4 ($2B\times 2D$) on the same line as *B*, and in the second column from the left, alongside *D* we put 9 ($5+4$). The product *E* is not directly expended in producing *A* but is nevertheless used indirectly, via products *C* and *D* ($2C\times 3E=6; 9D\times 2E=18$). We must therefore write 6 alongside *C* in column *E* and 18 in the same column alongside *D*. The total, 24, we put in the second column from the left alongside *E*. Similarly we fill in the table for all the end and intermediate products used in producing the product with which we are concerned. The results of our calculation are given in Table 9.

By summing the columns in each part of the table we obtain a line showing the combined material input norms for the production of the given

TABLE 9

Combined Material Input Norms

	A	*B*	*C*	*D*	*E*	*F*	*g*	*h*	*i*	
A		2		5		1		2		
B			1	2			1		1	
C					3			2	1	
D					2	1			1	
E						5	2	1		
F								3	1	
A	1	2		5		1		2		
B	2		2	4			2		2	
C	2				6			4	2	
D	9				18	9			9	
E	24					120	48	24		Columns of
F	130							390	130	matrix *R*
A		2	2	9	24	130	50	420	143	*A*
B	1		1	2			1		1	
C	1				3			2	1	
D	2				4	2			2	
E	7					35	14	7		
F	37							111	37	
B			1	2	7	37	15	120	41	*B*
C	1				3			2	1	
D	—									
E	3					15	6	3		
F	15							45	15	
C					3	15	6	50	16	*C*
D	1				2	1			1	
E	2					10	4	2		
F	11							33	11	
D					2	11	4	35	12	*D*

final product. The extreme right-hand of the table is the column of the matrix *R* relating to the given final product.

Matrix *R* starts with matrix vectors which are the variants of the production target (P_1 and P_2) from Table 7. Next comes the combined norms table converted from Table 9 in such a way that its totals columns for products *A*, *B*, *C*, *D* become the columns of Table 10. Each column then starts with a unit placed at the intersection of homonymous rows and columns. Multiplying the combined material input norms by the vectors of the matrix (production target) and summing these products we obtain the two extreme

TABLE 10

Direct Matrix for Combined Material Input Norms (R)

	4	80	4	34	P_2	
	12	96	5	34	P_1	
	A	*B*	*C*	*D*	M_1	M_2
A	1				12	4
B	2	1			120	88
C	2	1	1		125	92
D	9	2	—	1	334	230
E	24	7	3	2	1,043	736
F	130	37	15	11	5,561	3,914
g	50	15	6	4	2,206	1,560
h	420	120	50	35	18,000	12,670
i	143	41	16	12	6,140	4,324

right-hand columns giving the total volume of material production and supply (M_1 and M_2) for the first and second variants separately.

TABLE 11

Inverted Matrix of Combined Material Input Norms (R^{-1})

	4	88	92	230	736	3914	1560	12670	4324	M_2	
	12	120	125	334	1043	5561	2206	18000	6140	M_1	
	A	*B*	*C*	*D*	*E*	*F*	*g*	*h*	*i*	P_1	P_2
A	1									12	4
B	−2	1								96	80
C		−1	1							5	4
D	−5	−2		1						34	34
E			−3	−2	1					0	0
F	−1			−1	−5	1				0	0
g		−1			−2		1			0	0
h	−2		−2		−1	−3		1		0	0
i		−1	−1	−1		−1			1	0	0

The inverted matrix R^{-1} is constructed in the same way. In this case, however, the figures in the extreme right-hand columns of the direct matrix R, that is columns M_1 and M_2, appear on top as row vectors, and conversely, the target figures (P_1 and P_2) are set in the extreme right-hand columns of the inverted matrix.

The internal part of the inverted matrix is filled up as follows:

1. since the inverted matrix is a square matrix we copy out all the final and intermediate products and expenditures both horizontally and vertically.
2. At the intersections of homonymous columns and rows we set units (in the direct matrix the unit is written down for the final products).

3. We bring the intermediate input norms down from the top of the columns. All the intermediate-product and production-material norms now have a *negative* sign.

Verification is by multiplying both matrices, when if both have been correctly constructed we shall obtain an identity matrix. This will show that all the calculations are correct.

The identity matrix (I) has a unity all along its main diagonal—at the top from the left, at the bottom from the right, the remaining elements being all zeros.

We consequently have the following equations:

$$R \times M = P;$$
$$M \times R^{-1} = P;$$
$$R \times R^{-1} = \mathrm{I}.$$

Here R, R^{-1} and I denote the combined norm matrices, P a vector of the direct matrix (production target) and M a vector of the inverted matrix (volume of material production and input).

The use of matrices in planning calculations is particularly important when there are a great many final products, intermediate products and production materials and when it is necessary to construct many variants of the production target for final products.

Once the matrix has been constructed it can be used for a very wide range of combinations of final-product targets. Without matrices even the slightest alteration in planning the volume of production will necessitate starting all calculations over again from the very beginning. Calculations relating to the provision of materials are exceedingly complex unless matrices are used.

Matrices can be used in determining not only combined material input norms but also combined labour input norms (in man-hours or money wages) and combined norms for the input of electrical power, fuel (in units of conventional fuel) and so forth.

6. Marx, analysing simple and extended reproduction, used mathematical aids in the form of equations and inequalities. He established highly interesting mathematical ratios between the amount of past labour embodied in the means of production used in producing consumers' goods (c_2) and the amount of living labour—paid (v_1), and surplus (m_1)—expended in producing the means of production (v_1+m_1 being the value newly created by labour in producing the means of production). In simple reproduction (a static system of economic relationships) the equation is, of course,

$$c_2 = v_1+m_1$$

In extended reproduction (a dynamic system of economic interrelationships) we have, according to Marx, the inequality

$$(v_1+m_1) < c_2$$

Lenin attached exceptional importance to these relationships, pointing out that they would also hold good under communism. The inequality cited above can be transformed into the equation of balanced extended reproduction $v_1+m_1-c_2 = M$, where M is some variable. In simple reproduction $M = 0$; in extended reproduction M equals some quantity.

In simple reproduction the whole of the surplus product is consumed as income. In expanded reproduction the surplus product m is only partially expended as income. Let us denote that part of the surplus product consumed as income by the symbol pm (where p is less than unity but greater than or equal to zero).

In expanded reproduction there are in addition two other parts of the surplus product:

(*a*) that part accumulated in the form of extra means of production required for the next cycle of production (we shall denote this part by the symbol qm where q is smaller than unity but greater than or equal to zero);

(*b*) that part which is accumulated in the form of means for the creation of extra labour power (we shall denote this by the symbol zm where z is smaller than unity but greater than or equal to zero).

We then have: $p+q+z = 1$.

In all their numerical examples of expanded reproduction Marx and Lenin gave the following equations:

$$P_1 = c_1+c_2+qm$$
$$P_2 = v_1+v_2+zm+pm$$

If we substitute values for P_1 and P_2 such that

$$P_1 = c_1+v_1+m_1 \text{ and}$$
$$P_2 = c_2+v_2+m_2$$

in the above equations, we shall in both cases obtain the identical equation for a balanced extended reproduction

$$v_1+m_1-c_2 = qm$$

We can approach this relationship somewhat differently. To this end we consider the following master scheme of extended reproduction given by Marx:

$$\left.\begin{aligned} c_1v_1m_1 &= P_1 \\ c_2v_2m_2 &= P_2 \\ cvm &= P \end{aligned}\right\} \text{ current cycle of production}$$

$$\left.\begin{aligned} c_1'v_1'm_1' &= P_1' \\ c_2'v_2'm_2' &= P_2' \\ c'v'm' &= P' \end{aligned}\right\} \text{ next cycle of production}$$

Here the subscript 1 indicates production of the means of production and the subscript 2 production of consumers' goods; c is the value of the means of production expended, v the wage fund, m the surplus product and P the social product, equal in value to $c+v+m$.

In extended reproduction the social product P_1 (means of production) and P_2 (consumers' goods) must ensure respectively an expansion of the means of production and an expansion of the wages fund required for the next cycle of production.

Equating P_1 with c_1+c_2, we have

$$c_1+v_1+m_1 = c_1'+c_2'$$

From this we find $v_1+m-c_2 = \Delta c_1$ where $\Delta c = c'-c$, that is Δc is equal to the increment of material input in the next cycle as compared with the preceding one.

This is the equation of balanced extended reproduction of the means of production.

On the other hand, the social product of Department II (P_2) must ensure the means of subsistence to the workers in all spheres of material production in the next cycle of extended reproduction ($v_1'+v_2'$) and also cover the material means necessary for the non-productive sphere (pm). Here pm is the fraction of the surplus product required in the non-productive sphere. The increment in the means of subsistence for workers in the sphere of material production is essential in order to ensure expansion of production in the next cycle. This increment too is covered by the surplus product created at the given initial stage of production. By establishing the equation $P_1 = v_1'+v_2'+pm$ we obtain the same equation of balanced expanded reproduction $v_1+m_1-c_2 = \Delta c$.

This result is obtained when we have:

$$zm = \Delta v = v'-v = (v_1'-v_1)+(v_2'-v_2)$$

Under conditions of balanced reproduction the quantities qm and Δc are equal, as are zm and Δv. In the case of unbalanced expanded reproduction, however, they are different from each other. We therefore introduce quantities characterising the material basis (potential) of expanded reproduction in the case of the means of production (M) and in the case of articles of consumption (L) in the form of the following equation:

$$M = P_1-c_1-c_2$$
$$L = P_2-v_1-v_2-pm$$

Transforming these equations (by substituting values for P_1 and P_2) for conditions of unbalanced expanded reproduction (that is when $\Delta c \neq qm$, $\Delta v \neq zm$), we obtain the following very important relationships:

$$M = v_1+m_1-c_2$$
$$L = (q+z)\, m-M$$

If $(q+z)m$ is less than M, then L is a negative quantity. A negative value of the material basis (potential) of expanded reproduction indicates over-production.

If we examine this relationship it becomes clear that the conditions for balancing expanded reproduction are made up of a definite combination of value and material elements occurring in the current cycle of production. Here, particular importance attaches to the potential of expanded reproduction M, characterising the material basis of all expanded reproduction. The sign and value of the potential is of substantial importance for the characteristics of the disproportions formed. To measure the disproportions we can in addition introduce the balance coefficient.

$$B = \frac{(q+z)m}{M}$$

The more closely B approaches unity, the more balanced is the national economy. On the other hand, the more it exceeds unity the greater the excess investment, while the more it falls short of unity the greater the under-capitalisation and over-production.

The deviation of B from unity and of $(q+z)m$ from M indicates a disproportion in the development of the national economy. Under capitalism under-investment is the most characteristic feature (though not the cause) of a period of slump and crisis, while over-investment has a similar relationship to a period of rising production. These equations, then, enable us to determine the extent of disproportionality in the national economy.

The equation of balanced extended reproduction is true for an isolated dynamic economic system. The economic interrelationships with the external environment, regulated by the trade and payment balances, were not taken into account in this equation.

Let T_c denote the foreign trade balance and D_c the balance of payments (taking foreign trade into account). Then the potential of expanded reproduction (M') under conditions of balanced expanded reproduction and taking into account external economic connexions will be:

$$M' = M + D_c - T_c$$

Consequently the positive trade balance is in this case subtracted, whereas the positive balance of payments is added.

All the above equations and inequalities are of the greatest importance in analysing an expanding economy.

Simple reproduction and expanded reproduction thus have each their own quite definite equations. Balanced expanded reproduction can occur only when there is a quite definite relationship between the parts and elements of the social product and quite definite proportions characterising the structure of social production. Marx noted this point more than once. He refers to an allocation of the elements of social production *altered for the purpose of accumulation* and to the fact that 'the elements are classified by functions in such a way that reproduction begins again on the former scale' or 'the material basis for reproduction on an expanded scale is created'.[1] He often spoke of the value elements of the social product of Departments I and II, grouped for purposes of simple reproduction or, grouped differently, for purposes of expanded reproduction.

By no means every ratio between the parts and elements of the social product makes balanced simple or balanced expanded reproduction possible. The ratio is different for expanded and for simple reproduction. With balanced expanded reproduction there is a strict interdependence between the elements of the social product of the two departments. These elements cannot have an arbitrarily chosen value. They must have such values as would express a balanced exchange between the two departments of social production.

7. The input-output balance of production does not directly give all the quantities necessary in order to establish the equations cited for balanced expanded reproduction. The reason is that this balance differs from Marx's system of expanded reproduction. It is impossible to identify the two. Yet even in Marxist literature such identification is to some extent found. Oskar Lange, for example, in his paper 'Some Observations on Input-Output Analysis'[2] deals with Leontief's input-output analysis table and maintains that the difference between this table and the system of expanded reproduction lies in the replacement of Marx's two basic social categories by a very much larger number of production sectors in the Anglo-American table. Such identification is impermissible. The transition from a production input-output balance to Marx's model of expanded reproduction can be made only through a definite transformation of the former.

Marx's system of expanded reproduction is a theoretical model of a developing national economy. This model is based on dividing the sphere of material production into two main social categories: (*a*) production of means of production, (*b*) production of articles of consumption. In addition to this breakdown of the national economy into physically distinct categories, Marx's system envisages an analysis of the social product into its basic value elements, reflecting social character of labour expenditure: (1) *past* labour, embodied in the means of production (material expenditures, including both the input of materials created by labour and the wear and tear of production equipment and the instruments of labour); (2) the socially necessary paid *living* labour (the wage fund) and (3) surplus labour, creating the surplus product spent by society in expanded reproduction (accumulation) and in maintaining the social and cultural sphere (and on the parasitic consumption of non-labouring sections of society as well, under capitalist conditions).

The input-output balance by no means fully reflects such a subdivision of the social product according to its material and value content. The situation

[1] KARL MARX, *Kapital*, Vol. II, p. 508 (Russian edition), Gospolitizdat, 1955.

[2] See p. 191 of the present volume.

is particularly bad when it comes to dividing the surplus product, since in Anglo-American research the sphere of material production and the social-cultural sphere are usually confused, in particular material production and the sphere of services. In the Anglo-American table unearned income (profit, rent, interest) is generally not identifiable as such; the same applies to income obtained through redistribution of the basic income of the people (secondary income).

To form the category of 'production of the means of production' in Marx's sense we must collect these items in the input-output balance under a single head, as the output of objects produced by labour, capital investment and stocks, that is, items evident from various quadrants in this table. To form the category of 'production of objects of consumption' we must group under a single heading such items as personal expenditure by the public and materials used by institutions and organisations.

In order to divide the basic value elements among all these material categories we must subdivide both expenditure of the objects of labour, capital expenditure and stock-formation on the one hand and on the other hand personal consumption by the population, consumption by institutions and export into the following main value elements: (1) the value of the materials used up (c), (2) payment for the labour of workers in the sphere of material production (v) and (3) surplus product (m). The latter is spent on expanded reproduction and on maintaining that part of the social and cultural sphere which is not covered by redistribution through the wages fund.

The presence of an internal quadrant constructed in the form of a chess-board table and characterising the two way flow of the means of production among branches of the national economy enables us to reconstruct (transform), with some degree of approximation, the balance of input and output into Marx's scheme of expanded reproduction.

We have experimented with such a transformation of the English input-output table for the years 1935[1] and 1950.[2] The results are shown in Table 12. The input coefficients were obtained on the basis of a chessboard table (10 lines and 10 columns—consolidated branches). If, however, a more detailed chessboard table had been worked out with the aid of an electronic computer the result would have been somewhat different and more accurate.

Such a calculation enables us not only to determine the volume of production of the means of production and the volume of production of objects of consumption but also to establish for each category the material expenditure fund (c), the wages fund (v) and the surplus product (m).

The English table, however, does not enable us to do this with sufficient accuracy, for the following reasons: (*a*) amortisation (depreciation of capital equipment) is not distinguished in it; (*b*) the profit of independent producers

[1] T. BARNA, op. cit.

[2] *National Income and Expenditure 1946-1952*, pp. 22-23, London, 1953.

TABLE 12

Balance of Expanded Reproduction for the United Kingdom
(in millions of £ sterling)

Balance Items	Production of Means of Production				Production of Consumption Goods			Foreign Trade (export)	Grand Total
	Production of objects of labour (used up)	Stocks	Capital investments	Total	Private	State	Total		
I. 1935									
Material costs:	975	87	239	1,301	1,331	112	1,443	336	3,080
excluding imports	732	60	208	1,050	903	96	$999 = c_2$	229	2,278
Value added	1,181	96	279	$1{,}556 = v_1 + m_1$	2,377	333	2,710	458	4,724
Grand total	2,156	183	518	2,857	3,708	445	4,153	794	7,804
		$(q+z)m$							
II. 1950									
Material costs:	1,811	372	499	2,682	3,553	317	3,870	1,125	7,677
excluding imports	1,354	144	519	2,017	1,940	256	$2{,}196 = c_2$	655	4,868
Value added	3,401	328	944	$4{,}673 = v_1 + m_1$	5,200	1,740	6,940	1,615	13,228
Grand total	5,212	700	1,443	7,355	8,753	2,057	10,810	2,740	20,905
		$(q+z)m$							

personally taking part in production but having no hired labour, as well as directors' salaries, are included in the wage fund; (*c*) trading profits not connected with the continuation of material production (which includes only the storage, packing and delivery of goods to the consumer, but not the operation of commercial business which forms part of the surplus product) are not distinguished in the non-productive sphere of trading profit; (*d*) non-productive investment (housing and public amenity building) are not distinguished within capital expenditure. Moreover, the surplus product (in particular that due to profits and rent accruing from foreign investments) does not appear in the English table. We have accordingly abandoned the attempt to identify the surplus product and shall give only the newly created value as the sum of v and m. It must be emphasised that our calculation has only a methodological and illustrative character. In such a form, however, the English model of expanding reproduction does enable us to establish a series of proportions which have substantial economic significance.

To convert the input-output balance into Marx's scheme of expanded reproduction it is necessary to deduct the direct input coefficients as obtained from the figures in the columns of the inner quadrant (chessboard), by dividing each figure in the relevant column by the total of the row corresponding in number to the number of the column. The direct input coefficients thus obtained are then multiplied column by column for each absolute figure standing in one of the columns of the upper right-hand quadrant (final social product). The absolute figures obtained (as a result of multiplying a given absolute figure for final output by the direct input coefficients of the column corresponding to it) are written in the columns of a supplementary table. The totals of a column will then be equal to the transformed absolute figure.

In this way, the structure of input appears in the transformed balance table not by branches of production (as in the original input-output balance) but separately by objects of labour, objects of consumption and investments, that is separately for the production of consumers' goods and for the sphere of production of the means of production.

The English input-output balance table transformed into a model of expanded reproduction, despite certain inaccuracies, does enable us to establish the quantities required to determine the potentials M and L.

In Marxist methodology the most interesting feature is the ratio between the value of past labour embodied in the means of production used in producing consumers' goods (c_2) and the value of living labour (paid and surplus) expended in the sphere of production of the means of production (v_1+m_1).

The expanded reproduction balance table given above enables us to set up the necessary equations for balanced expanded reproduction for Britain in the years 1935 and 1950.

The expanded reproduction potential for 1950 was $M = v_1+m_1-c_2 = 4{,}673-2{,}196 = 2{,}477$. The capitalised surplus product $(q+z)m$ was $1{,}443+700 = 2{,}143$.

The disproportionality, or imbalance, in the national economy is described by the quantity L:

$$L = (q+z)m - M = 2{,}143 - 2{,}477 = -334$$

The balance coefficient is:

$$B = \frac{(q+z)m}{M} = \frac{2{,}143}{2{,}477} = 0{\cdot}865$$

The measure of balance of the national economy (in the direction of under-investment) was accordingly 13·5%. If we bear in mind, however, that in this case the foreign trade balance (−99 million £ sterling) and the active balance of payments (£352 million sterling) were not taken into account, we find that the expanded reproduction potential taken into account is $M' = 2{,}898$.

The balance coefficient, taking into account foreign trade, will be $B' = \frac{2{,}143}{2{,}898} = 0{\cdot}74$. The disproportionality of expanded reproduction is already 26% in the direction of overproduction.

For 1935 we obtain the following result:

$$(q+z)m = 691, \qquad M = 557, \qquad B = \frac{691}{557} = 1{\cdot}24,$$

$$L = 691 - 557 = 134$$

These are the results for 1935, a year of some improvement in the economic situation of Britain. The potential of expanded reproduction of consumers' goods (L) for 1950 is a negative value whereas for 1935 it was positive.

Our conversion of the English balance table into an expanded reproduction table was performed using the input coefficient, that is, the production cost elements (c, v, m).

Not long ago a conversion of the same English table for 1950 into a table of final demand distribution (private consumption, State consumption, capital investment and export) was published abroad with the following items: net production, import, indirect taxes (without subsidies). The recalculation was made proportional to the output coefficients calculated per unit of final product instead of proportional to the direct input coefficients. As the value elements c, v, m were not distinguished the converted table does not make it possible to determine the potentials M and L and it is therefore impossible to establish the deviations from the proportions of a balanced expanded reproduction which exist in real economic life.

* * *

I have merely given a few illustrations of the application of mathematics to economic research. These mainly relate to aspects of the national economic balance. Numerous other possibilities for the use of mathematics in economic research are described elsewhere in this symposium, some relating to national economic problems, others to economic problems within the factory.

Cost-Benefit Comparisons in a Socialist Economy

V. V. Novozhilov

CHAPTER I

STATEMENT OF THE PROBLEM

One of the most important economic problems in the USSR at present is the question of measuring outlays and their effectiveness in socialist production, the problem of measuring the effectiveness of labour.

This is a basic problem closely associated with a number of others of the highest importance, including measurement of the productivity of labour, calculation of prime cost, establishment of correct principles of price formation, determination of the effectiveness of capital investment, distribution according to the quantity and quality of labour, implementation of economic accounting and control by means of the rouble, organisation of socialist competition, and so on. The correct solution of all these problems depends to a greater or lesser degree on how correctly outlays on the production of goods and the results of these outlays are measured or calculated.

It is quite natural that Soviet economists should have paid a great deal of attention to the methods of economic accounting. Many books and articles have appeared dealing with problems of the calculation of prime cost, price formation, measurement of the productivity of labour, determination of the effectiveness of capital investment, and so on, and several conferences have been held to discuss these problems.

However, this huge amount of work has not yet led to the solution of the problem: practical economic accounting is still far from being perfected, using as it does various 'conventional' and theoretically unfounded methods. Moreover there is an essential divergence between practice and theory as far as the measurement of outlays and their effectiveness is concerned.

1. The Divergence between Practice and Theory in the Measurement of Outlays

Economic outlays are always labour outlays, whether human labour directly applied by man to the manufacture of certain goods, or stored-up or past labour, realised in the means of production. All costs are labour costs exclusively. It follows that they can be expressed in terms of one quantity. In practice, however, outlays are divided into several heterogeneous elements which cannot be added together. For example, prime cost, investment in fixed and circulating capital (for proposed production units) or indicators of capital utilisation (for existing enterprises) are used as independent indicators.

Until a short time ago a special procedure was adopted in planning practice by enterprises and by planning and investment estimating organisations for calculating outlays of particularly scarce means of production: they independently compared outlays of materials in short supply (so many tons of copper, say) with prime cost or capital investment, sometimes using coefficients of scarcity. Nowadays scarcity is taken into account in the prices of the means of production, thus making the problem of aggregating outlays considerably easier, and substituting a general addition to the price for the scarcity coefficients used by separate organisations.

However, the legalisation of scarcity as a factor in some sense increasing outlays made the problem of finding a theoretical basis for such calculations more urgent. It was one thing or the other: either some real labour outlays underlay the extra charge for scarcity, or such an extra charge distorted the measurements of real costs. If the first was correct, then what was this outlay of labour, and how was it to be measured? If an extra charge for scarcity did not reflect labour outlays, then it should not be taken into consideration in the measurement of outlays. These are purely theoretical problems since in practice no hesitation is felt in taking scarcity as a factor which increases costs.

The measurement of capital investment as a special type of outlay raises more complex problems. There are no set rules for comparing prime cost and investment in fixed and circulating capital, since theoretically the problem is still a subject of controversy.

As far as measurement of value is concerned, the separate assessment of capital investment, and also of indicators of utilisation of fixed and circulating capital, represents double counting: when we take investment in productive capital as an independent type of outlay, amortisation, the use of raw materials, fuel, etc., are counted twice.

It is true that prime cost does not completely represent the outlay of social labour, for it does not take into account that part of the outlay of living labour which creates a product for society. It might seem to follow from this that prime cost must be supplemented by a monetary expression of labour for society, as Academician S. G. Strumilin and others have suggested. In practice however the converse is done; to prime cost is added that outlay which is already fully reflected in it, investment in fixed and circulating capital, instead of what is not already included.

The heterogeneous composition of outlays would occasion no difficulty if all the elements always varied in the same direction, if an economic variant giving a higher prime cost always called for higher investment and a greater outlay of scarce inputs.

In fact, however, it often happens that a reduction in prime cost involves an increase in capital investment, so that it becomes necessary to compare the magnitude of the economies obtained by the decrease in prime cost with that of the additional capital investment. The methods of making such a comparison are still in dispute: either the various coefficients which compare investment and prime cost conceal labour outlays which are not included in prime cost, or investments should be taken into account in the course of their use as this is reflected in prime cost, i.e. they should not be considered a separate form of outlay.

It is because there is a difference between theory and practice that the measurement of outlays is full of imperfections, of which more important are:

1. the methods of comparing investment and prime cost. In particular, there are no standards for the pay-off period for investment in relation to economies in prime cost.
2. the pricing of ancillary products and scrap. This affects the calculation of primary goods.
3. the methods of assessing the significance of 'scarcity' in the prices of some forms of raw materials and fuel.
4. the valuation of fixed capital. The defects here lie not only in the fact that the methods are out of date, but also that the very principles of valuation are unclear. Thus, no methods have been devised to allow for wear and tear, and particularly for obsolescence.
5. the methods for pricing non-reproducible means of production (such as land, when determining loss from flooding in the construction of hydro-electric stations).
6. standards of amortisation. In particular, there has been little study of the problem of determining the economically optimal working life of instruments of labour and work tools.

The divergence between theory and practice points to the need for further development of the theory, without, however, simply legitimising practice. For the generalisation of existing practice would lead to the conclusion that there can be no single indicator of outlay; a conclusion which is inconsistent not only with the labour theory of value, but also with the requirements of practice itself. Practical workers acknowledge that their methods of comparison are imperfect, and are themselves looking to theory to help them, since they well understand the defects in the existing methods of measuring outlays and their effectiveness, when, instead of using a single indicator (as the theory would lead one to expect) they must allow for two (or more) heterogeneous quantities. In many cases this makes it difficult to establish which of the possible variants requires the least outlay.

Thus theory is called upon to construct better methods of measuring outlays and to light the way to improving practice.

2. The Strange 'Law' of Development of the Measurement of Outlays

Every process of development consists in progressive motion from the lower to the higher. There is no reason why the development of methods of measuring outlays should not be subject to the same law. As economics has developed from lower to higher forms, methods of measurement of outlays should have developed accordingly from the less to the more exact forms. For, as we know, the higher the level of economic development, the greater is the significance of economy of labour, and the fuller is the functioning of the law of economy of labour.

However, if the outlay of any good is measured by the labour expended in producing it, then the whole historical course of development of the measurement of outlays turns out to be retrogressive, from the higher to the lower. For it was only during the period of simple commodity production that the prices of individual commodities gravitated towards their values. With the rise of capitalism, the prices of individual commodities began systematically to deviate from their values and to approach the prices of production.

If value is an exact expression of real cost, then the deviations of production prices from values means that under capitalism the law of value performs its function as a measure of real cost less well than under feudalism. And as the capitalist method of production develops this process continues, since owing to the growth of the organic composition of capital the deviations become more and more significant.

We arrive at the paradox that at the higher stage of development outlays are measured less perfectly than at the lower stage. And what is even more remarkable, under socialism too outlays are measured not in accordance with value but with systematic deviations from it. It transpires that under socialism, when the economy of labour becomes more important than ever before, labour costs are measured less exactly than under feudalism. We obtain the following strange 'law': the more completely the law of the economy of labour functions, the less perfectly are labour costs measured.[1]

Thus, if value is taken to be the most perfect reflection of the real costs incurred on each separate product, then the law of development of methods of measuring costs is inconsistent with one of the most general laws of dialectical materialism. Therefore either the process of development from the lower to the higher is not a general law, or the labour expended on the

[1] It is interesting that this 'law' does not apply to the development of simple commodity production: 'The more fully simple commodity-production develops, the more the average prices over long periods uninterrupted by external violent disturbances coincide with values within a negligible margin.' (K. Marx, *Capital*, Vol. III, p. 876, Foreign Languages Publishing House, 1959.)

production of an individual product is not the best form of measurement of outlays.

It seems to us that we must give preference to the more general law, the law of dialectics. The reasons for doing so are not only that it is a conclusion derived from a much wider mass of facts than the proposition about measuring the outlay on any product in terms of the labour expended in its production (especially if we remember that, as we have shown, this statement does not explain what is done in practice) but also that it is only by the further application of dialectics to the measurement of outlays that we can eliminate all the contradictions between theory and practice that have been noted. As we shall prove, the measuring of the labour used in the production of each separate product is neither the sole nor the best method for the measurement of labour costs. At a certain stage in the development of the social economy other, better ways arise.

3. The Gap between Theory and Practice in the Measurement of the Results of Labour

Difference between theory and practice also occurs in the measurement of the results of labour. Reasoning logically we should expect the value expression of the results to reflect the labour socially necessary for the production of the given goods. Then by comparing the actual labour cost with that which is socially necessary we should obtain a measure of the effectiveness of the actual cost. For example, if the actual cost is half the necessary cost, we should consider that the labour utilised for the given output has yielded a product twice as great as the social average.

However, it is doubtful whether the prices of goods offer a true reflection of the labour it was necessary to expend, so that in practice value indicators are looked on with suspicion. Thus the low profitability, or even loss, of an industry does not always indicate that it is economically ineffective, and conversely high profitability may not mean high effectiveness of labour. For this reason the results of labour are often measured by the quantity of output, although the substitution of a quantitative measurement for a value measurement encourages quantitative goals to the detriment of quality and of genuine effectiveness in the use of labour.

These are the defects in the measurement of the results of the outlay of living and past labour.

There is a still more remarkable gulf between theory and practice in the measurement of living labour.

Theoretically, the economic result of living labour is measured by a single indicator—net production, i.e. the contribution to the national income; but in practice there is no synthetic indicator of the results of living labour. The net product of enterprises is not even calculated. Those indicators which are used in practice suffer from basic defects. It is difficult to imagine a more serious error in economic accounting than the blurring of distinctions between income and expenditure, results and costs, and yet elements of this error occur in the commonest methods of measuring the results of living labour by gross output (on a factory basis) or by the quantity of output produced.

In fact, the gross output of an enterprise is a measure of the result of the work of a number of other enterprises as well, namely those supplying the means of production used in producing the gross output. Therefore gross output of an enterprise might increase at the cost of an increase in the utilisation of producer goods obtained 'on the side'. It is clear that by including material outlays in the indicator of results we encourage excessive use of materials, instead of economy in them. This defect of the indicator of gross output has been so well illustrated in our Press that it would be superfluous to give any examples here.

The same error (although in a less conspicuous form) appears in the measurement of the results of living labour by the quantity of goods produced. For the quantity of output often depends on the quantity of utilised producer goods and not only on the effectiveness of living labour. For example, if output is measured by weight, it sometimes turns out to be directly dependent on the material input per useful unit of output.

This means that the measurement of the results by living labour by the quantity of output contains elements of the same confusion of results with outlay which is characteristic of taking gross output as an indicator of the results of living labour.

Finally, the indicators used to measure the output of enterprises suffer from the essential defect that they do not reflect economies of past labour. But the use of past labour is a component part of the result of living labour. Moreover it is an important part: the use of past labour constitutes on the average 76% of the prime cost of industrial output.

It is true that the use of past labour is considered in the net return (profits) of the enterprise. However, the role of this indicator is contradictory. On the one hand, it is the most general quantitative indicator of the operation of an enterprise, more general than prime cost. On the other, enterprises sometimes should not be guided by it, for it can conflict with their plan (for example, with the planned product-mix).

Moreover, profit does not reflect satisfactorily such elements of the result of living labour as the use of fixed and circulating capital, since this affects profit only in so far as it is reflected in prime cost. At the same time the relation between the use of capital and prime cost is not a simple one; in some cases an improved use of capital is accompanied by a decrease in prime cost, and in other cases by an increase.[1] Therefore prime cost has to be supplemented by indicators of the use of productive capital, and so practice still possesses no synthetic indicator of the results of living labour.

This leads to the need for a large number of indicators of the results of

[1] For example, a decrease in the batch size of mass produced machines accelerates the turnover of circulating capital but increases the prime cost of the goods.

the operation of various productive units (the enterprise, works or sector). A multiplicity of indicators makes it difficult to draw any general conclusion about the measure of success of the operation of the various productive units, and also complicates payment by results. In particular, because of the absence of general rules for weighting the different indicators, qualitative indicators are often underrated compared with quantitative ones, especially those concerning the use of fixed and circulating capital.

Recently the search for a synthetic indicator of the results of living labour has been resumed. This is a step forward, but the new proposals still do not solve the problems.

The defects we have noted in the comparisons of output with input lead to the difference between theory and practice in the measurement of the effectiveness of resource utilisation, i.e. in the comparison of results and costs. For example, in measuring the productivity of labour, the product of living and past labour (gross output, quantity of goods produced) is compared with the outlay of living labour. But in calculating profitability, profit (i.e. the net effect of the use of living labour) is compared with the living and past labour costs, with the prime cost of the marketed output. In both cases the correspondence between the magnitudes being compared (of input and output) is destroyed.

Yet another example of the divergence between theory and practice in the comparison of output with input is afforded by the use of what is known as 'unit' capital investment as an indicator of the effectiveness of investment, this being the ratio of investment to the quantity of output produced in a given time-period. This indicator ascribes too large a result to investment, including all the output produced with its aid.

4. The Significance of the Problem of the Measurement of Outlays and their Results

Our economists certainly have paid much attention to the problem of the comparison of outlays with results. However, it is so large a problem that the amount of work being done on it at present is still insufficient.

Because of the complexity of economic interdependencies, the losses caused by defects in the accounting of outlays and their results are spread over a number of stages, and so are not easily noticed or determined.

If a worker spoils an article, the loss is obvious and easily calculated. It is much more difficult to calculate losses from bad organisation of the plant or works, although these can be much larger than losses from rejects. But the most difficult task of all is that of the economist who tries to note and measure losses from incorrect accounting methods, which amount to many milliards of roubles.

The table below shows losses that could be caused by the lack of a common standard of investment effectiveness.

Suppose that there are alternative projects, one based on a standard pay-off period of two years, and the other on a standard pay-off period of 20 years.[1]

We have the two proposed production units A and B with the following expenditure for each variant:

TABLE 1

	A				*B*		
Variant	Capital Invest-ment (roubles m.)	Prime Cost of Annual Output (roubles m.)	Pay-off Period (Years)	Variant	Capital Invest-ment (roubles m.)	Prime Cost of Annual Output (roubles m.)	Pay-off Period (Years)
I_A	50	75	—	I_B	50	50	—
II_A	100	50	2	II_B	100	47·5	20
				III_B	550	25	20

If we stipulate that all the variants for each unit fulfil identical tasks (i.e. give identical output) and are identical in the qualitative elements of their effect (conditions of labour, and so on), then each combination of variants for the units A and B will also fulfil identical tasks (as far as output and the purposes of economic policy are concerned).

Let us further assume that additional investment in both production units is not associated with additional outlay of scarce forms of input, since otherwise economies in prime cost would result not only from the additional investment, but also from the additional outlay of scarce materials, and so on.

Let us find the cost (in million roubles) required by various combinations of variants of A and B given the standard pay-off periods:

$$\text{for } A = 2 \text{ years}$$
$$\text{for } B = 20 \text{ years}$$

TABLE 2

Combination	Investment	Prime Cost of Annual Output
$I_A + II_B$	150	122·5
$I_A + III_B$	600	100

The first combination is formed if the limits of investment in the production unit B are relatively restricted; the second, for wider investment limits.

Consider now the combination of variants of A and B which is formed for a common standard pay-off period between 2 and 20 years.

TABLE 3

Combination	Investment	Prime Cost of Annual Output
$II_A + I_B$	150	100

[1] It should be noted that even greater differences between the pay-off periods of accepted variants can occur in practice. It often happens that for a long time there are variants of investment which would pay off over a period of less than two years which are not put into effect, while variants with pay-off periods of 20 years and more are being implemented.

Let us compare this combination with the two previous ones.

The first two entailed large losses. The first ($I_A + II_B$) involved additional cost outlays to the tune of 22·5% for the same total investment. (We compare the numbers underlined once in Tables 2 and 3.)

The second combination of Table 2 ($I_A + III_B$) requires four times as large an investment as that with a common standard pay-off period without giving any economy in prime cost. (We compare the numbers underlined twice in the two tables.)

Since the combinations we are comparing give identical output, those using different standard pay-off periods needlessly entail net losses which would be huge on a nation-wide scale.

These losses are greatest when we attempt to be guided by minimum prime cost (or individual value) of output; for when capital expenditure is restricted the principle of minimising prime cost involves the greatest difference between pay-off periods for investment. Although there are still some supporters of the view that minimum prime cost can be a criterion of the effectiveness of outlays, nevertheless in practice some pay-off norms or other are used. The average difference between those periods is less than in the example we have given. Therefore the relative overspending in prime cost and investment (caused by the use of incorrect norms for the effectiveness of investment) is less than in our example. However, the absolute overspending can probably be expressed in milliards of roubles per year.

Let us consider our example more fully.

If we take the variants separately, we see that it is not possible for us to know which, if any, is ineffective by itself. This means that if one variant is 'worse' than the other in terms of prime cost, then it is 'better' from the standpoint of investment, and vice versa: the example contains no variant which would be worse than the others without some compensations. But we find that combinations of these separately effective variants can be ineffective. It is for this reason that the project-maker, working in his own sphere, is not in a position either to notice or to prevent economically ineffective combinations of variants in the economy as a whole if he is not guided by an appropriate standard pay-off period.

We have been considering only one form of loss resulting from the incorrect measurement of costs. Calculations of costs are used not only to determine investment effectiveness, but also to make good use of existing means of production, both reproducible and non-reproducible.

Suppose that we change the headings in our example, and instead of 'investment in million roubles' we put 'outlay of scarce raw materials in thousands of tons per year', and instead of 'pay-off period of investments' we put 'outlay of scarce raw materials in kg. per rouble of economy in prime cost'.

Then we find that if the prices of the scarce raw material do not regulate its use in the necessary way, we can form combinations of variants which require either a four times greater outlay of scarce raw materials (for the same prime cost of output) or excessive prime cost for the same total outlay of scarce raw materials.

Similar examples could be found for any means of production. Almost all capital (plots of land, ore deposits, buildings, machinery, etc.) can be used in various ways and to varying effect. And, as with capital investment, combinations of separately effective variants of the use of every relatively better means of production can be ineffective.

It is difficult to imagine the scale of losses due to the ineffective use of productive capital and natural resources, but they probably exceed the losses caused by errors in the calculation of the effectiveness of investments, for annual investment comprises only a small part of all productive capital.

Our example illustrates only those losses which arise in the process of planning, whereas defects in the measurement of costs also affect the fulfilment of the plan, economic accounting, distribution according to labour, and the organisation of industrial management.

An improvement in economic accounting must consist not only in an extension of the independence of enterprises (which is the easiest of all to achieve) but, primarily, in the perfection of this method as a tool in economic planning.

The potentialities for doing this are great.

We know that the targets set by a plan are a long way from being always consistent with the financial stimuli at enterprise level. There are 'profitable' and 'unprofitable' targets for enterprises. Financial advantage often conflicts with the interests of the economy, with the plan.

We have already noted the defects in using gross product as an indicator in this respect. Due to them, it often becomes unprofitable for an enterprise to economise on materials, since this has a negative effect on the gross product, as well as on the indicators of labour productivity. For the same reason it is often not worthwhile for an enterprise to fulfil the product-mix plan. The same must be said about such indicators as profitability and the utilisation of productive capital. The profitability of an enterprise often fails to measure its economic effectiveness, and the indicators of the use of capital which are applied do not reflect the effectiveness with which it is utilised.

Differences between enterprise profitability and national economic advantage are so common that they are thought to be unavoidable. Indeed, some economists believe the divergence between the economic effectiveness and the profitability of enterprises (i.e. losses incurred in productive operations which are run from the standpoint of the entire economy) to be an advantage of socialism.

But is this so?

It is natural under capitalism for private gain to be different from social gain. If, when socialist construction began, many important sectors of industry still made losses, this was understandable. It is undoubtedly true that in the past, at the dawn of socialist industrialisation, planning bodies could make much less use of the law of value than today. Essential sectors of industry were still unprofitable, and so it was a good thing that the industrialisation plan could be realised without the support of its law of value, even in spite of this law.

But, as the proverb goes, 'Every vegetable has its season'. Now that socialism has become so strong, it is time to attempt a wider appreciation of the law of value as a planning tool. Differences between economic advantage and enterprise profitability make economic accounting and the planning based on it more difficult, and complicate the determination of the results of work and distribution according to work done.

All economic accounting indicators should correctly reflect the corresponding economic phenomenon. The main difficulty lies in achieving this in dynamic terms, i.e. so that each increment in the enterprise profitability indicators corresponds to the same increment in terms of wider economic advantage.

On the accuracy of measuring outlays and production depends the correctness of planning proposals made in the localities, i.e. the correctness of all basic work of formulating the plan. The correctness of payment according to quantity and quality of labour depends on the reliability of the economic accounting indicators. The principal difficulty here lies not in the determination of the standard of payment per unit of final-product, but in the measurement of the product of labour. The better this is measured, the closer is the connexion between labour and payment for it, and the more fully material interests in the results of production are ensured.

The reliability of the indicators is at the same time a necessary condition for the democratisation of production management. Otherwise the extension of the rights of enterprises to take decisions also increases the possibility that they will pursue profitability when this will not coincide with the interests of the economy as a whole.

Thus, an increase in the reliability of economic accounting indicators is essential for the improvement of planning, of industrial management organisations, of distribution according to work done and of the growth of the material interest of the worker in the results of his labour. This is one of the most important preconditions for the perfection of socialist production relations, a decisive factor in the development of production.

It is difficult even to imagine what scope there would be for the development of the creative activity of the workers, for the development of economic accounting and democratic centralism in economic life, if it were possible to measure easily and exactly what each enterprise, shop and worker gives to society. Inexhaustible sources of new wealth, more plentiful than the richest natural resources, would be tapped.

The problem of making the best use of the creative energy of many millions of workers is in essence the problem of using the immense internal energy of the 'atoms of society'. The significance of this problem can clearly be compared with that of the use of atomic energy. Of course, there are basic differences between these two problems: in particular, the energy reserves of 'atoms of society' are not available to every social system. But it is just for this reason that the study of the use of these reserves is worthy of special attention from our economists.

There is little doubt that it should be possible to construct prices and economic accounting indicators in such a way that economic accounting would become a reliable planning tool. We can imagine the basic lines of accounting and pricing methods to be so formulated that the production of the planned range of goods would be more profitable for an enterprise than violation of the plan, that savings in the accounting prime costs at enterprise level would be a reflection of savings in real cost from the standpoint of the economy as a whole, and that enterprises would have an interest in technical progress, in the best use of its productive capital.

Why is it then that, despite the enormous significance of the measurement of outlays and their results, in practice these measurements are still so imperfect, and that they are, probably, the greatest obstacle in the development of the socialist economy, restricting the fullest use of its advantages?

A basic reason for this situation lies in the fact that partial problems of the measurement of outlays and their results (price formation, accounting, measurement of output, effectiveness of capital investment and so on) are still not counted as a single problem. Economists trying to solve these problems do not think of the whole aggregate of interconnexions, yet without doing this not a single particular problem in the determination of the effectiveness of social labour can be solved.

For example, the problem of the effectiveness of capital investment necessarily involves questions concerning the prices of producers' goods, the calculation of prime cost, the determination of obsolescence, and so on. In their turn, problems of the economic effectiveness of new techniques, the effectiveness of mechanisation and automation and so on cannot be solved without solving the problem of the effectiveness of investment.

The present work is concerned with the general problem of measuring outlay and its results, measuring the effectiveness of labour in a socialist economy. We attempt to put the problem as a whole and to point the way to its solution. The work is based on articles published between 1939 and 1958, now revised and supplemented specially for this edition.

CHAPTER II

MEASUREMENT OF THE RELATIVE EFFECTIVENESS OF OUTLAY ON LABOUR WITHOUT MEASUREMENT OF OVERALL SOCIAL BENEFITS

1. The Effectiveness of Social Labour

Outlay and the return to outlay are measured in order to solve a major question of practical economics—how to find the effectiveness of social labour. This is one of the broadest concepts of economics, and for this reason is not easy to define.

First of all we must define 'effectiveness' in general. The general concept is a wide one, applicable in various spheres. Effectiveness is the ratio of return (or effect) to outlay costs. By comparing various types of outlay with the specific components of the useful return they produce, we obtain such indicators of effectiveness as labour productivity, efficiency and the rate of machine utilisation. Indicators of effectiveness are often expressed in reciprocal form as the ratio of costs to return, e.g. prime cost per unit of output and cost of fuel per unit of output.

However, all the indicators of effectiveness which are in use are imperfect; they take insufficient account of either outlay or return or usually of both. Yet, in order to make economic decisions or to choose between alternative plans (or projects) it is necessary to know the relationship between the overall economic effect and all the economic outlays involved for each of the variants being compared. It is necessary to know their overall or social effectiveness.

Since outlays consist in reality only of labour costs, social effectiveness of labour is the same thing as the effectiveness of social labour.

The effectiveness of labour is usually identified with its productivity, although in fact the product of labour and the social return to labour are not the same thing. The overall return to labour does not consist only of output. The construction and operation of new enterprises make it possible both to produce more and to solve other problems.

Thus, the construction of a factory in a culturally backward region is a factor in raising the cultural level of the population. A technological process which makes it easier to convert the industry concerned with defence strengthens the defence potential of the country. These benefits from outlays usually cannot be measured. Nevertheless we must take them into account when attempting to find whether outlay is appropriate to return.

The distinction between labour productivity and the effectiveness of labour is not due only to the fact that effectiveness includes components which cannot be measured; even if it did not include them, labour effectiveness would still not be identical with labour productivity. The productivity of labour is the ratio of the amount of output to outlay on labour, but the useful effect of output is not measured by its amount: a product can be useful or useless, necessary or superfluous. The measurement of output in physical terms does not take these factors into account. Yet the overall economic effect of outlays is both to satisfy material wants and to achieve other goals of the socialist government.

If there is an increase in unwanted production, labour productivity may rise, but its effectiveness may fall. The essence of the definition of the effectiveness of labour is expressed in the following remark by Engels about planning in a communist society: 'The useful effects of the various articles of consumption, compared with each other and with the quantity of labour required for their production, will in the last analysis determine the plan.'[1]

According to Engels, in order to construct a plan it is necessary to compare the useful effects of products, and not only the amount produced. The relative significance of different lines of production has to be discovered, and at the same time the useful effects of consumer goods must be compared with the labour costs necessary to produce them. In this way we can establish both the amount of each product and the total volume of material production.

Of course the society Engels had in mind was a communist society with historical conditions different from those of the USSR; in particular, he assumed that the law of value had already lost its force. However, the idea that a plan should be constructed on the basis of comparing the 'useful effects' of goods and not their quantity is completely valid also in our conditions. It is impossible to determine whether a certain product justifies the costs incurred in producing it without comparing the different use-values qualitatively. It would be impossible to determine in what proportions to produce goods if we took into account only the quantity of output without considering how quantities correspond to needs, for quantities of heterogeneous products are incommensurable, and so the ratios of their outputs cannot by themselves give any basis for determining what their proportions should be.

It follows that the effectiveness of social labour is represented by the productivity of labour if one takes into account not only the quantity of output but also how it corresponds to needs, and also to the other component parts of the overall return to labour which are not measureable.

2. A Basic Rule for Comparing the Effectiveness of Labour Outlays

From what has been said it will be clear that it is impossible to determine

[1] Engels, *Anti-Dühring*, p. 293, Gospolitizdat, 1957.

the absolute level of labour effectiveness, taking both measurable and unmeasurable elements of effect into account. However this does not prevent us from measuring the relative effectiveness of labour. While the effectiveness of social labour may not be expressible by a number, the relationship of the effectivenesses of outlays on two alternative plans (or projects) may, under one condition, be expressed by a number.

This condition is that the social benefits from the alternatives being compared shall be identical.

We cannot measure overall social benefits, but we can establish whether the goals attained by the variants will be identical. It is essential to be able to do this (to determine whether the economic effect is identical or not) in order to compare the economic effectiveness of various projects. When the social benefit from them is identical, the ratio of the economic effectiveness of each is inversely proportional to the ratio of the costs incurred in each case.

Thus, when the effect of all the variants being compared is identical, the comparison is based on outlays. The outlays on the different alternatives are commensurable, and also the investments required for different alternatives. We can determine the ratio of the operational costs of one alternative to those of another.

This gives us the first rule for comparing the overall economic effectiveness of alternative projects, which can be called 'the rule of identity of effect'. It may be stated as follows: the alternative projects to be compared must fulfil identical overall economic purposes, i.e. must be equivalent in (*a*) volume; (*b*) composition; (*c*) location; (*d*) timing; (*e*) the needs they satisfy; and (*f*) they must serve the same aims of economic policy in their nature, volume, location and time.

Let us amplify the various points of this rule separately.

Point (*a*). It may seem at first glance that differences in the extent to which need is satisfied should not prevent comparison of the economic effectiveness of alternatives: but in fact they do. The point is, that different levels of output in a projected productive unit affect the effectiveness of the output of the same product elsewhere.

Clearly, having chosen a project which covers a certain portion of the requirements for the given product, we thereby limit the volume of output of other new enterprises in the same field. From a social standpoint, what matters most is the effectiveness with which total, not partial, requirements are satisfied. Therefore we cannot make firm decisions by comparing the indicators of effectiveness of alternatives which meet different portions of a partial need.

For example, if one alternative satisfies 100% of society's need for a product and another only 50% we cannot establish which will satisfy all the needs at minimum cost by comparing costs of production. The first alternative satisfies all the needs, and the second only half of them. Therefore we know the total operational costs of the first alternative in satisfying the given needs, but in the second case we know only part of these costs. It is quite possible that the cost of production satisfying the rest of the needs is very much higher than the cost of the output in the second alternative. As a result, the average cost of the total output in the second case will be higher than in the first, even if the second alternative (in satisfying 50% of the needs) produces output which is cheaper per unit than the first.

It follows that indicators of effectiveness can be compared only when the same proportion of wants is satisfied, i.e. when there is the same volume of production. Only then does the effectiveness of the production of the rest of the output not depend on which alternative project is selected.

Point (*b*). It is hardly necessary to prove that the prime cost of production of one kilowatt-hour of electricity is not commensurable with the prime cost of production of one ton of pig iron. Similarly we cannot compare different investment expenditures per unit of different kinds of output. In addition, differences in the qualitative composition of the effect prevent comparison of the benefits deriving from alternative projects not only when their effects contain different components, but also when they contain the same components, but in different proportions.

Point (*c*). Different locations of projected enterprises do not in themselves prevent us from comparing the outlays on these enterprises, provided that the alternatives being compared are intended to satisfy needs which are the same in their location and in all other respects. It is not necessary for the plan to locate the project variants in the same place for their effectiveness to be compared, but the area supplied must be identical. The outlays on the different alternative projects of a machine-building works which is to supply the whole of the Soviet Union can be completely commensurable even though the sites which are being examined are several thousand kilometres apart.

Point (*d*). Two different projects with output identical in composition, quantity and location of consumption area will nevertheless be incommensurable if they do not produce the output at the same time. Thus, if for some reason or other one factory is to begin to produce three years later than another, the outlays on the alternatives will be incommensurable: for over the course of three years the effects of the outlays will be very different; the second factory will produce when the first does not.

Point (*e*). The physical or chemical properties of different output need not be completely identical for the effectiveness of alternatives to be compared. Provided that the two products serve to satisfy identical wants, then we can compare the outlays on their production.

For example, we can compare the benefits from alternative methods for supplying fuel energy, although the chemical composition and physical properties of peat, coal, slate and other forms of fuel are different.

Point (*f*). The effectiveness of alternatives cannot be compared if there are different non-measurable components of the return, i.e. differences in the way in which, or the extent to which, the variants realise aims of economic policy, such as the development of backward areas and the strengthening of the defence potential. Thus, if the alternatives which are being compared give identical output, but one of them facilitates the economic and cultural development of a backward area to a greater degree than the other, then the ratio of their effectiveness will not be inversely proportional to the ratio of their expenditure.

3. Reduction of Alternative Projects to a Common Effect

The rule of identity of effect makes such rigorous demands on the methods of comparing effectiveness that it might seem to be impracticable. In practice alternative projects rarely produce effects which are identical in all respects. Moreover, even if some did so, they would almost never exhaust all possible alternatives satisfying the given aims. Yet it is necessary to examine all possible alternatives, and even sometimes to compare their effectiveness, in order to determine which requires the least outlay.

The effectiveness of variants even with quite different effect can be compared, provided that they can be reduced to a common effect.

The method of reduction is essentially very simple. Suppose that we have to compare the economic effectiveness of two alternatives, one giving the effect $(a+b)$, and the other $(a+c)$ with the same outlay.

In this case it would be incorrect to determine the relative effectiveness of both projects by comparing the differences in the indicators of effectiveness with differences in the degree of overall economic usefulness of the output of each, $(a+b)$ and $(a+c)$. It would only be necessary to make such a comparison of outlay and usefulness if, when one of the variants was selected, the first, say c, could not be produced elsewhere, and when the second was selected, there was no possibility of producing b. Then it would be necessary to take into account the value of c and b to the economy, to compare this with the outlay and decide which one to select.

In fact, when alternative projects with differently composed effects are compared, it is not necessary to do this. As a rule, the choice of one particular alternative does not make it impossible to produce the goods or obtain the benefits which were available in the rejected alternatives but are absent from the one selected. The benefits absent from the selected alternative can be obtained by other means. In our example, choosing the alternative which will produce $(a+b)$ and rejecting the one producing $(a+c)$ does not normally mean that the economy will have to do without c, or cut its consumption of it. All it means is that c must be produced by other means.

If c can be produced by other methods then it is possible to reduce the variants to a common (identical) effect and, therefore, to compare their effectiveness.

In fact, if we select the project producing $(a+b)$ instead of the one producing $(a+c)$ then we must specify how, and at what cost, the demand for

c could be satisfied. Conversely, if we select the project producing $(a+c)$ instead of that producing $(a+b)$ we must specify how and at what cost the demand for b could be satisfied. In other words, we must in either case consider the outlay on the production of $a+b+c$ by the various methods, in the first case $a+b$ being produced together and c separately, and in the second $a+c$ being produced together and b separately.

We can reduce the alternatives to an identical effect by adding to each one the production of that output (or components of the effect) which the others produce and it does not. We must then increase the outlay on it by the amount required to produce the additional components of the effect. The effect of all the transformed variants will then be the same and therefore the outlays on each will be commensurable.

Thus in order to reduce to a common effect one must find those combinations of projects which include the compared alternatives of the proposed production unit and produce an identical social effect. It is clear that such combinations can be formed from different numbers of alternatives. In fact the condition of identity of effect is completely satisfied also by the project alternatives transformed in such a way that each of them is supplemented by the rest of the whole economy, so that the alternatives become:

1. the whole economy including the first alternative $(a+b)$ and the production of the product c separately;
2. the whole economy including the second alternative $(a+c)$ and the production of the product b separately.

However there is no need to increase in this way the number of alternatives being compared. We can restrict ourselves entirely to as many as are necessary and sufficient to attain identity. We must supplement each alternative by the goods produced by the others but not by it (or else produced by it in smaller quantities). Their production must be taken to be as large as it is in that alternative in which it is the largest.

The following is a scheme for reducing the alternatives to a common effect.

Suppose that we are comparing four alternatives, given by the following data:

TABLE 4

Variants	Annual Output	Operational Costs (roubles per year)	Capital Investment (roubles)
I	$100a+100b$	1,000	2,000
II	$100a+50c$	1,100	2,300
III	$100a+50c+50d$	1,300	2,250
IV	$100a+150e$	900	2,000

In this form these alternatives are incommensurable. Suppose further that the goods b, c, d and e can be produced separately with a comparatively higher effectiveness than by any other method. Then the common effect of the variants I to IV is

$$100a+100b+50c+50d+150e.$$

Let us suppose that the costs of producing *b*, *c*, *d* and *e* separately are:

TABLE 5

Output	Operational Costs (roubles per year)	Capital Investment (roubles)
$100b$	200	50
$50c$	200	300
$50d$	100	200
$150e$	50	50

Now we can reduce all the variants to a common effect by adding to each the additional outlay necessary to produce an output equal to the common effect. As a result we obtain the following total outlay on each of the reduced alternatives (where the reduced output of each is equal to

$$100a+100b+50c+50d+150e):$$

TABLE 6

Variants	Output before Reduction	Ouptut added for Reduction to Common Effect	Additional Operational costs (roubles per year)	Additional Investment (roubles)	Outlay on Reduced Alternatives: Operational costs (roubles per year)	Outlay on Reduced Alternatives: Capital investment (roubles)
I	$100a+100b$	$50c+50d+150e$	350	550	1,350	2,550
II	$100a+50c$	$100b+50d+150e$	350	300	1,450	2,600
III	$100a+50c+50d$	$100b+150e$	250	100	1,550	2,350
IV	$100a+150e$	$100b+50c+50d$	500	550	1,400	2,550

Since the reduced variants have identical output, the outlays on them are commensurable, and we see that of the four it is I which has the highest effectiveness. It is true that the alternative I requires more capital investments than alternative III, but the difference in these once-for-all outlays is compensated by economies in operational costs over one year. Therefore in this case there is no doubt as to which variant should be chosen.

4. EXAMPLES OF THE REDUCTION OF PROJECT ALTERNATIVES TO A COMMON EFFECT

Let us illustrate what we have said with some obvious examples of the reduction to a least common effect.

1. *Reduction to the Same Volume of Output*

Problem: It is proposed to recapitalise an electric power station with the following indicators:

Output of electrical energy:

before recapitalisation	125	million kwh/year
after recapitalisation	250	million kwh/year

Investment required for recapitalisation	17·5 million roubles
Prime cost of electrical energy:	
before recapitalisation	10 kopecks/kwh
after recapitalisation	8 kopecks/kwh

Is the recapitalisation effective?

Let us try first of all to solve this problem without reducing the alternatives to a common effect. The recapitalisation results in an economy in prime cost of two kopecks per kilowatt-hour, and so the investment required for the recapitalisation will be compensated by economies in prime cost. However, in attempting to find out the annual savings in prime cost we run into serious difficulties. By what volume of annual output should one multiply the economy in prime cost per unit of output: by the amount which was produced before recapitalisation (125 million kwh/year), or by the output after it? If it is the former, then clearly our result will not reflect the economies in prime cost resulting from the increase in output. But if we multiply the economies in prime cost by the output after recapitalisation, then in this case it is clear that we are spreading the economies over that part of the output which did not exist before, and so a fictitious saving will creep into our calculation.

Suppose that in order not to overestimate the effectiveness of recapitalisation we cautiously accept the first solution. Then the investment required for the recapitalisation is offset by an economy in prime cost within seven years $\left(\frac{17{,}500{,}000}{0{\cdot}02 \times 125{,}000{,}000} = 7\right)$. Therefore we can conclude that even on the most conservative estimate the recapitalisation pays off in a comparatively short time, and is therefore effective.

Unfortunately this conclusion is based on the erroneous comparison of alternatives with different volumes of output. Therefore, it may be true, but only by accident. For, even if it was decided not to recapitalise the power station the need for an additional production of 125 million kwh would still have to be satisfied. Suppose that this could be achieved by building a new power station, requiring an investment of 20 million roubles due to its more favourable location in relation to fuel resources, and producing at the average prime cost per kwh (to the consumer) of five kopecks.

By considering other possible methods of satisfying the energy requirements we have obtained the data needed to reduce the project variants to a common effect.

The reduced variants are shown in Table 7.

It is clear that we were previously mistaken about the effectiveness of recapitalisation. When we solved the problem without reducing to a common effect we found that the recapitalisation would afford an economy in prime cost, and would pay off its cost in seven years. After reducing the variants to a common effect, we find that the recapitalisation increases prime cost by 1,250,000 roubles per year. True, it economises on capital investment, but

TABLE 7

Variant	Output	Investment	Prime Cost of Annual Output
I (without re-capitalisation)	125 (old station) + 125 (new station) = 250 million kwh/yr.	20 million roubles	$0{\cdot}1 \times 125{,}000{,}000 + 0{\cdot}05 \times 125{,}000{,}000 = 18{,}750{,}000$ roubles per year
II (recapitalisation)	250 million kwh/yr. (recapitalised station)	17·5 million roubles	$0{\cdot}08 \times 250{,}000{,}000 = 20{,}000{,}000$ roubles per year

the extra cost of the new station is offset by economies in prime cost after two years:

$$\left(\frac{20{,}000{,}000 - 17{,}500{,}000}{20{,}000{,}000 - 18{,}750{,}000}\right)$$

It will now be easy to discover the cause of the difficulties encountered in attempting to determine the total economy in prime cost from recapitalisation without reducing to a common effect. They arise from the fact that our accounting was based on the erroneous comparison of variants which gave unequal volumes of output. Because of this, both the possible methods of determining the total economy were incorrect. When we multiplied the economy obtained from a decrease in the prime cost per unit of output by the volume of production before recapitalisation we were allowing for economies (in this case negative[1]) on the increased production brought about by the recapitalisation. On the other hand, in multiplying the economy in prime cost per unit of output by the volume of production after recapitalisation, we were assuming without any justification that if the recapitalisation was not carried out the need for the additional 125 million kwh per year could only be satisfied with operational costs as high as those of the old power station.[2]

2. *Reduction to Common Composition and Volume of Output*

Suppose we are considering a hydro-electric power station with a production of 200 million kwh per year which is combined with the starting up of navigation which will reduce the prime cost of the transportation of two million ton-kilometres of freight per year between the points $a, b, c, \ldots k$ along the river A. Even if we decide against constructing this station, the need for electricity and transportation of freight remains, and so must be satisfied in some other way—either by providing another hydro-electric power station, or by constructing a thermal power station together with a railway line, or by constructing a thermal power station and undertaking dredging works. These are the possible alternatives. They all have the same object of satisfying the

[1] In comparison with the new construction.

[2] This example shows that variant I has a higher effectiveness than variant II. But it does not prove that of all possible variants satisfying the requirements in electrical energy variant I has the highest effectiveness; for not all possible variants were considered.

requirements for which the first hydro-electric power station was intended. If it was to provide surplus power for transmission to remote areas, we must show how both the local shortage of energy and that of the distant areas can be met.

Assume that the alternative to this hydro-electric power station is one in the same region, but on another river, supplying 100 million kwh per year, and improving navigation to the extent of three million ton-kilometres of different freight between the points $a_1, b_1, c_1, \dots k_1$ along the river B. We cannot yet compare the effectiveness of the two variants, so we must reduce them to a common effect. We determine the total effect of both by deducting repeated quantities:

1. 200 million kwh of electricity;
2. transportation of freight between the points $a, b, c, \dots k$;
3. transportation of freight between the points $a_1, b_1, c_1, \dots k_1$.

It is easy to see that we have obtained the sum of the maxima of each type of output for the variants we are comparing. This sum represents the smallest size of these economic sectors which, firstly, are commensurable (for they have the same output) and, secondly, include one of the two stations.

Let us try to describe each variant in more detail.

Variant I (reduced to a common effect). Hydro-electric power station on river A.

1. Production of electricity: 200 million kwh per year;
2. two million ton-kilometres of freight transport per year along river A;
3. three million ton-kilometres freight transport per year along river B in small boats at a comparatively high prime cost.

Variant II (reduced to a common effect). Hydro-electric power station on river B.

1. Production of electricity: 100 million kwh per year;
   A power station with production of 100 million kwh per year;
2. 1·5 million ton-kilometres of freight per year by rail, the same amount as would be taken by river A in the first alternative (the same quantity of freight is taken a shorter distance);
3. three million ton-kilometres of freight per year by river B in large boats at a low prime cost.

These variants have identical effects, and so their effectiveness can be compared merely by comparing the annual operational costs and capital outlays on each.[1] This comparison may be made in two ways—either by

[1] In this example we have assumed that the maximum production of the individual goods in the variants does not exceed the needs of the respective regions. If this were not so, we would either have to reject the variant or have to prove that it would be expedient to transport the surplus to other regions. In general it must be remembered that the use of the given scheme must either be based on detailed data about the requirements for all

calculating the total operational costs and capital outlays required to produce output for each variant, or by adding the positive and negative differences (economies and diseconomies) of operational costs and capital outlay for one variant compared with the other. For example, we can take either the total prime cost of transporting three million ton-kilometres along river B for each variant, or just the sum of the economies in prime cost afforded by variant II in comparison with variant I (including this sum in the total economy on operational costs which is obtained).

The latter method can be called *net-accounting* and the former *gross-accounting*. Correctly used, both methods must give the same results, but since it gives a more complete picture of the outlays and is more easily checked, gross-accounting is to be preferred.

3. *Reduction to a Common Consumption Area*

Suppose that we have several alternative locations for an enterprise, such that the respective areas of product-consumption do not completely coincide. Then, in considering each variant, it is necessary to state how, and at what costs, those requirements of the region which the given variant does not satisfy but which the others do, can be met.

For example, suppose the first site for the projected enterprise has requirements A and B, and the second site B and C. Then, in considering the first variant we must specify how the requirements C will be satisfied, and in considering the second, how the requirements A will be satisfied. Having found the necessary outlays on the variants thus reduced, we can determine which one satisfies the requirements A, B and C with minimum outlay.

4. *Reduction to Common Time*

If one project begins to produce output two years later than another, then in order to compare their effectiveness, it is necessary to determine how, and at what costs, the demand for output over the course of the two years between the beginning of production of the first project and that of the second will be satisfied.

This is in practice one of the most difficult cases of reduction to a common effect. The difference in time between the appearance of output for the different variants is usually less than the standard amortisation period. Therefore, if an attempt is made to make up the time lag by constructing new enterprises, this will not, as a rule, give the necessary effect. Minor re-capitalisation, too, is not effective enough in these cases, since it is usually not able to make up for the scarcity of output, while major recapitalisation would have an effect lasting longer than the time-lag.

types of goods it produces, or must be critically re-examined by subsequent study of these requirements. Otherwise the choice might be made of a variant producing a surplus of some good or having an incorrect ratio of essential to non-essential production from the point of view of a business-like development of production.

5. *Reduction to Identical Goals of Economic Policy*

Example. We wish to compare two variants of the production of the same quantity of the goods *A*.

Variant I_A in a backward area, and variant II_A in a developed area.

The outlays on these variants are (in millions of roubles):

TABLE 8

Variants	Capital Investment	Annual Opreational Costs
I_A	110	95
II_A	100	90

The question is, which variant is more effective?

To answer this question, it might at first seem necessary to compare the additional outlay on variant I_A with its additional effect compared with II_A, i.e. to compare the development of the backward region which is promised by variant I_A with the extra million roubles of capital outlay and five million roubles of annual operational costs which this would entail.

However, to compare them in this way would be correct only if the given variant was the only way to develop the backward region economically. In fact, it rarely happens that only one industry can be used to develop a region. The problem then becomes one of deciding whether it is possible to develop the region to the same extent with less additional outlays than variant I_A requires.

Suppose the production of *B* and *C* in this backward region requires the following outlays (in million roubles):

TABLE 9

Variant	Capital Investment	Annual Operational Costs
I_B	80	60
I_C	60	70
Total	140	130

Suppose that the joint installation of these production processes leads, on the whole, to the same degree of economic and cultural development of the backward region as the variant I_A. We then find out the outlay necessary to produce the same quantity of goods *B* and *C* in a developed region:

TABLE 10

Variant	Capital Investment	Annual Operational Costs
II_B	75	60
II_C	61	67
Total	136	127

We now reduce the variants I_A and II_A to a common economic effect by taking into account the variants for producing *B* and *C*.

TABLE 11

Combination of Variants	Reduced Variants (combination of variants of production of *A*, *B* and *C*)	Capital Investment	Annual Operational Costs
I	$I_A + II_B + II_C$	246	222
II	$II_A + I_B + I_C$	240	220

Both combinations of variants in Table 11 (I and II) produce the same effect, i.e. the same quantity of goods *A*, *B* and *C*, and the same degree of development of the backward region. Therefore we can assess the relative effectiveness of these two combinations from the expenditure. In this example it is clear that the combination II is more effective than I.

The greatest difficulty in this reduction to a common economic effect lies in determining when the aims of economic policy are identical. How can we judge the degree of economic and cultural development of a region achieved in carrying out a project? This is a question which has not been studied. In our view, its solution depends on the actual aims of economic policy in developing a region. In some cases, for example, the basic aim of the development might be to increase the material well-being of the backward local population engaged in non-productive forms of labour. In other cases the main object might be to exploit extensive natural resources by populating an uninhabited region.

In the first case one of the important indicators of the extent of economic and cultural development would be the number of workers attracted from the local population to industrial jobs with a high productivity. In the second case the main indicator would be the effectiveness of the use of the local resources.

Thus in order to reduce the variants to common aims of economic policy it is necessary first to determine what specific aims each variant fulfils. We should not, as project-making organisations often do, restrict ourselves to the general consideration that the construction develops the backward region, industrialises it, and so on; we must give a detailed qualitative and quantitative assessment of the way in which our aims are realised in the region. Only then can we judge, on some grounds, how the compared variants contribute to the fulfilment of these aims.

5. Difficulties in the Reduction of Alternative Projects to a Common Effect

The reduction of planning (or project) variants to a common effect is frequently accompanied by such complications that project-making organisations have difficulty in overcoming them. The trouble is that those elements in the effect, which in the cases we have considered are obtained in combination with the basic effect, can rarely be produced independently. For example it often happens that a by-product of a given industry cannot, in general, be produced on its own, but can only be a by-product of other industries.

Expressing this in general terms we can say that the products *b*, *c*, *d* and *e* can be produced with the product *a*, and also with the products *f*, *g* and *h*, i.e. together with components of the effect not contained in any of the four project variants being compared. As a result the common effect of the variants is broadened even further, and it can become practically impossible for the project-maker to make a complete reduction of the projected variants to a common effect; for project-making organisations are divided into sectors, and in a number of cases the common effect will go beyond the bounds of their particular sectors. In such cases, it must be the function of the planning organs to reduce to a common effect, for by collecting all the basic data for each projected variant they can form complex combinations giving identical effect.

We observe that it is in some cases possible to determine the relative effectiveness of the variants even when they are not completely reduced to a common effect. This happens when we know that one variant has a larger effect than the others, but requires the same, or smaller outlay.

Let us examine the difficulties involved in the reduction to a common effect of hydro-electric power stations in backward regions. Our simplified example of the reduction of two variants of such stations related to a developed region: the hydro-electric power station was intended to satisfy requirements which existed whether it was there or not. Therefore the volume (of output) of the production units of the economy that are being compared was equal to the sum of the maximum values of the separate elements of the direct effect of the different variants.

In planning a power station in a backward region it is necessary first of all to plan the power requirements, since in this case the operation of the station is completely bound up with the needs of consumers who do not yet exist. Hence, the question is not only whether or not to construct the station, but also whether or not to create a whole number of consumers of power from this station.

Of course, in such a case it is not so much the effectiveness of creating individual consumers which is important, as their effectiveness as a whole or, in other words, the effectiveness of the given variant of development of the region. This means that, when projecting a power station on some large river in a backward region we must, for example, specify in what other ways we could produce as much aluminium, synthetic ammonia and other products as the group of enterprises supplied by the projected power station is intended to produce. Such a group may be so large than an examination of other variants for producing the identical products can become a very difficult problem.

However, this difficulty is not a result of the method itself, but is due to the variety of composition and the immensity of the proposed construction. If the construction embraces ten different lines of production, then the number of different variants for obtaining the same products can be very large. The main difficulty in this case boils down to one of making an exhaustive choice of the data (indicators) for variants realising the same aims. But since these indicators are required whatever method of determining the economic effectiveness of a hydro-electric power project in a backward region is used, the method of reducing to a common effect does not in itself create new difficulties: it only reveals more clearly what is needed to solve the problem.

6. Reduction to a Common Effect as a Method of Justifying Projects of Socialist Enterprises

The purpose of reduction to a common effect is to specify how, and at what cost, in realising one of the project variants, it is possible to satisfy those requirements which the other comparable variants satisfy and this one does not. It follows that this method makes sense in an economy which is directed to the fulfilment of social needs and of other aims of the government, rather than to the receipt of profits. In a capitalist economy it is impossible to use this method in order to choose between variants with different outputs, as it does not show which will give the higher rate of profit.

By comparing the rate of profit of a project producing $(a+b)$ with that of another producing $(a+c)$ the capitalist obtains what is, for him, a necessary and sufficient answer to the question of choice. He will not worry how the need for c in the economy as a whole will be satisfied when he chooses the variant producing $(a+b)$.

But the purpose of a socialist economy is not the extraction of maximum profit, but the fullest satisfaction of the needs of the members of society. Therefore the main problem, in deciding which variant to select, is to specify how the needs for the products or the aims which are not reflected in the given variant will be satisfied. In a socialist society the question of the degree of profitability of each specific variant can be answered only from this point of view.

Project variants reduced to a common effect are variants of small productive units of the economy meant to fulfil a number of aims, and not just of enterprises. These units may be the individual, widely scattered parts of different enterprises which are not directly interconnected. Thus the variant of construction of a new machine-building plant can compete with a variant of the reconstruction of a number of shops in several existing plants.

The reduction of variants to a common effect does not make non-measurable components of effect measurable; nor does it relieve the planning organs of the need to compare non-measurable components of effect with outlay, and somehow to 'weigh up' or compare them.

In fact the reduction of variants to an identical effect is based on the premise that none of them goes beyond the requirements of the region or of the whole economy. For example, if the production of an additional $50c$ was superfluous to the economy, then variants II and III (see above, p. 50) could be dropped, or, more precisely, either the $50c$ is dumped as unusable waste, and the worthwhile products of variant II remain $100a$, and of variant III, $100a+50d$, or else the $50c$ are used with a lower effect than that of the other part of the production of c in the economy. In the latter case the reduction to identity in the material composition of output does not relieve us from considering the extent to which the products of the variants being compared are necessary for the economy as a whole.

Thus the reduction of variants to identical effect assumes that the requirement for their output is already established, and that none of them goes beyond these requirements. This means that the value of the separate lines of production to the economy as a whole is already established, and the level of production in the sectors is determined proportionately.

In establishing the requirements and the perspectives of developing production we are taking for granted the same comparison of the components of effect and outlay that cannot be directly measured and which we tried to avoid by reducing the variants to a common effect. However, the important point is that the reduction method is of value not because the planning organisations in general need no longer establish the relation between aims and production costs, or compare and 'weigh-up' non-measurable components of effect (which is both impossible and worse than useless), but because such a comparison need not be carried out every time two or three variants are to be compared, but only when the basic construction problems are being solved. The main advantage of the reduction method is that it makes it possible to find which variant requires the least outlay to fulfil a certain set of aims.

Without reducing variants to a common effect, it is in many cases impossible to compare their effectiveness, and so it is impossible to determine which one will require a minimum of costs for the economy as a whole.

For this reason it is worth taking care, in the reduction to a common effect, to select the correct variant, ensuring the most effective use of social labour and the development of its productivity.

7. Concealed Forms of Reduction to a Common Effect which are used in Practice

The effectiveness of project variants is often compared by implicitly reducing them to a common effect.

Take the simplest case of the comparison of effectiveness of production of variants with a different composition of their effect: the production of metal goods with different proportions of scrap. In practice this problem is solved by pricing the scrap, although the pricing methods to be used are a matter of controversy. It might appear that scrap, as such, is worth nothing, and that the pricing must include only the cost of transporting it, storing it and dividing it up, and so on. However, the example below shows how incorrect this view is.

Suppose that two variants of production of metal goods which are of the same quality need equal capital investment and operational costs, but leave different amounts of scrap. Is it correct, in determining the effectiveness of these variants, to put the value of the scrap at zero? Obviously not: for scrap used as raw material for open-hearth furnaces can replace pig iron and so save the labour outlays on the production of the corresponding quantity of pig iron. Owing to such considerations, the practice in project estimates has been to value the scrap at the prime cost of pig iron.

Similarly in the project-making of chemical factories, ancillary products are usually valued in terms of the prime cost of similar products or substitutes produced by other methods.

The practice of pricing by-products in terms of the prime cost of the products for which it is a substitute, is no more than a concealed way of reducing the variants to a common effect.

Suppose that we are comparing the operational costs of two project variants:

TABLE 12

Variant	Output	Operational Costs
I	$100a+100b$	E_1
II	$100a+50c$	E_2

Since the output of these variants is heterogeneous, we must first of all simplify them. We do this in two ways: (1) by reducing them to the least common effect; (2) by putting the valuation for the ancillary products b and c at the cost of their production by other methods, and subtracting this amount from the total operational costs.

For either method it is necessary to have some data concerning the operational costs necessary to produce b and c in other ways.

Suppose that the

costs for the production of $100b = S_b$
costs for the production of $50c = S_c$

Then to reduce both variants to their least common effect it is necessary to add

$50c$ of output and S_c of outlay to variant I
$100b$ of output and S_b of outlay to variant II.

But to determine the cost of production by subtracting the valuation of the ancillary product it is necessary to subtract

$100b$ of output and S_b of outlay from variant I
$50c$ of output and S_c of outlay from variant II.

In other words, comparing the variants by reducing to a common effect gives the inequality

$$E_1+S_c \gtrless E_2+S_b \qquad \ldots [2.1]$$

The comparison of the operational costs for the same variants after subtracting the prime cost of the ancillary products obtained in other ways gives

$$E_1 - S_b \gtrless E_2 - S_c \qquad \ldots \quad [2.2]$$

Clearly the second inequality is a transformation of the first. This means that the comparison of the operational costs of variants with heterogeneous output by subtracting the prime cost of the ancillary products obtained from other sources is equivalent to the comparison of the operational costs of the same variants by reducing to a common effect. This is what we were required to prove.

Although, when they are correctly used, concealed forms of the reduction of project variants to a common effect give the same result as the explicit method, it is considerably more difficult to use them correctly. Moreover, mistakes are more easily made. In particular, the method of valuation of the ancillary product by the cost of the same products produced in other ways has the following disadvantages:

1. It replaces the reduction to a common social effect by a reduction to a common output. The valuation of ancillary products and scrap attributes all the expenditure to output alone, and so the difficulty of comparing the effectiveness of variants fulfilling non-identical aims of economic policy remains unresolved.

2. It ascribes the whole differences between the operational costs of the different variants of production of the whole product-mix to only one 'basic' product. Thus the difference between the 'prime cost' of 100*a* for variants I and II is $(E_1 - S_b) - (E_2 - S_c)$ which is equal to $(E_1 + S_c) - (E_2 + S_b)$.

This causes us to overemphasise the relative significance of this difference. Thus, if $E_1 = 100$, $E_2 = 120$, $S_c = 85$, $S_b = 70$, then the difference between the prime costs of the basic product for the two variants in our example is 16·7% of the prime cost of the basic products for variant I $[(5 \div 30) \times 100]$, while in relation to the total operational costs for the reduced variant I this difference is only 2·7%, $\{[(120+70)-(100+85)] \times 100 \div (100+85)\}$. The first ratio (16·7%) is sufficiently large, all other conditions being equal, for the advantage to lie with the first variant. The second ratio, 2·7%, is not significant, for even if all other conditions are equal, at least at the project-making stage this difference could be accounted for by possible errors.

3. This way of reducing to a common effect gives the false impression that by assessing the ancillary product according to its prime cost when produced by other methods we can determine the true prime cost of the basic production. If the same technological process is used for several products, only the total prime cost for the entire product-mix can be ascertained. The prime costs of the individual products are conditional magnitudes.

This conditional character is most clearly revealed when the prime cost is negative, as can happen when the other variants of obtaining the ancillary products require greater operational costs.

The valuation of ancillary products according to their prime cost when produced by other methods enables us to compare the overall effectiveness of variants with different product-mix according to only one of the basic indicators of effectiveness—that of operational costs. To compare their effectiveness with respect to capital investment we must determine the investment in the basic product by a method similar to the determination of its prime cost, i.e. from the amount of investment needed to produce the given ancillary products by other methods.

The valuation of scrap and ancillary products according to their prime cost is not a unique example of how the reduction of variants to a common effect is carried out in practice. We could give many such examples. The reduction of variants to a common effect is virtually done already, when the project-maker, comparing variants producing effects with different compositions, asks how those requirements and objects which are not fulfilled by the given variant can be fulfilled in other ways.

This question arises, for example, when one of the variants starts production later than another. In this case the question is how, and at what costs, we can make up for the shortage in the product during the time that the given variant is still not producing, while the other variants could be. Answering this question is no more than beginning to reduce the variants to a common effect according to their gestation period.

Thus project-making practice uses various implicit ways of reducing the variants being compared to a common effect. But when implicit, these methods do not make the meaning of the operations carried out very clear, nor do they make it possible to estimate the degree of accuracy obtained. Moreover, implicit ways of calculations usually require more work than estimates using explicit methods. Therefore it would be advisable to replace the former by the explicit method we have been describing.

It must be noted that these implicit ways of reduction to a common effect are still not *the* serious fault of project-making or planning practice. There are very much worse methods of comparing the effectiveness of project variants. Various methods are used for the valuation of ancillary products and for the allocation of capital investment between individual 'components of the product-mix'. In this respect there is no unconditional method. All accepted methods are conventional, or, it would be more accurate to say, invalid. This means that serious errors can occur.

We have encountered cases where estimates of the indicators of effectiveness of one and the same project have differed widely, because of the various ways of assessing the valuation for ancillary products or scrap. It is an intolerable position, when calculations must depend on the subjective free-will of the project-maker. The method of reduction to a common economic effect gives an objective basis for the comparison of the effectiveness of variants with non-identical effects, a basis which is independent of any subjective judgment.

CHAPTER III

EXISTING METHODS FOR COMPARING PRIME COST AND INVESTMENT

1. The Maximum Effect of Investment in the Economy as a Whole and how it is Reflected in Project-making Practice

Since every industry can produce the same quantity of goods with different amounts of investment, the output stipulated by the national economic plan can be produced with very different allocations of the total investment between the various sectors of the economy and construction projects.

There will be, it is true, a certain minimum investment for each line of production under socialist conditions of production (due perhaps to the conditions of labour). Hence directives concerning what must be produced and in what way, determine, within certain limits, both the total volume of investment outlay and its sectoral allocation. However, these limits within which there can exist many variants differing in the size and the direction of the investments are very wide.

The mere planning of the composition and volume of output does not in itself determine the allocation of investment as between the sectors and individual projects. Given the same overall investment, there are various ways in which it can be distributed for the production of the given final output.

However, the social benefit from the same volume of overall investment will not be the same. Very different economies of social labour result from equal investments, depending on where, how and to what they are applied, and on their allocation between the different construction projects.

We may then ask how we can find the allocation of investments in a socialist economy producing the maximum total effect for all the capital outlay on the production of the given final output, i.e. leading to the minimum expenditure of social labour on the production of the given output.

The practical significance of this problem is obvious, and the need for it to be solved correctly is acknowledged in practice. However, the current methods for finding the maximum effectiveness of investments do not get to the essence of the problem. These are confined merely to a comparison between investments and the consequent savings in prime cost.

When some variants require more capital but produce at a smaller prime cost than others attaining the same objectives, it becomes necessary to compare the extra capital cost with the economies in prime cost. However, investment is an outlay which is made once only, whereas the prime cost is incurred repeatedly in the production of each new batch of output. For this reason we cannot compare an extra investment of one rouble with a rouble's economy in prime cost of the annual output. The problem therefore is reduced to determining what fraction of a rouble's economy in prime cost of the annual output is equivalent to one extra rouble in investment.

Put in this way the question relates only to that part of the problem which is reflected in the economic indicators of the individual enterprise. If, when projecting an enterprise or even a group of enterprises, we go no further and ignore the effect of our proposals on the whole economy, then the problem of the maximum effectiveness of all investments shrinks to the comparatively restricted one of comparing the prime cost and the capital of the projected units. It cannot therefore be solved; for it is not enough to have the most detailed data concerning only the individual project or even a significant part of the economy. We need some data for the whole economy.

Therefore although planners and project-makers have made many efforts to produce different methods and standards for comparing capital and prime costs, the problem not only remains unsolved but is not even properly stated. And since in practice the project-makers cannot do without a comparison of investment and prime cost, they use unjustifiable standards.

This results in a considerable loss for the economy as a whole, probably amounting to milliards of roubles per year, although it is rather difficult to estimate.

The most effective investment of capital cannot take place automatically, but must be contrived. The methods used to compare capital and prime cost do not do this and so investments in our economy produce somewhat less than the maximum possible effect. The economy loses either the difference between the maximum and the actual effect of the investment made, or the difference between the actual investment and that which would be necessary to produce the same effect when used most effectively.

It is true that these losses are an insignificant fraction of the huge and increasing national income of a socialist country, but they should still be of concern to our economy and can, and must, be eliminated.

2. The Methods Applied in Practice for Comparing Prime Cost and Investment

In long-term planning and project-making practice it is often necessary to choose between variants requiring comparatively large investment but producing at a low cost and those requiring comparatively small investments but requiring higher costs of production.[1]

There is a very large number of such variants, as almost every problem in any production project has alternative solutions which differ in investment

[1] We ignore those variants requiring greater investment without giving any economy in prime cost, since they are obviously ineffective.

needs, and in operational costs. As random examples of the problem where we often need to compare extra capital investment with economies in operational costs we may mention the choice of technological processes and the type and construction of equipment (for example, the determination of the optimal coefficient of utilisation of a boiler), the choice of a building site, the choice of a variant about internal transport in a factory (such as the choice of the guiding slope), the choice of building material or a route for the laying of roads and railways, or of the kind of structure (for example, the choice of the capacity of a water-reservoir when planning the long-term control of a water current).

In their everyday operation also, enterprises are concerned with problems requiring the comparison of capital and prime costs, e.g. in the determination of the optimal batch size for articles produced serially.

Thus in practice problems of the following type occur frequently. We are given three project variants with the following data:

TABLE 13

Variants	Prime Cost per Unit of Output (roubles)	Capital per Unit of Output (roubles per year)
I	50	100
II	52	80
III	56	50

The question is which of these variants is the most effective, if each gives identical output?

Project-makers have attempted to solve this problem in different ways.

First of all they tried to compare investment and operational costs by including in prime cost a definite percentage of the investment. Thus, when considering power projects the general rule was to include 6% of the investment in the 'commercial value'.[1]

Certainly it was at the same time acknowledged that there is no place for capital or for interest on capital in a socialist economy, and so this 'interest on capital' was often said to be a conventional one. However, the essence of a 'conventional interest on capital' remained obscure, as did the methods for determining its magnitude, making it difficult to use; for the choice of variant to a certain extent depended on the magnitude of this rate of interest. This meant that if there was no reason for its being what it was, then all the estimates carried out with it, and the solutions based upon it, were somewhat arbitrary.

[1] A directive from the Energotsentr', in November 1931, proposed that when calculating the 'commercial value' of a kilowatt-hour on bus-bars the expenditure should include 6% of the capital in addition to amortisation and the cost of capital repair. When calculating the cost, the percentage of capital was not included. See 'Provisional Directive on compiling estimates in the provision of new and expansion of existing power stations (thermal stations, hydro-electric power stations, substations and electric transmission lines)', Moscow (1931).

With our example of three variants we can show how the magnitude of this 'conventional interest' affects the indicators of their effectiveness.

The table gives prime cost including 'interest on investments', and illustrates the relation between the relative effectiveness of the variants and the rate of interest.

TABLE 14

Variant	At 6%	At 10%	At 14%
I	56·0	60·0	64·0
II	56·8	60·0	63·2
III	59·0	61·0	63·0

This makes it clear that at a rate of 6% variant I is the most effective, at a rate higher than 10% but lower than 13·3% the most effective is variant II, while if the interest exceeds 13·3% then the optimal variant is III.

It is obvious that to provide some economic justification for selecting a variant by using this 'interest on investment', this interest must be given some overall economic content. Attempts to do this have been made. Project-makers have often started out from the idea that interest on investments must represent the interest paid in the State lottery loans (equating the payment of winnings to the payment of interest).

However, very little consideration is required to show that such a notion is unjustifiable. First, the State Loan finances only a very small fraction of all capital investments in construction; second, the winnings and interest paid out do not reflect the real expenditure (the expenditure of social labour), but constitute a method for redistributing the national income and for financing construction. It would be incorrect to base production decisions on the size of payments which are not essentially related to the conditions of production.

The attempt to interpret conventional interest on investments as the standard of accumulation was more sensible, but still involved an arbitrary choice of the period of time to which this standard would refer—whether it should be the average over five, ten or more years. Thus this interpretation was not free from conventions.

The practice of including the interest on investment in the prime cost became discredited and project-makers began to avoid its use. However, their rejection of it was less real than apparent, for the other methods they used to compare prime cost and investment also lacked any economic basis; they were usually just a disguised form of the conventional interest on investment.

In fact the most common method at the present time is the comparison of economies in prime cost with the extra investment required by one projected variant compared with another. By comparing extra investment with economies in prime cost, we obtain the 'pay-off period' of the extra investment from future economies in prime cost.

As an illustration we give in Table 15 the pay-off periods for the variants given above (p. 66).

It appears that the second variant should be selected, as it has the shortest

TABLE 15

Variants Compared	Extra Investment	Economy in Prime Cost	Pay-off Period (years)
	1	2	1:2
Var. I compared with II	100 – 80	52 – 50	10
Var. II compared with III	80 – 50	56 – 52	$7\frac{1}{2}$
Var. I compared with III	100 – 50	56 – 50	$8\frac{1}{3}$

pay-off period (7·5 years), assuming that 7·5 years is a sufficiently short period. If it is not, then we must choose the third variant. Of course, in using the 'pay-off period' to assess the effectiveness of investment we are assuming that a standard pay-off period has already been fixed. Thus if the project-makers are persuaded that the pay-off period must be less than 7·5 years, they will prefer the third variant. If it was decided that the standard pay-off period lies between 7·5 and 10 years, the preference would be given to the second variant; while, finally, if the standard pay-off period was considered to be more than 10 years, the second variant would be more effective than the third, and the first more effective than the second and the third.

In our comparison of the effectiveness of these variants using pay-off periods we notice a similarity with the comparison of these same variants using the 'interest on investments'. In both cases a standard is required—in one case a standard rate of interest, and in the other a standard pay-off period. In both cases the choice of the optimal variant depended on the standard. If we examine the critical standard pay-off periods for which the optimal solution moves from the third variant to the second, and then to the first, we notice that they are the reciprocals of the 'interest on capital' determining the transition of the optimal solution between the same variants. For 7·5 is the reciprocal of 13·3%, and 10 is the reciprocal of 10%.

Thus the standard pay-off period is no more than a disguised form of 'conventional interest on investment'.

Let us prove this statement. Denote the capital investment per unit of yearly output for one variant by K_1, and for a second by K_2; and let the prime cost per unit output for the first be C_1 and for the second C_2. We make the condition that $K_2 > K_1$ but $C_2 < C_1$. The pay-off period can be expressed by the following formula:

$$T_{2/1} = \frac{K_2 - K_1}{C_1 - C_2} \qquad \ldots \quad [3.1]$$

The magnitude of this expression by itself tells us nothing about the effectiveness of a variant: this pay-off period must be compared with some standard.

Suppose that we take t years as the standard pay-off period. Then the condition comparing the effectiveness of two variants can be expressed by the inequality

$$\frac{K_2 - K_1}{C_1 - C_2} \gtreqless t \qquad \ldots \quad [3.2]$$

This inequality means that the actual pay-off period of the second variant compared with the first is more than, less than or equal to the standard period. However, it can be written in another form. Multiplying both sides of the inequality by $\frac{C_1 - C_2}{t}$ (a positive quantity) we have

$$C_2 + \frac{1}{t} K_2 \gtreqless C_1 + \frac{1}{t} K_1 \qquad \ldots \quad [3.3]$$

Each side of [3.3] is the prime cost plus the 'interest on capital' at a rate equal to the reciprocal standard pay-off period.

Hence, if we take as the standard 'interest on capital' a quantity equal to $100/t$, this will be equivalent to taking the standard pay-off period as t.

The use of the pay-off period sometimes involves concealed comparisons of extra investment with economy in prime cost.

Provided that it is not known that the variant with the least capital is not effective, then in comparing the pay-off periods of all the other variants it is necessary to have an explicit standard pay-off period. Otherwise it would be impossible to establish whether the shortest pay-off period is sufficiently short, or to be sure that the most effective variant is not the one with the smallest investment having a zero pay-off period. Without an explicit pay-off period it is impossible to determine the effectiveness of the variant with the smallest capital and the highest prime cost.

But if we know the base variant for calculating the pay-off period to be ineffective, with an exceptionally high prime cost, then this excludes the possibility of the base variant (the variant with the lowest investment) being the optimal one.

This method implies that the project-maker need not determine the standard pay-off period exactly, although in fact the standard is contained in a disguised form in the indicators of the base variant, since the choice of this variant—of the basis for calculating the pay-off period—predetermines which of the compared variants will have the minimum pay-off period. The higher the prime cost and capital for the base variant, the less significant are economies in prime cost and the more significant are economies in capital. In other words, the more backward the method of production for the base variant is, the less advanced will be the method of production chosen because of its minimum pay-off period.

We can see that this is so from the following argument. Let the prime costs per unit output of the base variant be C_0, and of the other variants C_1 and C_2; let the capital investment per unit of annual output of the base variant be K_0, and the others K_1 and K_2. Let the pay-off periods be T (with corresponding subscripts).

We make the conditions that $C_0 > C_1 > C_2$ and $K_0 < K_1 < K_2$. Then the pay-off periods of variants 1 and 2 relative to variant 0 are, respectively,

$$\left.\begin{aligned} T_{1/0} &= \frac{K_1 - K_0}{C_0 - C_1}; \\ T_{2/0} &= \frac{K_2 - K_0}{C_0 - C_2}. \end{aligned}\right\} \qquad \ldots [3.4]$$

To determine what effect the choice of the base has on the relative magnitude of each of these fractions, we assume that C_1, C_2, K_1 and K_2 remain unchanged, while C_0 and K_0 are varied in turn.

Let us look at the behaviour of $T_{1/0}$ and $T_{2/0}$ (see formula [*3.4*]). From the conditions $C_0 > C_1 > C_2$ and $K_0 < K_1 < K_2$ it follows that the numerator and denominator of the first fraction are respectively less than the numerator and denominator of the second, i.e. that

$$K_1 - K_0 < K_2 - K_0; \qquad \ldots [3.5]$$

$$C_0 - C_1 < C_0 - C_2. \qquad \ldots [3.6]$$

This does not mean that the first fraction is less than the second, for [*3.5*] and [*3.6*] are quite compatible with the inequality

$$\frac{K_1 - K_0}{C_0 - C_1} > \frac{K_2 - K_0}{C_0 - C_2}. \qquad \ldots [3.7]$$

In economic terms, this means that although the capital investment per unit of annual output for variant 1 is less than that for variant 2, the economy in prime cost promised by variant 2 in comparison with 1 is so great that the pay-off period of 2 is less than that of 1.

Let us assume now that C_0 is increased, and K_0 remains unchanged. Then both sides of [*3.7*] become smaller, but to a different extent: the left-hand side will decrease more rapidly than the right-hand side. This is because a fraction which has a smaller numerator and denominator than another will decrease more rapidly when their denominators are increased by the same amount.

When both these conditions apply, the left-hand side of the inequality [*3.7*] can be smaller than the right-hand side.[1]

Thus the higher the prime cost for the base variant, the more probable it is that the minimum pay-off period belongs to the variant requiring comparatively high operational costs but comparatively low capital investment (per unit of annual output).

Let us assume now that K_0 is increased, and C_0 is unchanged. Then both sides of the inequality [*3.7*] will decrease, the left-hand side more quickly than the right-hand one; for when the numerators of fractions are decreased by the same quantity the smaller their numerator and the smaller their denominator, the more quickly they decrease.

[1] This will happen when $C_0 > \dfrac{C_1(K_2 - K_0) - C_2(K_1 - K_0)}{K_2 - K_1}$.

When both these conditions apply, the left-hand side of the inequality [*3.7*] may be less than the right-hand side.

Thus, the higher the capital investment per unit of output in the base variant, the more probable it is that the minimum pay-off period belongs to the variant requiring a comparatively small capital investment but producing at comparatively higher costs.

This argument leads to the following general conclusion. The more backward the method of production for the base variant is, the less technically advanced will be that which has the minimum pay-off period.[1]

But if the base variant has a decisive influence and, to a certain extent the relative pay-off periods of the variants are predetermined, this means that the selection of this base is no more than a choice of standard fulfilling the same function as the 'conventional interest on investment'. Then the degree of ineffectiveness of the base variant has the same effect as this rate of interest: the worse the indicators of effectiveness of the original variant are, the less significant is the economy in prime cost and the more significant is the economy in capital investment in the accounting. In just the same way the higher the 'interest on investment' added to the prime cost, the more evident are the advantages of the variants which require a low capital investment but comparatively high costs of production.

This means that if we adopt as our base variant one which we know to be ineffective, this is equivalent to adopting as a standard a high rate of effectiveness of capital outlay, which will hold back the technical renovation of the given productive system. Clearly this property of the method of comparison conflicts with the aims of our economic policy.

In practice this method is usually used in a form which seems to be very convincing. The calculation of the pay-off periods is based on information from existing factories in the same line of production. This method 'buys

[1] As an illustration of this statement we give the following arithmetic example, which presents these relations clearly. Let

$$K_0 = 100; \quad K_1 = 150; \quad K_2 = 200;$$
$$C_0 = 120; \quad C_1 = 110; \quad C_2 = 100.$$

Then the pay-off periods of variants 1 and 2 with respect to the variant 0 are equal to

$$\frac{150-110}{120-110} = \frac{200-100}{120-100} = 5 \text{ years.}$$

We can follow through the effect that the magnitude of prime cost of the base variant has by changing C_0 (i.e. 120). It is not difficult to see that when C_0 is reduced, the pay-off period for the first variant increases much faster than that of the second. Thus, for $C_0 = 110$, the pay-off period of variant 1 is equal to $\frac{50}{0} = \infty$, while that of variant 2 is only 10 years. Conversely, for C_0 bigger than 120, $C_0 = 132$ say, the pay-off period of the first variant will be less than that of the second—2 years as compared with 2·9 years. We can follow through the influence of the amount of capital investment for the base variant by changing K_0 (i.e. 100). For $K_0 = 50$ the pay-off periods are 10 years and 7·5 years respectively. Here it is the second variant which is the more effective. For $K_0 = 150$ the pay-off periods are 0 years and 2·5 years. In this case the first is the more effective variant.

off' its connexions with the economic life, its own objectivity, and independence of the project-maker's individual judgment.

However, this form of comparison tends not to eliminate but rather to strengthen existing differences between the technical levels in different branches of the economy. For if the calculation of the pay-off periods of projected variants is based on accounting indicators, then technically backward industries with a high prime cost of output will be prevented in the future from carrying out technical renovation. This is in clear contradiction with the goals of Soviet economic policy.

One of the most persistent errors in project-making practice is the identification of the standard pay-off period with the average life of instruments of labour or with the average turn-over time for capital as a whole. No theoretical foundation has been put forward for this point of view: its supporters probably consider its truth to be self-evident. In fact, using the following simple argument, we can justify even this idea.

Productive capital is used for a limited length of time, and so additional capital outlays must be covered by economies in prime cost of output over this time, as otherwise the extra payment would not be refunded.

This argument is built on an error which lies in confusing productive capital as a constantly renewed stock of objects and instruments of labours with the individual objects of which the capital consists. Productive capital, both fixed and circulating, is renewed as the elements it contains are consumed, and the renewal is included in the prime cost of the produced goods. Thus although the elements making up this capital have a limited life, and capital itself (in the economic sense) 'lives' for an unlimited period—for as long as its worn-out elements continue to be replaced.

If we wish to take the life of fixed capital as its pay-off period, we must exclude amortisation from the components of prime cost. But if we do this, then at best the comparison of the pay-off period of extra investment with economies in prime cost, excluding amortisation, leads to a result similar to the comparison of prime costs. This means that this method for comparing capital and prime cost is imaginary, as it does not in fact compare them, but instead gives, in complicated and obscure form, a comparison of prime costs.

Let us prove this statement. We use the following notation:

TABLE 16

	Project-variant 1	Project-variant 2
Prime cost of a unit of output	C_1	C_2
Fixed capital per unit of annual output	K_1	K_2
Turnover period for the fixed capital	t_a	t_a

We assume that $C_1 > C_2$ and $K_1 < K_2$.

We have made the capital turnover periods for these variants the same (t_a) in order to simplify the interpretation of our results.

The amortisation per unit output is $\frac{K_1}{t_a}$ and $\frac{K_2}{t_a}$.

Therefore the economy in prime cost, after subtracting amortisation from it, is

$$\left(C_1 - \frac{K_1}{t_a}\right) - \left(C_2 - \frac{K_2}{t_a}\right)$$

Taking the ratio of the additional investment required by the second variant and this economy in prime cost (without amortisation) we have the pay-off period of the second variant compared with the first:

$$T_{2/1} = \frac{K_2 - K_1}{\left(C_1 - \frac{K_1}{t_a}\right) - \left(C_2 - \frac{K_2}{t_a}\right)}$$

Let us see under what conditions this pay-off period is greater or less than the amortisation period:

$$\frac{K_2 - K_1}{\left(C_1 - \frac{K_1}{t_a}\right) - \left(C_2 - \frac{K_2}{t_a}\right)} \gtreqless t_a \qquad \ldots \text{[3.8]}$$

Multiplying both sides of [*3.8*] by the positive quantity

$$\left[\left(C_1 - \frac{K_1}{t_a}\right) - \left(C_2 - \frac{K_2}{t_a}\right)\right]^1$$

and simplifying further we obtain $C_2 \gtreqless C_1$.

Thus in this method for comparing prime cost and capital, the effectiveness of the second variant compared with that of the first depends only on the indicator of prime cost. The second indicator (capital) has no effect on the result. This means that this method for calculating the pay-off period does not compare prime cost and capital, but is only a complicated form of the comparison of prime costs.

If we take standard pay-off period to be the average capital turnover period and calculate the economy in total prime cost without subtracting amortisation, then we obtain an obviously absurd result, as the following argument shows.

The trouble is that the turnover period for capital with non-identical elements is very different. If each portion of capital must 'pay off' through economies in prime cost over its turnover period, then the variant requiring both greater investment and greater operational costs will prove to be more effective than the others. This result is obtained whatever variant is taken as the base for the calculation of economy in prime cost and of additional investment.

[1] By hypothesis $C_1 > C_2$ and $K_1 < K_2$. Therefore

$$C_1 - \frac{K_1}{t_a} > C_2 - \frac{K_2}{t_a}.$$

Consider the following example:

TABLE 17

	Variant 1	Variant 2	Variant 0 taken as base for comparison
Prime cost per unit of output	C_1	C_2	C_0
Capital per unit of output	K_1	K_2	K_0
Average turnover period for the capital	t_1	t_2	t_0

We assume that $C_0 > C_1 > C_2$ (or $C_0 - C_1 < C_0 - C_2$) and that $K_0 < K_1$, $K_0 < K_2$ but $K_1 > K_2$.

Thus variant 1 requires both greater capital investment and greater prime cost than variant 2.

Nevertheless the economy in prime cost which variant 1 affords compared to variant 0 over the turnover period of K_1 can be greater than the economy in prime cost for the second variant (instead of variant 0) for the turnover period of K_2.

That this is possible can easily be demonstrated by means of the inequality

$$(C_0 - C_1)\, t_1 > (C_0 - C_2)\, t_2 \qquad \ldots [3.9]$$

By hypothesis, $(C_0 - C_1)$ is less than $(C_0 - C_2)$. But for a sufficiently large ratio $\frac{t_1}{t_2}$ [3.9] is perfectly possible, and all we need is

$$\frac{t_1}{t_2} > \frac{C_0 - C_2}{C_0 - C_1}.$$

Nor is this all. Not only the absolute magnitude of the economy in prime cost over the capital turnover period, but also the ratio of this to the amount of capital for variant 1 can be higher than that for variant 2 (if we take variant 0 as the base variant).

We can see that this is so by looking at the inequalities:

$$\frac{(C_0 - C_1)\, t_1}{K_1 - K_0} > \frac{(C_0 - C_2)\, t_2}{K_2 - K_0}; \qquad \ldots [3.10]$$

$$C_0 - C_1 < C_0 - C_2; \qquad \ldots [3.11]$$

$$K_1 - K_0 > K_2 - K_0. \qquad \ldots [3.12]$$

The inequality [3.10] expresses the fact that the effectiveness of K_1 (counting the effect over its turnover period) is higher than that of K_2 (over the turnover period of K_2).

Let us determine for what value of t_1/t_2 inequality [3.10] is possible. Transforming this inequality, we have

$$\frac{t_1}{t_2} > \frac{C_0 - C_2}{C_0 - C_1} \cdot \frac{K_1 - K_0}{K_2 - K_0} \qquad \ldots [3.13]$$

which, it is easy to see, is perfectly compatible with the inequalities

$$(C_0 - C_1) < (C_0 - C_2) \text{ and } (K_1 - K_0) > (K_2 - K_0)$$

and so also with the inequalities

$$C_1 > C_2 \text{ and } K_1 > K_2$$

since it is quite possible for t_1 to be considerably larger than t_2 and for t_1/t_2 to exceed the right-hand side of [*3.13*].

Thus, if we take as the standard pay-off period the turnover period of the capital which is required by the given variant, this can create the impression that the investment producing smaller volume of annual output per unit of outlay at a higher prime cost, is the most effective.[1]

It is true that using the average life of productive capital as the standard pay-off period does not usually lead to such a ridiculous result, but this is because in practice this method is applied only nominally.

For when they are comparing variants with different average capital turnover periods the supporters of this method have to take the same turnover period for all variants, so that the standard itself is deprived of all real content. For example, in taking as the standard pay-off period the average turnover period of two portions of capital, one of which lasts 20 years and the other 10, they are rejecting the principle that each portion of capital should pay off over its lifetime; while the requirement that each portion of capital should pay off over the lifetime of some other portion not only lacks any economic sense, but any sense at all.

Thus, all the current methods we have considered for the comparison of the basic indicators of effectiveness turn out, for various reasons, to be unsuitable. The defects of all these methods have one common root, and reduce to the same common mistake, in that each of them uses either an explicit or a concealed standard for comparison which is not associated with the development plan of the economy.

In effect, the conventional interest on investment is used without deriving its magnitude from the long-term plan. Moreover the question of whether it is possible from the long-term plan to derive a 'conventional interest' suitable for comparing prime cost and capital in project-making is not even discussed.

Further, the use of the pay-off period presupposes an explicit or implicit standard, expressed either in the standard number of years to pay-off, or in the indicators of the variant taken as a base for the calculation of the pay-off periods, or, finally, in the information from existing factories (if these are taken as a basis for the calculation of the pay-off periods).

[1] To illustrate this point we give an arithmetic example. Let $K_1 = 100$; $K_2 = 90$; $K_0 = 50$; $C_1 = 80$; $C_2 = 78$; $C_0 = 90$. Then the effectiveness of the investment K_1 (with K_0 as base) will be greater than that of K_2 (with the same base) if the turnover period of K_1 is more than $1\frac{1}{2}$ times as long as that of K_2.

In each case the standard which rules the comparison is independent of the long-term plan. Besides we have seen that the use of such standards can directly conflict with the broad lines of Soviet economic policy.

Everything that we have said leads to the simple conclusion that in order to compare basic indicators of overall economic effectiveness in a planned economy we must not use standards and methods which are unrelated to the long-term development plan of economics.

In the absence of any guidance from theory, practice has bestowed on superficial distinctions the virtue of distinctions of principle. This has made it more difficult to find an effective solution of the problem. The naïve belief that once we have rejected conventional interest on investment and begun to use the pay-off period, we have rejected capitalist methods of comparison of investment and prime cost, thereby creating socialist ones, in no way gives a correct approach to the solution of this important question of socialist economics.

On the other hand, the pay-off period has made it easier to confuse the standard of comparison of investment and prime cost with the amortisation period or turnover period of capital than did the conventional interest on investment. The identification of the standard pay-off period with the average life of fixed capital might appear to be convincing. But the perfectly analogous equating of the standard effectiveness of fixed capital with the average rate of amortisation raises very serious doubts. It is still more doubtful whether it would be correct to identify the annual standard of effectiveness of all productive capital (fixed and circulating) with its average turnover during the year. Yet this is equivalent to equating the pay-off period of investments to their average turnover period.

Finally, as we have seen, the use of the pay-off period leads to the least desirable, concealed, forms of comparing additional investment with economies in prime cost.

CHAPTER IV

METHODS OF FINDING THE MAXIMUM EFFECT OF CAPITAL INVESTMENT IN A SOCIALIST ECONOMY

1. General Considerations

It is well known that the possibilities of effective investment exceed the extent of existing accumulation. A great deal of very effective capital outlay could be made over and above the plan, if this were not prevented by the lack of sufficient accumulation. Nor is this an accidental transient phenomenon. Whatever the volume of accumulation in the economy, if all the newest potentialities of effective investment are put forward immediately after a study of natural resources and technical inventions, then the relative shortage of accumulation will be evident.

If more effective investment can be made than the present means allow, then it is important to concentrate investment on those subjects which will be sufficiently effective. If the amount of accumulation is too small for all the effective uses, then the investment must be used only for the most effective ones among them, so that their total effect shall be a maximum. This conclusion is so obvious that it does not require proof.

However, it is not at all simple to implement it in practice. There are still no scientifically based methods for establishing the permissible minimum of effectiveness of investment enabling each project-maker to distinguish between investments which are effective enough and those that are not. It is clear that this minimal effectiveness can be established only when the fullest satisfaction of the needs of the economy as a whole is taken into account.

Although this problem of finding the maximum effect of investments is simple in conception, technically it is very complex. Its solution assumes the development of new forms of planning, since at present each project-maker is forced to decide for himself what is the permissible effectiveness of investment; and this can only lead to the result that the total effect of investment is below its maximum. This is natural, since the maximum cannot result from different variants selected on the basis of different solutions to what constitutes the permissible effectiveness of investment.

But is it possible in general to attempt to find the maximum effect of investment in the economy? Such an attempt will presuppose that the effects of the investment in the production of different goods are commensurable. For a long time, however, our economists have thought that since investments in different lines of production give qualitatively dissimilar effects (in metallurgy, metals; in textiles, cloth; in agriculture, grain, and so on) the effectiveness of investments can be compared only within the same line of production.

Those who support this view assert that when we say that investment in one sector is so many times more effective than in another, we mean that the output of the first sector is so many times more necessary than that of the other. But since different use-values are incommensurable, it follows that the different sectors in which capital is invested show incommensurable degrees of effectiveness. Having uncritically adopted this theoretical position, project-makers take as their basic indicator of the effectiveness of capital investment the ratio of annual output to capital investment, or the 'return to capital'.

However, this is an incorrect interpretation of the effect of investments. Output is the result not only of capital investment, but also of other outlays of social labour. If capital investments alone produced output without any operational costs, then all outlays of labour apart from those directed to the construction of productive capital, would be ineffective and unnecessary.

It follows that the indicator of 'return to capital' is economically imperfect. Despite this, it continues to be used in project-making practice under a different name. Thus, in 'Recommendations to the All-Union Scientific-Technical Conference on Problems of the Determination of the Economic Effectiveness of Capital Investments and New Techniques in the National Economy of the USSR' (June 1958) we read: 'Another indicator of the effectiveness of capital investments is the special index—that of the volume of capital investment per unit of output.'[1]

Those who support this view are inconsistent. When speaking of the effectiveness of investment they compare output not only with investment, but also with operational costs. For example, the 'Recommendations' we have quoted restrict the function of special indices as follows: 'However, the special indices do not sufficiently reflect the cost-side of the effectiveness of capital investments, since they do not include the prime cost of output'.

Marxist-Leninist political economy provides the correct theoretical foundation for devising practical ways of measuring the effect of investment. 'The productiveness of a machine is measured by the human labour-power it replaces.'[2] Correspondingly, the effect of investment is measured by the economy of labour to which it contributes. However different may be the advantages of a more capital-intensive construction-project over less capital-intensive ones, in the majority of cases these advantages can be reduced to the economy of labour, and can be measured by it. This can be done by reducing the compared variants to an identical effect for the economy as a whole.

[1] *Voprosy ekonomiki*, 1958, No. 9, p. 156.

[2] K. Marx, *Capital*, Vol. I, p. 391 (Foreign Languages Publishing House, Moscow, 1954).

The economy of labour obtained in the production of different goods can be compared just as much as the labour outlays on the production of different use-values can. This applies equally when calculation is made in value (i.e. money) terms. In money terms, the economy of labour which must, for example, be obtained by investment in an electric power station can be compared with the economies of labour which can be obtained from the same total investment in a tunnel which shortens a road. In every case, in each sector and industry, the effect of investment is measured in the same units. But investment itself is also measured in the same units, in whatever sector it is used.

Thus, the ratio of the effect of investments to their magnitude, i.e. the effectiveness of investment, has the same dimensions in all sectors and industries. We cannot determine by how much pig iron is more (or less) necessary than footwear, but this does not prevent us from measuring how much more (or less) effective a given sum of investment in a metallurgical plant is than in a boot and shoe factory.

However, we must make an important reservation here. We cannot measure the effect of the total investment in some production unit or other, for to do this it would be necessary to compare the given investment variant with the production of the same goods with no investment at all. But production without investment is not only ineffective, as we know (due to the high labour outlays involved), but often technically impossible (as in the smelting of pig iron) and it does not satisfy the qualitative requirements of a socialist economy (such as the conditions of labour). And in practice, the question of whether to produce the given product with or without the use of means of production is never posed. The problem is whether to choose a more or less capital-intensive variant, i.e. whether to spend more or less of labour on the capital construction for the production of a definite output. In order to solve this problem there is no need to know what economy is afforded by the total sum of investments; it is quite sufficient to be able to determine the additional economy in the labour outlays which is given by the first variant compared with the less capital-intensive variant in the same line of production.

The minimal necessary total investment is determined by the production programme for the final output of the economy, and it is distributed among the various sectors according to this programme. The problem of finding the maximum effect of investment arises only for that part of it which exceeds the minimum necessary to complete the final output programme during the planning period. The difference between the accumulation of the economy and the necessary minimum investment can be allocated in various ways between the sectors and construction projects without necessitating any change in the final output programme. This is where there also arises the problem of comparing the effectiveness of different variants of the additional investment, and of finding the total maximum effect of investment.

To put it shortly the problem is as follows. Given

1. the production programme of the final output of the whole economy;
2. the minimum sum of investment necessary for its fulfilment, divided by sector;
3. the planned accumulation of the whole economy;
4. the variants of extra investment in all construction projects needed to fulfil the production programme of the final output[1];

how to allocate the additional investment between its possible uses, so that the total effect of all investment is as large as possible.

When the problem is put in this way, the indicator of effectiveness of investment will be the ratio of the economy in prime cost, obtained by means of additional investment, to the size of this investment.

Denote the cost of production of annual output for two project variants by C_1 and C_2, and their investment by K_1 and K_2. Here we shall make the condition that the additional investment for the second variant yields a positive effect, i.e. that

$$K_2 > K_1 \text{ and } C_2 < C_1$$

Then the indicator of the effectiveness of the additional investment for the second variant is

$$E_{2/1} = \frac{C_1 - C_2}{K_2 - K_1} \quad \ldots [4.1]$$

This quantity shows what proportion of the additional investment is contained in its annual effect. The indicator [*4.1*] can be expressed inversely:

$$\frac{1}{E_{2/1}} = \frac{K_2 - K_1}{C_1 - C_2} \quad \ldots [4.2]$$

It then denotes the pay-off period in years of the additional investment

[1] The final output of the whole economy in any one period consists of consumer goods (individual and social) defence goods and those means of production which are to be used to expand production in the future (in the subsequent periods). Strictly speaking, these means of production are not themselves the final goal of production, but this comes to light only at the end of the planning period. However, we start by assuming a continuous growth of production. The planning period is always restricted to a definite period of time. Therefore, however far into the future the long-term plan might extend, and however far the end of the planning period might be from the beginning, the output in this period will still include some means of production whose function is not yet defined. Therefore although means of production are not a goal in themselves, nevertheless the final output of the plan includes a certain part of them—that part which is to be used for the growth of consumption beyond the planning period.

due to the economy in prime cost given by this investment. In practice the second (inverse) indicator is preferred, clearly because it is thought that it more closely corresponds to the nature of a socialist economy; but in fact there is no distinction between the two. Both [*4.1*] and [*4.2*] mean the same thing, but express it differently (directly and inversely). Therefore it is impossible for one of them to correspond to the nature of a socialist economy while the other does not.[1]

In calculating the indicator of the effectiveness of investment it is necessary to observe the basic rule of the comparison of the overall economic effectiveness of project variants, the rule of the identity of the overall economic effect. We can measure the relative effectiveness of different variants only on condition that they fulfil identical needs and goals of economic policy.

The measurement of the effectiveness of investment is a particular case of the measurement of the overall economic effectiveness of labour outlays, or, more precisely, one of the operations in its measurement. Therefore, the general rule of this measurement applies also to the calculation of the indicator of the effectiveness of investment. If the variants requiring the additional investment give a different effect for the economy as a whole (such as a different by-product), then they must be transformed by conversion to an identical effect.[2]

Let us show that the effect of additional investment expressed in the form of increased output can be measured by the economy of labour.

Suppose that for a given labour outlay (denoted by C) an increase in invesment from K to $(K+\Delta K)$ causes an increase in output from Q to $(Q+\Delta Q)$. The effects are different, the first being Q and the second $(Q+\Delta Q)$. Therefore we cannot measure the relative effectiveness of the labour outlays directly, nor can we calculate any indicator of effectiveness of the additional investment (ΔK) which would be comparable with the same indicators in the production of other outputs, by expressing the effect of investment in terms of the increase in output (ΔQ). For the numerator of the indicator $\frac{\Delta Q}{\Delta K}$ is output in physical terms, so that when there is a qualitative difference in the output of the compared project variants, their indicators cannot be compared in this form.

If ΔQ is pig iron, and $\Delta Q'$ cloth, then it is impossible to determine which is larger, $\frac{\Delta Q}{\Delta K}$ or $\frac{\Delta Q'}{\Delta K'}$.

Let us reduce the variants of production of Q and $(Q+\Delta Q)$ to an identical effect for the entire economy. To do this we evaluate the first variant for the same volume of production as given by the second variant, i.e. for $Q+\Delta Q$. We have

[1] See Chapter III for more detail.

[2] See Chapter II about the law of the identity of effect and methods of reduction to an identical effect.

TABLE 18

	Overall Economic Effect	Investment	Costs of Production of the Annual Output
First variant (reduced)	$Q+\Delta Q$	$K\times\frac{Q+\Delta Q}{Q}$	$C\times\frac{Q+\Delta Q}{Q}$
Second variant		$K+\Delta K$	C

From this we can find the effectiveness of the additional investment of the second variant relative to the reduced first variant:

$$\frac{C\dfrac{Q+\Delta Q}{Q}-C}{K+\Delta K-K\dfrac{Q+\Delta Q}{Q}}=\frac{C\dfrac{\Delta Q}{Q}}{K\left[\dfrac{\Delta K}{K}-\dfrac{\Delta Q}{Q}\right]}$$

The numerator of this indicator contains costs of production, which are homogeneous and commensurable in all sectors. The units of the denominator are also the same in all sectors, as it represents investment. This means that indicators of the effectiveness of investment of this kind can be compared not only within one line of production, but also when variants of production of different products are being compared.

The comparison of the effectiveness of investment in different sectors is based on the fact that whatever investment variant is selected, the final overall economic effect of labour will be the same. It is only the allocation of expenditure between production units and the total sum of outlays which change. Suppose, for example, that we are comparing the effectiveness of investment in the production of *A* with that in the production of *B*. The investment variants are as follows:

TABLE 19

A				*B*			
Variant	Cost of Production of the Annual Output (million roubles)	Investment (million roubles)	Effectiveness of Additional Investment	Variant	Cost of Production of the Annual Output (million roubles)	Investment (million roubles)	Effectiveness of Additional Investment
I_A	50	50	—	I_B	45	25	—
II_A	49	75	0·04	II_B	35	50	0·4

Suppose that each variant of the production of *A* gives the same effect, and that each variant of the production of *B* also gives the identical overall economic effect. This means that every combination of variants of *A* and *B*, one for each product, gives the same total effect for the whole economy. Hence the comparison of the effectiveness of an investment equal to 25 million roubles in the production of *A* with the effectiveness of the investment of the same sum in the production of B is equivalent to a comparison of two combinations of variants with the identical overall economic effect, $A+B$ but with a different allocation of investment between the two products. One consequence (effect) of the different allocations of investment will be differences in the labour outlays. And these are commensurable.

Thus a comparison of the indicators of effectiveness of investment in different sectors is based on the fact that the calculation of these indicators is possible only after the reduction of the variants entering into them to an identical overall economic effect, so that the same units can be used to express the effect of the investment in all products.

2. The Simplest Example of Finding the Total Maximum Effect of Investment

Problem 1

The basic idea in finding the maximum effect of investment is very simple, and can be illustrated by an elementary example. Suppose that a trust has at its disposal 340 million roubles in order to fulfil a production programme for the five goods: *A, B, C, D* and *E*. The outlays necessary to fulfil the programme for each product are as follows:

TABLE 20

A			*B*			*C*			*D*			*E*		
Variant	Cost of production of the Annual Output (million roubles)	Investment (million roubles)	Variant	Cost of production of the Annual Output (million roubles)	Investment (million roubles)	Variant	Cost of production of the Annual Output (million roubles)	Investment (million roubles)	Variant	Cost of production of the Annual Output (million roubles)	Investment (million roubles)	Variant	Cost of production of the Annual Output (million roubles)	Investment (million roubles)
I_A	91	50	I_B	76	50	I_C	64	50	I_D	53·2	50	I_E	42·6	50
II_A	81·2	80	II_B	71	80	II_C	60·8	80	II_D	50·7	80	II_E	40·6	80

As we see, each type of production has only one variant of additional investment.

Each variant is in accordance with the programme, and those with the same suffixes (*A*, *B* etc.) are reduced to identical overall economic effect. Therefore all combinations of the variants containing one for each product give the same total effect for the economy as a whole.

The question is: which of the possible combinations of variants uses the available investment with the maximum total effect?

It is very easy to answer this question by making a direct selection of the most effective variants requiring additional investment.

1. We calculate the effectiveness of the additional investment for each variant with the larger investment.

We obtain the following group of indicators of effectiveness of investment.

TABLE 21

Variant	Effectiveness of Additional Investment (as % of Annual Investment)
II_A	32·7
II_B	16·7
II_C	10·7
II_D	8·3
II_E	6·7

2. We arrange all the variants in decreasing order of effectiveness of investment showing the total additional investment required. At the beginning of the series we put the minimum necessary total investment, i.e. the sum of the investments for the variants I_A, I_B, I_C, I_D and I_E. We obtain the following table.

TABLE 22

Variant	Annual Effectiveness of Additional Investment (% of Investment)	Total Investment Used with Given Effectiveness (million roubles)	
I_A, I_B, I_C, I_D, I_E	∞[1]	250	340 (250 + 30 + 30 + 30)
II_A	32·7	30	
II_B	16·7	30	
II_C	10·7	30	
II_D	8·3	30	
II_E	6·7	30	

[1] It is conventional to denote the effectiveness of the minimum necessary investment as indefinitely large. The sign ∞ here means only that the production programme could not be completed without this investment.

3. Starting from the top of this table we select as many rows as we can before the investment limit is reached. For example, with a limit of 340 million roubles, it would be necessary to pick out the top four rows.

4. For each line of production we take the variant with the greatest investment from those which are included in the total. With a limit of 340 million roubles we must select the variants II_A, II_B, II_C, I_D and I_E. The reason for this rule is that in Table 22 the variants with larger investment do not figure in the total sum of investment, but appear only as additional investment over and above the minimum necessary total outlays. But the larger investment includes the necessary minimum investment as well as the additional investment (30 million roubles), so that the selected variants II_A, II_B and II_C preclude the realisation of I_A, I_B and I_C.

The balance of accumulation and investment formed in this way can be said to be the most effective, or optimal, balance, since the variants II_A, II_B, II_C, I_D and I_E will give the most effective use of the amount available for investment. In other words, this combination ensures that we obtain the planned output with a smaller total prime cost than any other possible combination of variants with the same investment limit.

3. A More Complicated Case of Finding the Total Maximum Effect of Investment

Problem 2

Suppose now that the limit to capital is raised to 410 million roubles, and each production unit has several variants requiring additional investment, instead of only one:

TABLE 23

A			B			C			D			E		
Variant	Cost of production of the Annual Output (million roubles)	Investment (million roubles)	Variant	Cost of production of the Annual Output (million roubles)	Investment (million roubles)	Variant	Cost of production of the Annual Output (million roubles)	Investment (million roubles)	Variant	Cost of production of the Annual Output (million roubles)	Investment (million roubles)	Variant	Cost of Production of the Annual Output (million roubles)	Investment (million roubles)
I_A	91	50	I_B	76	50	I_C	64	50	I_D	53·2	50	I_E	42·6	50
II_A	90	60	II_B	72·8	70	II_C	63·5	60	II_D	50·7	80	II_E	40·6	80
III_A	88	70	III_B	71	80	III_C	62·9	70	III_D	50	100	III_E	40	100
IV_A	81·2	80	IV_B	70	100	IV_C	60·8	80						
V_A	80	100				V_C	60	100						

Here the solution is complicated by the problem of selecting a base for the calculation of the indicators of effectiveness of investment. Should we take a constant base—the variant with the smallest investment of all—or a variable one—the variant with the next smallest investment? If the first, then the calculation will give us the effectiveness of the total additional investment, while if we take the second, we shall find only the effectiveness of the marginal investment.

It might appear that the unity of the principle of construction of the series demands the use of a single base in calculating the effectiveness of investment, but in fact this is not so. For a constant base is suitable only when the effectiveness of the successive investments increases continuously. Hence the most effective investment must be either technically impossible or cause a negative effectiveness for further investments. On the other hand, a variable base is appropriate only when the effectiveness of successive investments decreases continuously.

Let us prove these statements:

1. When each successive sum of investments in a given line of production is more effective than the previous one, then the effectiveness of the total sum of additional investments over and above the minimum will always be lower than that of the marginal investments. However, we cannot make the marginal investments without making all the previous ones: it would be no more

possible to do this than it would be to fill the top half of a glass without filling the bottom half first. Therefore when the effectiveness of successive investments increases, the indicators must be calculated on a constant base. We can show why it would be incorrect in this case to use a variable base with the data of Table 23. In the table, the ratio of the effectiveness of variant IV_C (E) compared with that of III_C is equal to

$$\frac{62{\cdot}9-60{\cdot}8}{80-70} = 21\% \text{ per year,}$$

and compared with that of variant I_C is equal to

$$\frac{64-60{\cdot}8}{80-50} = 10{\cdot}7\% \text{ per year}$$

At the same time, the ratio of the effectiveness of variant III_B compared to that of variant II_B is equal to

$$\frac{72{\cdot}8-71}{80-70} = 18\% \text{ per year,}$$

and compared to that of variant I_B is equal to

$$\frac{76-71}{80-50} = 16{\cdot}7\% \text{ per year}$$

In calculating the effectiveness on a variable base, i.e. with the variant with the next smallest investment as base, the variant IV_C takes a higher place than IV_B.

If the investment limits do not allow us to select any variants whose effectiveness is less than 20%, then these chain indicators of investment effectiveness make the variant IV_C stay, and the variant III_B go (since $E_{IV_C/III_C} > 20\%$ but $E_{III_B/II_B} < 20\%$). At the same time, in the implementation of variant IV_C it is not only the marginal investment $80-70 = 10$ which must be made, but also all the preceding layers, which have a lower effectiveness.[1] As a result, the effectiveness of all the additional investments as a whole for variant IV_C will not only be lower than 20%, but also lower than the investment effectiveness of the variant III_B

$$E_{IV_C/I_C} = 10{\cdot}7\% \text{ per year}$$
$$E_{III_B/I_B} = 16{\cdot}7\% \text{ per year}$$

2. But when each successive sum of investments in the given production is less effective than the previous one, then the effectiveness of the total sum of additional investment will always be higher than that of the marginal

[1] Thus $E_{IIIc/IIIc} = \frac{63{\cdot}5-62{\cdot}9}{70-60} = 6\%$ per year, and

$E_{IIc/Ic} = \frac{64-63{\cdot}5}{60-50} = 5\%$ per year.

investment. Therefore in this case it is impossible to determine whether the effectiveness of the marginal investment is large enough by looking at the effectiveness of the total sum of additional investment. We may reject the marginal investment without rejecting the intra-marginal ones (just as we can fill the lower half of a glass without filling the upper half).

Therefore in this case it would be incorrect to calculate the effectiveness of investments on a constant base, and would lead to the implementation of less effective investment at the cost of rejecting the more effective ones. For example, from Table 23 we see that $E_{\mathrm{V}_A/\mathrm{I}_A}$ is equal to 22% per year, while $E_{\mathrm{V}_A/\mathrm{IV}_A}$ is no more than 6% per year.

If we judged the effectiveness of the variant V_A on the strength of the first of these indicators (calculated on a constant base) then this variant would be ahead of the variants III_B, IV_C, II_D, II_E which have smaller indicators when these are calculated on a constant base, but are considerably more effective than the marginal investment.

Thus, when the effectiveness of successive investment decreases, we must calculate indicators of effectiveness by the chain method for each marginal investment. The margin must be narrow so that all the possibilities of more effective investment are exploited more fully, and that at the same time investments which are ineffective are not concealed by including in one lump (in the same margin) along with more effective investments.

In practice the effectiveness of successive investments (in the same product) can both increase and decrease: when the transition is made from a low technical level to technically newer variants, the effectiveness of successive investments often increases, but when variants at identical technical levels are being compared, the effectiveness of successive investments usually falls. How should the indicators be calculated in this case?

There can only be one answer: by alternating the bases. Where the effectiveness of successive investments increases these indicators must be calculated with the variant where the growth of effectiveness of successive investments first begins as the base; where this effectiveness falls, their effectiveness must be measured by the chain method, i.e. with the variant with the next smallest investment as a base.

However, this conclusion raises doubts at once. Can we collect indicators calculated with different bases into one decreasing series in order to select which of the most effective investments lie within the total limit for accumulation?

4. Variants which are such that, however great their Effectiveness may be, they can Never be Included in the Most Effective Balance of Investments

This question can easily be answered if we try to construct such a series. To save time, let us do it with the variants for the product *A* only.

We calculate the indicators of effectiveness on constant and variable bases:

TABLE 24

Variant	Investment (million roubles)	Cost of production of the Annual Output (million roubles)	Annual Effectiveness of Investment (as % of Investment)	
			constant base	chain method
I_A	50	91	∞	∞
II_A	60	90	10	10
III_A	70	88	15	20
IV_A	80	81·2	32·7	68
V_A	100	80	22	6

As we see, the effectiveness of investment increases between variants I_A and IV_A, and then falls (V_A). From what we have proved we know that in order to solve our problem we must use I_A as a base for II_A, III_A and IV_A, and we must use the chain method with the variant with the next smallest investment as a base for V_A.

Let us see what the result will be if we use these indicators (outlined in Table 24) and arrange them in a decreasing series, formed in the same way as in Table 22 (see Table 25).

Suppose that the limit to investment is increased, starting from a quantity such that only the variant with the minimum investment can be implemented, and reaching an amount for which the variant with the greatest investment can be accepted.

Then, whatever may be the limit to investment, the variants III_A and II_A cannot be included in the most effective balance of accumulation and investment. For, from Column 2 of Table 25 we see that the variant III_A could be

TABLE 25

Variant and Base	Effectiveness of Investment (as % per year)	Investment with the Given Effectiveness[1] (in million roubles)	Total Investment of Variant[2] (in million roubles)
1	2	3	4
I_A	∞	50	50
IV_A / I_A	32·7	30	80
III_A / I_A	15	20	70
II_A / I_A	10	10	60
V_A / IV_A	6	20	100

[1] Column 3 contains the difference between the investments of the variant to which the indicator of effectiveness of investments refers and the investment of the variant used for the calculation of this indicator.

[2] Column 4 gives the total sum of investments of the variants to which the indicators of effectiveness of investment refer. Thus, the second row in this column gives the investment of the variant IV_A, the third row gives that of variant III_A and so on.

included only when the investment limit allowed us to make an investment with an effectiveness of the order of 15% per year both in the production of *A* and in other lines of production. From Column 4 of the same table we see that if the total limit to investment is increased, the investment in the production of A must be reduced, for the variant III_A requires less investment than the variant IV_A. Already here we can see that there is an inconsistency, in that as the total limit of investment is increased (other conditions remaining the same) investment in the production of A is decreased.

What is even more absurd is that the highly-effective additional investment of variant IV_A must be rejected in favour of the less effective additional investment in other products. In fact, transferring from variant IV_A to variant III_A means rejecting additional investment with an effectiveness equal to 68% per year, as Table 24 shows, while in the other production units, due to the extended limit of accumulation, these investments can be used with an effectiveness of the order of only 15% per year.

Thus, whatever the limit of accumulation is, the variant III_A cannot be included in the most effective balance of accumulation and investment.

Similarly it can be shown that variant II_A must go the same way, for its indicators of effectiveness show that it is acceptable for higher limits of accumulation than III_A and IV_A but that the size of its investment makes it correspond to smaller limits of accumulation.

Variant V_A is in a different position. It has the lowest indicator of effectiveness but nevertheless, given sufficiently large accumulation, can be included in the most effective balance. This will be possible if the volume of accumulation allows us to use investments with an effectiveness of the order of 6% or less. The variant V_A requires a higher investment than IV_A, and so once V_A is accepted, instead of all the preceding 'layers' of investment being ruled out, they are included with that of variant IV_A among them. This is because only the marginal investment, i.e. the 20 million roubles of additional investment of variant V_A over and above the investment of IV_A, has an effectiveness of 6%. The other 'layer' of investment of V_A, the 30 million roubles of additional investment of IV_A over and above the investment of I_A, has the same effectiveness as that of IV_A.

Thus although II_A and III_A have a greater effectiveness than V_A, nevertheless under certain conditions the variant V_A can be included in the most effective balance of investments while II_A and III_A cannot. The reason for this is not that their effectiveness is not high, but that it is lower than the effectiveness of a larger investment in the same production (variant IV_A). The point is that the variants II_A and III_A occupy an intermediate position among variants with an increasing effectiveness for successive investments, and however high the effectiveness of such variants may be, they cannot be included in the most effective balance; at the same time less effective variants of the same production units among those with a falling effectiveness for successive investment (for example, variant V_A) can be included.

This leads to important practical conclusions. When the effectiveness of successive investment is falling, allocation of the additional investment must be made comparatively uniformly between different production units. When the accumulation is small, additional investment must be directed to many products, but in small quantities, whereas when the accumulation is large, it must go to many lines of production in larger quantities.

In this way we attain the maximum effect of investments when the effectiveness of successive investment is falling.

When this effectiveness is increasing, a different method must be used. Here restrictions on accumulation, instead of leading to the selection of variants with small additional investments in many products, must lead to the selection of those variants with the greatest effectiveness of investment in a small number of products and variants with the necessary minimum investment in the others. If the additional investments were allocated uniformly in this case we would have not the most effective, but the intermediate, variants, which can never be included in the most effective balance, i.e. those variants in the range of increasing effectiveness for successive investment.

Consequently in a period of rapid technical progress, when in many cases the effectiveness of successive investment is increasing, the development of the technical level of the economy must not be uniform, gradually climbing from one rung of the ladder to the next, but must move abruptly, in jumps. The shortage of accumulation in this case will express itself by a restriction in the number of 'jumping' industries and enterprises, rather than in a reduction in the height of the jump. Conversely, the average height of each jump will be even greater than when the volume of accumulation is larger, since only the most effective investment variants must be accepted. But of course the increase in the technical level of the whole economy (including enterprises which are not 'jumping') will be more significant, the greater the volume of accumulation.

Socialist construction in the USSR is in accordance with this principle of the allocation of investments when the effectiveness of successive outlays is growing. Although the construction is being carried out with a considerable shortage of accumulation in comparison with the amount of potentially effective investments, it is nevertheless being done according to the last word in techniques. The combined effect of the advantages of a socialist system and the transition from a very low technical level to an advanced one, has increased the effectiveness of successive investments in many sectors with substantial successive outlays.

Any variants lying between those with the necessary minimum investment and those with the greatest effectiveness of investment do not here comply with the principle of the maximum effect of investment. This is why investment is concentrated on the most effective production units. Direct instructions concerning this question are contained in resolutions of the CPSU. Thus in one of the resolutions at the XVth Congress of the CPSU (B) it was stated that the plan of capital construction 'must proceed from the greatest effectiveness of capital outlays, as far as both the time taken to finish work and the productive effect of the construction enterprises are concerned. Therefore the capital outlays of every year must specify capital investment in a relatively limited number of new factories and existing enterprises selected for reconstruction.'[1]

Thus variants which occupy an intermediate place among those with a increasing effectiveness for successive investment are never under any circumstances compatible with the total maximum effect of investments. If these variants are accepted, then the total effect of investment is reduced to a level below that which is required by the production programme of final output and by the accumulation; and of course the total prime cost of this output is raised.

If we eliminate those variants with less effective investment than those with larger investment in the same product, we obtain a series of variants whose indicators are calculated by the chain method (see Table 26).

TABLE 26

Variant and Base	Investment (in million roubles)	Cost of production of the Annual Output (in million roubles)	Annual Effectiveness of Investment (as % of investment)
I_A	50	91	∞
IV_A / I_A	80	81·2	32·7
V_A / IV_A	100	80	6

Once variants II_A and III_A have been dropped, I_A takes a place immediately next to IV_A, so that the effectiveness of IV_A, previously calculated on the base of the variant which preceded the growth of the effectiveness of successive investments, is now calculated on the base of the variant with the next smallest investment. At the same time, when the intermediate variants among those with an increasing effectiveness for successive investment are dropped, the series of variants either is reduced to the two variants with the least and the greatest investment, or becomes a series with falling effectiveness for successive investment.

The first possibility occurs if the original series was such that the effectiveness of successive investment increases until the end, although it might decrease from time to time.

The second arises if in the original series the increasing effectiveness of successive investment is replaced by falling effectiveness.

5. The Solution of a More Complicated Problem of Finding the Total Maximum Effect of Investments

Let us return to the solution of Problem 2 (p. 85), and calculate the indicators of effectiveness for the variants of the other products (*B*, *C*, *D* and *E*), using the rules we have given.

The chain method of calculation gives the series of indicators shown in Table 27, above the line.

Remembering that the variants are numbered in the order of increasing

[1] The CPSU in the *Resolutions of Congresses, Conferences and Plenary Sessions of the Central Committee*, Part II, pp. 338-9 (7th ed.).

TABLE 27

B		*C*		*D*		*E*	
Variant and Base	Effectiveness of Investment (as % per year)	Variant and Base	Effectiveness of Investment (as % per year)	Variant and Base	Effectiveness of Investment (as % per year)	Variant and Base	Effectiveness of Investment (as % per year)
II_B/I_B	16	II_C/I_C	5	II_D/I_D	8·3	II_E/I_E	6·7
III_B/II_B	18	III_C/II_C	6	III_D/II_D	3·5	III_E/II_E	3
IV_B/III_B	5	IV_C/III_C	21				
		V_C/IV_C	4				
III_B/I_B	16·7	IV_C/I_C	10·7				

investment, we see that II_B, II_C and III_C (outlined in the table) must be dropped, as they are intermediate variants with increasing effectiveness of successive investment. We must then re-evaluate the indicators of effectiveness of the variants III_B and IV_C on the bases I_B and I_C. These indicators are also in boxes. We obtain

$$E_{III_B/I_B} = 16{\cdot}7\%; \quad E_{IV_C/I_C} = 10{\cdot}7\%$$

We have put these indicators in the table (below the line). As a result we have the indicators of effectiveness of the variants which can be included in the most effective balance of investments (see Table 27, the indicators not in boxes).

We put these investment variants in the order of decreasing effectiveness and give the size of investment to which the corresponding indicators of effectiveness refer (including the data for product *A* from Table 26).

TABLE 28

Variant	Effectiveness of Investment (% per year)	with this effectiveness (in million roubles)	Cumulative Investment (million roubles)	Total Cost of Production of Output (*A, B, C, D, E*) (with Investment of Column 4) (in millions of roubles/year)
1	2	3	4	5
I_A, I_B, I_C, I_D, I_E	∞	250	250	326·8
IV_A	32·7	30	280	317·0
III_B	16·7	30	310	312·0
IV_C	10·7	30	340	308·8
II_D	8·3	30	370	306·3
II_E	6·7	30	400	304·3
V_A	6·0	20	420	303·1
IV_B	5·0	20	440	302·1
V_C	4·0	20	460	301·3
III_D	3·5	20	480	300·6
III_E	3·0	20	500	300·0

From this Table we start with the largest investment which lies within the investment limit. To make the selection easier, Column 4 gives the sum of investments obtained by summing Column 3, and we can see that the combination of variants with a total investment of 400 million roubles is compatible with the conditions of the problem, which stipulated an investment limit equal to 410 million roubles.

The combination of variants with the next highest investment is not within the limit (requiring 420 million roubles). This means that we cannot combine the variants in our problem so as to use 410 million roubles investment and at the same time be most effective. It is true that 30 different combinations of the variants, which give the output of *A*, *B*, *C*, *D* and *E* and have an investment equal to 410 million roubles, can be found (after those which cannot be included in the most effective balance have been eliminated), but not one of them gives a solution to our problem.[1] Therefore the investment limit must be reduced to 400 million roubles.

The total investment found in this way also determines which variants in the combination solve our problem. For each product (*A*, *B*, *C*, *D* and *E*) we must take that variant with higher investment which is still within the limit as far as its additional outlays are concerned. This method is justified by the fact that the investment for this variant is equal to the sum of its additional investment and all the preceding 'layers' of investment for the line of production. For example, in our problem the 'layers' of investment in the production of *A* which were within the limit were:

minimum investment of variant I_A	50 million roubles
additional investment of variant IV_A over and above the investment of I_A	30 million roubles
Total	80 million roubles

which is equal to the investment of variant IV_A.

If we take that variant for each product which is the lowest of those in Column 1 of Table 28 above the line separating accepted variants of investment from rejected ones, we obtain the combination of variants which solves our problem:

$$IV_A,\ III_B,\ IV_C,\ II_D,\ II_E.$$

[1] Twenty-eight combinations (with an investment of 410 million roubles) produce output with a higher prime cost than that of the above combination requiring only 400 million roubles investment, and one gives no relative economy in prime cost. Finally, there is one combination with an investment of 410 million roubles which gives some relative economy in prime cost, but the effectiveness of its additional investment is very much lower than the lowest limit of effectiveness for the variants included in our combination. The best combination with 410 million roubles investment is that of V_A, IV_B, IV_C, II_D and I_E. Its prime cost is 304·1 million roubles. Therefore the effectiveness of additional investment for this combination compared with the one we have chosen is equal to 2% per year $\left(\frac{304{\cdot}3 - 304{\cdot}1}{410 - 400}\right)$ which is only a third of the lowest limit of effectiveness of the variants in our combination (6·7% per year).

By finding this combination, we have at the same time drawn up the most effective (optimal) balance of investments (in millions of roubles).

TABLE 29

Allocation of Investment

	Variant	Investment
Total Investment Limit—400	IV_A	80
	III_B	80
	IV_C	80
	II_D	80
	II_E	80
	Total	400

This balance ensures that the total investment will be equal to the absolute limit, and also that the limit will be most effectively used.

6. A Possible Inaccuracy in the Solution

The balance we have drawn up ensures the most effective use of the investment limit, assuming that there are no other variants of investment in these products than those given in the problem. But the total effect of the investment could be still greater if there was an increase in the number of variants with an effectiveness exceeding the lowest effectiveness of the accepted variants (6·7%). The highest effectiveness indicators for each product can remain unchanged; all that the additional variants whose effectiveness is lower than the highest effectiveness of the accepted variants, but higher than their lowest effectiveness, can do is to increase the total effect of investment.

Suppose that the products *A*, *B* and *C* have new variants with an investment greater by 10 million roubles than that of each of IV_A, III_B and IV_C, and that the effectiveness of the additional investment of these variants is, respectively, 15%, 12% and 9% per year. Then we must reject variant II_E with its effectiveness of 6·7% per year, and replace it by I_E, distributing the 30 million roubles additional investment (the investment of II_E less that of I_E) between the new variants. The total effect of investments will increase by $30 \times \left(\frac{15+12+9}{3} - 6{\cdot}7\right) \times \frac{1}{100} = 1{\cdot}6$ million roubles per year.

We have achieved this increase in the effect of investment without increasing the effectiveness of the most effective investment, by increasing the number of intermediate variants among those with a falling effectiveness for successive investments. Another result has been that the differences between the effectiveness of the marginal investments selected for the various projects have been reduced. Thus in our example before the new variants appeared, these differences ranged between 6·7% and 32·7%, and afterwards were between 8·3% and 15%.

The introduction of further variants with an effectiveness of additional investment greater than 8·3% but less than 15% would lead to a further increase in the total effect from the same investment limit (owing to the rejection of less effective in favour of more effective additional investments).

Continuing this argument, we arrive at the conclusion that an increase in the number of intermediate variants among those with a falling effectiveness for successive investments, all other conditions being the same, will increase the total effect of the investments, raise the minimum effectiveness of the accepted variants, and reduce the difference in levels of effectiveness of the marginal investment in the various production units.[1] It follows that it will be profitable to elaborate new variants of investment as long as the increase in the total effect of investment obtained exceeds the cost of elaborating them.

7. The Standard Effectiveness of Investment—the Indicator of the Correspondence of Individual Investments to their Maximum Total Effect

The most effective balance of investments cannot embrace all possible variants, for their number is practically unlimited. For this reason, when selecting the material for machine parts, or choosing the diameter of a pipeline or the thickness of a wall, or in answering similar questions, one is faced with the problem of comparing prime cost and investment. The solution of such problems cannot be centralised, i.e. we cannot solve them by constructing an optimal balance of investment. Moreover, due to technical progress, new variants of investment arise daily, even hourly, yet it is impossible to determine their effectiveness by preparing new optimal balances.

This makes it clear that we require a standard so that in each individual case we can determine whether the given investment corresponds to the maximum total effect of investment of the whole economy, and whether it can be included in the optimal balance of investments. This standard will be a direct result of the optimal balance. In fact, if we consider the variants which are included in the optimal balance, we see from Table 28 that the following two properties distinguish them:

1. The effectiveness of each accepted variant is greater than that of each rejected variant, and greater than or equal to the minimum effectiveness of the accepted variants.
2. The investment requirement of each accepted variant is equal to or less than the investment limit.

Let us see how we can find the variants possessing these properties.

From the first property, it follows that the minimum effectiveness of the accepted variants must be greater than, or at least equal to, the maximum effectiveness of the rejected variants. This means that having found the minimum effectiveness of the accepted variants from the optimal balance we

[1] The complete equality of the effectiveness of the marginal investments in all the production units is only conceivable under unrealistic conditions, when the effectiveness of successive investments is a continuous function of its size and when the number of variants of successive investment in each production unit is indefinitely large.

have obtained the standard on the basis of which we can judge whether the level of effectiveness of the projected investment is sufficient, and whether it can be included in the optimal balance.[1]

By comparing the actual effectiveness of a number of variants of investment with the standard, we can determine which of them should be included in the optimal balance. In making this comparison it is necessary, first, to exclude variants occupying an intermediate position among those with an increasing effectiveness of successive (additional) investments, and, second, to calculate the indicators of effectiveness of the remaining variants by the chain method. Then the variant with an effectiveness slightly greater than or equal to the standard will be the optimal one, and must be included in the optimal balance of investments.[2]

Let us explain this rule. We recall that when making a direct selection of the most effective investments (from Table 28) for each product we took the variant with the largest investment of all those above the line separating the accepted variants from the rejected ones. But the variant with the largest investment is at the same time that with the least effectiveness of all those variants of the same product above the line. This is a consequence of the basic rules for the direct selection of the most effective investments, those for selecting the base for the calculation of the effectiveness of investment, and those for eliminating variants occupying an intermediate position among those with an increasing effectiveness for successive investments.

The standard effectiveness of investment can also be used in another selection method. Putting the above method in mathematical terms, let the investment according to the project variants for any one product be

$$K_1, K_2, \ldots, K_m$$

and the prime cost of annual output for the same variants be, respectively,

$$C_1, C_2, \ldots, C_m$$

Suppose that

$$K_1 < K_2 < \ldots < K_m$$

$$C_1 > C_2 > \ldots > C_m$$

[1] The maximum effectiveness of the rejected variants could also be used as a standard. In our example this maximum is not an absolutely clear criterion of whether the level of effectiveness is high enough: it merely shows that the optimal balance can include investments with an effectiveness greater than the standard, without indicating by how much. In actual optimal balances, when there is a very large number of investment variants, the maximum effectiveness of the rejected variants practically coincides with the minimum effectiveness of those which have been accepted. It is clear that the standard effectiveness of investment determined from the optimal balance will only be suitable for small changes in the optimal balance. When large changes in the balance are made the standard effectiveness might also have to change.

[2] It would be incorrect to suggest that the optimal variant is that with the highest effectiveness of investment, just as it would be inaccurate to say that the variant with an effectiveness greater than the standard was optimal, for there can be several such variants.

We also suppose that these variants include none which occupy an intermediate position among those with an increasing effectiveness of successive investments. This is expressed by the following inequalities:

$$\frac{C_1-C_2}{K_2-K_1} > \frac{C_2-C_3}{K_3-K_2} > \ldots > \frac{C_{m-1}-C_m}{K_m-K_{m-1}}$$

We call the permissible minimum effectiveness of investment the standard effectiveness of investment and denote it by r.

Let the variant f have an effectiveness which is equal to, or slightly greater than, the standard.

Symbolically this can be written

$$\frac{C_1-C_2}{K_2-K_1} > \frac{C_2-C_3}{K_3-K_2} > \ldots > \frac{C_{f-1}-C_f}{K_f-K_{f-1}} \geqq r > \frac{C_f-C_{f+1}}{K_{f+1}-K_f} > \ldots > \frac{C_{m-1}-C_m}{K_m-K_{m-1}}$$

It follows that

$$\frac{C_1-C_2}{K_2-K_1} > r$$

$$\frac{C_2-C_3}{K_3-K_2} > r \qquad \frac{C_f-C_{f+1}}{K_{f+1}-K_f} < r$$

$$\ldots\ldots \qquad \ldots\ldots$$

$$\frac{C_{f-1}-C_f}{K_f-K_{f-1}} \geqq r \qquad \frac{C_{m-1}-C_m}{K_m-K_{m-1}} < r$$

These inequalities can be transformed into a series of inequalities such as:

$$C_1+K_1r > C_2+K_2r$$

$$C_2+K_2r > C_3+K_3r \qquad C_f+K_fr < C_{f+1}+K_{f+1}r$$

$$\ldots\ldots \qquad \ldots\ldots$$

$$C_{f-1}+K_{f-1}r \geqq C_f+K_fr \qquad C_{m-1}+K_{m-1}r < C_m+K_mr$$

From which

$$C_1+K_1r > C_2+K_2r > C_3+K_3r > \ldots > C_{f-1}+K_{f-1}r \geqq$$
$$\geqq \boxed{C_f+K_fr} < C_{f+1}+K_{f+1}r < \ldots < C_m+K_mr$$

Of all the sums of the form $C+Kr$ the sum C_f+K_fr is the least.[1] But the variant f is the variant with an effectiveness equal to, or slightly larger than, the standard, i.e. the variant corresponding to the total maximum effect of

[1] The equation $C_{f-1}+K_{f-1}r = C_f+K_fr$ means that the additional investment has only the least permissible effectiveness.

investments. Hence the variants with an effectiveness equal to or slightly larger than the standard can be replaced by those for which the sum of the prime cost of annual output and the product of investment and the norm of investment efficiency is least.

In other words, instead of determining the optimal variant according to the minimum negative difference between the actual and the standard effectiveness of additional investment, we can find the variant from the formula $C+Kr$ min., where the product Kr expresses the standard effect of the investment K, i.e. the minimum economy of labour which the investment K must yield so that it may be included in the optimal balance. Thus, the sum $C+Kr$ is the sum of the prime cost and the standard economy of labour from the projected investment.

Here the reader may wish to ask why it is not necessary, when selecting the variant by this method, to exclude in the beginning variants occupying an intermediate position among those with an increasing effectiveness for successive outlays of limited means. The answer is simply that for all economically possible values of the standard of effectiveness such variants cannot have least sums of the form $C+Kr$.

We can see that this is true from the following argument. Suppose that we have three variants of production of some output. The respective outlays on these variants are: investments, viz. K_1, K_2, K_3; and prime cost of annual output is C_1, C_2, C_3.

We have

$$K_1 < K_2 < K_3 \text{ and } C_1 > C_2 > C_3 \qquad \ldots \quad [4.3]$$

Moreover, the effectiveness of additional investments for variant 3 is greater than that for variant 2:

$$\frac{C_2-C_3}{K_3-K_2} > \frac{C_1-C_2}{K_2-K_1} \qquad \ldots \quad [4.4]$$

This means that variant 2 occupies an intermediate position among those with an increasing effectiveness for successive investments.

The conditions [*4.3*] and [*4.4*] preclude the possibility that variant 2 shall have the least sum $C+Kr$, i.e. it is impossible, when $r \geqq 0$, that

$$C_2+K_2r < \left| \begin{matrix} C_1+K_1r \\ C_3+K_3r \end{matrix} \right.$$

For these inequalities are equivalent to

$$\frac{C_2-C_3}{K_3-K_2} < r < \frac{C_1-C_2}{K_2-K_1},$$

giving

$$\frac{C_2-C_3}{K_3-K_2} < \frac{C_1-C_2}{K_2-K_1},$$

which contradicts [*4.4*].

This means that the variant 2 cannot have the least sum of the form $C+Kr$ for any value of r other than a negative one.

It is not difficult to see that it is simpler to select variants by finding the minimum of $C+Kr$ than by finding the minimum non-negative difference between the actual and the standard effectiveness: we no longer require several extra rules and stipulations, which might be forgotten and lead to errors. However, the advantages of this method are immeasurably more important than its simplicity or convenience.

From the theoretical point of view, the calculation of the sum $C+Kr$ is a special method of the measurement of labour outlays, a method directed to finding its overall minimum. In practice, however, this measurement of outlays is the only possible way of drawing up the optimal balance of accumulation and investment and also of solving a number of other important questions in economic planning.

8. The Need for Another Method of Finding the Maximum Effect of Investments, apart from the Direct Selection of the Most Effective Variants of Investment

The method we have given for finding the maximum effect of investments is very simple. In practice however it is applicable only on a modest scale, for it is only in rare cases that we can calculate the indicator of the effectiveness of investment.

The indicator $\frac{C_1-C_2}{K_2-K_1}$ can be calculated only when the economy in prime cost (C_1-C_2) is the result of the additional investment (K_2-K_1) alone. But economy of labour (and this means economy of prime cost) is afforded not only by investment, but also by the use of better natural resources (better soil, better minerals) and other relatively good means of production. Usually better means of production are not available in sufficient quantities for the needs in them to be satisfied. In this respect they are similar to investment: the volume of effective uses is greater than their supplies. The problem then arises of finding the most effective use of the better, but limited, means of production, and this is a problem similar to that of finding the maximum effect of investment.

At first glance it would appear that these problems can be solved separately for each type of the limited means of production.

However this is not so, because we cannot divide the economy in prime cost (C_2-C_1), which is the combined effect of several limited means of production, into a number of terms representing the effect of outlay of each of these means separately, for this would imply solving one equation with several unknowns.

On the other hand, with the joint outlay of two or more limited means we cannot consider the economy in prime cost as the effect of only one limited means, say investment. For if we did, the effectiveness of those variants of investment which presuppose the use of scarce means of production would be overestimated owing to the effect of the use of these means. As a result the most effective balance of investments, formed on the basis of incorrect indicators, would require a greater quantity of scarce means of production than was available. Having selected as many of the investment variants placed in order of decreasing effectiveness as are consistent with the investment limit, we would obtain a balance of investments which could not be put into effect, due to the insufficiency of better natural resources, scarce types of raw material and fuel.

Thus we can only apply the method of direct selection of the most effective investment when the compared variants require the identical outlay of each scarce means of production and different investment. It is therefore clear that our examples of determining the maximum effect of investments (see above, Tables 20 and 23) omitted the one important reservation that for each product (*A*, *B*, *C*, *D* and *E*) the outlay of any limited means apart from investment is identical for all variants.

It should be noted that we are here referring to those better means of production which are available, or produced, in smaller quantities than necessary; or to be more precise, in smaller quantities than the volume of their effective uses. Here it is not the quality of the means of production that is decisive, but the restriction on their volume.

We can see this clearly by imagining that rich deposits of raw materials have been discovered, excelling the best of the previously known scarce varieties of the same raw materials, and exceeding in quantity all possible effective uses. Then this material, though better than the former scarce raw material, will not be scarce, and the latter will become non-industrial (ineffective). Although the new abundant raw material will be more effective than the old scarce one, differences in expenditure of it in the compared variants will not prevent us from finding the maximum effect of investment by the given method, since in constructing the most effective balance of investments we shall not come up against any shortage of raw material.

Problem 3

Let us illustrate this by a simple example. Suppose that to produce the three products *A*, *B* and *C* we have the following limited means: 260 thousand roubles of investment, and 40 tons of scarce raw material per year.

The annual production programme of each of these products can be fulfilled in several ways with various investments and different outlays of the scarce raw material. The necessary outlay for each variant to complete the annual programme for each product is shown in Table 30.

The question is to find the combination of variants for which

1. the production programme of all three products will be fulfilled;

TABLE 30

A				B				C			
Variant	Prime Cost of Annual Output (thousand roubles)	Investment (thousand roubles)	Outlay of Scarce Raw Material (tons/year)	Variant	Prime Cost of Annual Output (thousand roubles)	Investment (thousand roubles)	Outlay of Scarce Raw Material (tons/year)	Variant	Prime Cost of Annual Output (thousand roubles)	Investment (thousand roubles)	Outlay of Scarce Raw Material (tons/year)
I_A	102	80	0	I_B	200	100	0	I_C	130	110	0
II_A	96	70	10	II_B	180	80	20	II_C	100	100	20
III_A	90	120	10	III_B	175	120	20	III_C	95	110	30

2. investment and outlay of scarce raw materials will not exceed their limits;
3. the total effect from the use of the scarce raw materials and investment will be as large as possible (i.e. the total prime cost of the products *A*, *B* and *C* will be as small as possible).

Let us try to solve this problem by the same method as before. We determine the indicators of the effectiveness of investment on the assumption that the economy in prime cost afforded by a variant is the effect of investment only. In other words, we assume that the effectiveness of the outlay of the scarce means of production is equal to zero. Then clearly on this assumption variants I_A, I_B, I_C must be dropped, since the additional investment for these variants entails an extra outlay in prime cost of output (compared with variants II_A, II_B and II_C).

Let us calculate the effectiveness of the additional investment for the variants III_A, III_B and III_C:

$$E_{III_A/II_A} = \frac{96-90}{120-70} = 12\% \text{ per year}$$

$$E_{III_B/II_B} = \frac{180-175}{120-80} = 12{\cdot}5\% \text{ per year}$$

$$E_{III_C/II_C} = \frac{100-95}{110-100} = 50\% \text{ per year}$$

We form a table to select the most effective variants.

TABLE 31

Variant and Base	Effectiveness of Investment (% per year)	Investment with this Effectiveness (in thousand roubles)
II_A, II_B, II_C	∞	250
III_C/II_C	50	10
III_B/II_B	12·5	40
III_A/II_A	12	50

It is obvious that variants II_A, II_B and III_C are within the investment limit, but that the scarce raw material which this combination requires is not; it requires $(10+20+30) = 60$ tons per year, whereas the limit is 40 tons per year.

We shall obtain a similar result when we solve this problem by finding the maximum effectiveness of use of the scarce raw material, if we ascribe to it all the economy in prime cost promised by one variant in comparison with another.

The effectiveness of scarce raw material represents the ratio of the economy in prime cost obtained from its use to its outlay (expressed in natural units). Taking the effectiveness of investment equal to zero, we obtain the following indicators of the effectiveness of scarce raw material for Problem 3:

The variants III_A and III_B have infinitely greater effectiveness of use of scarce raw material than II_A and II_B, for the economy in prime cost is obtained without additional expenditure of it. Therefore variants II_A and II_B drop out.

For the remaining variants, the effectiveness of outlay of scarce raw material is given by the following quantities:

$$E_{III_A/I_A} = \frac{102-90}{10-0} = 1{\cdot}2 \text{ thousand roubles/ton}$$

$$E_{III_B/I_B} = \frac{200-175}{20-0} = 1{\cdot}25 \text{ thousand roubles/ton}$$

$$E_{III_C/I_C} = \frac{130-100}{20-0} = 1{\cdot}5 \text{ thousand roubles/ton}$$

$$E_{III_C/II_C} = \frac{100-95}{30-20} = 0{\cdot}5 \text{ thousand roubles/ton}$$

We form a table to select the most effective variants.

TABLE 32

Variant and Base	Effectiveness of outlay of Scarce Raw Materials (thousands of roubles/ton)	Amount of Scarce Raw Materials which can be Expended with this Effectiveness (tons/year)
I_A, I_B, I_C	—	0
II_C/I_C	1·5	20
III_B/I_B	1·25	20
III_A/I_A	1·2	10
III_C/II_C	0·5	10

The combination of variants I_A, III_B and II_C satisfies the limit of scarce raw material, but not the investment limit: the investment in this case is $(80+120+100) = 300$ thousand roubles, and the limit is 260 thousand roubles.

Thus both attempts to solve the problem have failed. The reason is the same in both cases: the whole economy in prime cost was attributed to only one of two limited means, while in fact, by hypothesis, some economy in prime cost is afforded by both investment and outlay of the scarce raw material. This is clear from Table 30. Thus the additional investment for variant III_A compared with II_A is accompanied by an economy in prime cost, for the same outlay of the scarce raw material. On the other hand, the outlay of scarce raw material for variant II_A is accompanied by an economy in prime cost, despite the reduced investment in comparison with the variant I_A. Similar relationships can be seen for the variants II_B and III_B, I_B and II_B, III_C and I_C.

Yet both investment and scarce raw material are limited: there is less of them than is required for all the uses which economise on labour (within the limits of the production programme for *A*, *B* and *C*). Hence, both investment and scarce raw materials must be used with the maximum effectiveness, i.e. so that the total effect of their use is as large as possible.

From this it is clear that our mistake was to try to solve the problem by finding the maximum effect of the use of only one limited means of production, while the problem is to find the maximum total effect of the use of two limited means of production.

To solve problems such as this, this method is not suitable. In fact the direct selection of the most effective variants is based on the comparison of the indicators of effectiveness of the use of limited means of production. When there is joint outlay of two (or more) limited means, the economy in prime cost afforded by their use is the joint effect of several heterogeneous means.

But we cannot calculate the indicator of effectiveness of the outlay of several heterogeneous means of production: to do so it would be necessary to calculate the ratio of the economy in prime cost obtained from the joint outlay of the different means of production to the sum of the expended means. When these means are heterogeneous, they cannot be summed: we cannot add roubles of investment to tons of copper or hectares of land. In practice the joint outlay of several limited means is the rule, and so, in general, the calculation of the indicators of the effectiveness of investment, to a greater or less extent, contains the same error which we committed when we calculated them from Table 30 (giving Table 31) and said that the effectiveness of the scarce raw material was equal to zero.

Thus the problem of finding the maximum effect of investments of the whole economy cannot be solved in isolation from the more general problem of finding the maximum effect of all limited means of production. It is obvious that this is a different problem from that which we have solved so far. We have been looking for the maximum effect of investment only. Now we have the wider problem of finding the most effective use of several limited producer goods. Nor is this all. The problem of finding the total maximum effect of limited means of production is, in its turn, part of the problem of the most effective use of all means of production in general.

In fact limited or scarce means of production are, strictly speaking, those for which the number of effective uses is greater than their supply (or production). This means that all the means of production which are better than the worst ones of the same kind are used to satisfy the requirements. Every means of production which helps to produce output with a lower outlay than the worst of the necessary means will be limited: its use will afford an economy of labour, and its possible effective uses (i.e. those economising labour) will be fewer than its supply, for otherwise there would be no need to use the less effective means.

Thus the composition of the limited means of production is very wide, and includes all exploited natural resources apart from the worst of them, and those reproducible means whose stock is restricted by the limits of accumulation. But in finding the most effective use of limited means of production it is necessary also to take into account the use of the worst of the means of production required, for it is on the quality of these that the relative effectiveness of the possible uses of the limited means depends.

Hence the most effective balances of limited means of production can be drawn up only when 'non-scarce' means of production are included in them.

The problem of the maximum effectiveness of investment has therefore led us to a much more general problem going outside the limits of this chapter. However, if we keep within these limits (restricting ourselves to the one means —investment) we can justify a method for comparing optimal balances suitable for any number of limited means by considering it in its simplest form.

9. Potentially-Optimal Combinations of Variants

We have considered the standard effectiveness of investment as a criterion for introducing small additions to the optimal balance of investments. In addition this standard can be used to draw up the optimal balance as a whole. For, if we could know in some way the standard effectiveness of investment, then we could at once solve the whole problem. All that would be necessary would be to select the variant (for each product) either with an effectiveness slightly larger than or equal to the standard, or with the least sum of the form $C+Kr$. The question is only how to find out this standard.

We have seen that the standard follows from the optimal balance of investments. Therefore it is reasonable to suggest that any method for determining the standard is at the same time a method for drawing up the optimal balance of investments.

The direct selection of the most effective investment variants is not the only method or even, as we shall see below, the most accessible one. It is just that it is the simplest and most easily understood. Starting with it, we can more easily explain another method of constructing optimal balances which, although more complicated, is more in accordance with the conditions of contemporary economics.

This more complicated method is based on the property of the standard of effectiveness of investment being the lower limit of effectiveness of the accepted variants. This property is obvious when it is used in the formula $\frac{C_1 - C_2}{K_2 - K_1} - r = \min \geqq 0$ or (using the pay-off period) in the formula

$$\frac{1}{r} - \frac{K_2 - K_1}{C_1 - C_2} = \min \geqq 0$$

Obviously, if the selected investments satisfy these formulae, then their effectiveness will not be lower than the standard.

But as we have shown, the standard of effectiveness possesses the same property when it is used with the formula $C + Kr = \min$. It follows that for any non-negative standard effectiveness the variants selected on this basis form a combination for which the total investment gives a greater effect (greater economy of labour) than any other possible use of the same total investment in the production of the same output.

It is true that the magnitude of the standard effectiveness affects the sum of the selected investments, and, therefore, their total effect. When the standard effectiveness is high both the total sum of selected investments and their total effect will be less than when it is low. But for any non-negative standard effectiveness we can select a combination of variants which is relatively more effective than any other possible combination with the same (or smaller) total investment.

Therefore the combinations of variants formed by a selection on the basis of any non-negative standard effectiveness of investment can be said to be potentially-optimal.

These combinations will be optimal if the total investment they require is equal to the investment limit. It follows that the optimal balance of investments can be found by forming several potentially-optimal combinations on the basis of trial standards of effectiveness. The criterion in these trials must be the relation between the required investment and the limit. If the former exceeds the fixed limit, then the trial standard of effectiveness must be lowered, while if it is considerably less than the limit the standard must be raised. The potentially-optimal combination for which the required investment is equal to the limit, constitutes the outlay side of the optimal balance of accumulation and investment.

Each potentially-optimal combination is distinguished by the following properties:

1. It has the lowest prime cost of output of all combinations requiring equal (or less) investment;
2. It requires the lowest investment of all combinations having equal (or lower) prime cost of the same output.

Let us prove this in the simplest case of the production of two products, 1 and 2.

Suppose that, having fixed the standard effectiveness ($r>0$) we select the variants of production of these outputs with the least sums of the form $C+Kr$

$$C'_1+K'_1r = \min,$$

$$C'_2+K'_2r = \min,$$

where the suffixes 1 and 2 denote the product, and the dashes denote that these are the prime cost of annual output and investment of the selected variants.

If we now replace the variants with a dash in this combination by two others chosen so that the total sum of investments of the combination does not increase:

$$K''_1+K''_2 \leqq K'_1+K'_2, \quad \ldots \quad [4.5]$$

where K''_1 and K''_2 are the new investments, the total outlay (of the form $(C+Kr)$) will increase (or at least remain the same):

$$C''_1+K''_1r+C''_2+K''_2r \geqq C'_1+K'_1r+C'_2+K'_2r \quad \ldots \quad [4.6]$$

This increase in the total outlay (for a given value of r) is possible only through an increase in the total cost of output. In fact, multiplying both sides of [*4.5*] by r (which is positive) we obtain:

$$K''_1r+K''_2r \leqq K'_1r+K'_2r \quad \ldots \quad [4.7]$$

Subtracting this from [*4.6*] in such a way that we subtract the larger side of [*4.7*] from the smaller side of [*4.6*], and the smaller side of [*4.7*] from the larger side of [*4.6*], we have

$$C''_1+C''_2 \geqq C'_1+C'_2$$

Thus we have proved that potentially-optimal combinations have the lowest prime cost of output of all possible combinations requiring the same (or less) total investment.

If we now replace the selected variants by others in such a way that the total cost of both products does not increase (denoting the prime cost for the variants in the changed combination by C'''_1 and C'''_2)

$$C'''_1+C'''_2 \leqq C'_1+C'_2 \quad \ldots \quad [4.8]$$

the total outlay of the form $C+Kr$ will increase (or at least remain unchanged):

$$C'''_1+K'''_1r+C'''_2+K'''_2r \geqq C'_1+K'_1r+C'_2+K'_2r \quad \ldots \quad [4.9]$$

Given r, this increase in total outlay is possible only through an increase in the total investment in the production of both outputs.

In fact, subtracting [*4.8*] from [*4.9*] we obtain

$$K'''_1r+K'''_2r \geqq K'_1r+K'_2r$$

Dividing both sides of this inequality by r ($r>0$) we obtain

$$K_1''' + K_2''' \geqq K_1' + K_2'$$

This proves that potentially-optimal combinations require a lower investment than any other possible combination of variants with the same (or less) total cost of the same output.

Thus the formation of potentially-optimal combinations of variants of investment can be used for the solution of two problems:

1. the problem of the maximum total effect from the use of a definite limit of investment (or, in other words, of the minimum total cost of the given output);
2. the problem of the minimum total investment (for a given limit to the total cost of output).

The economic meaning of these two problems is distinct. The first is a result of the laws of socialist economics, while the second is at variance with them. The problem of the minimum capital investment is based on the implicit assumption that the economy attempts to reduce to the minimum the time taken to produce and circulate the required output, rather than the working time needed to produce it.

In fact, the relation between the prime cost of output and the capital necessary for its production and circulation is $K = C\bar{t}$, where K is the capital, C the prime cost of annual output and $\bar{t}$ the average period of production and circulation of capital, weighted according to the size of the outlay. It follows that the problem of the minimum of K for limited C is a problem of the minimum of $\bar{t}$.

As we shall see below, the existence of potentially-optimal combinations of variants can be used to construct optimal balances not only of investments, but also of any means of production (material balances). This method lacks the clarity which distinguishes the direct selection of the most effective variants. When forming trial potentially-optimal combinations of variants we are, so to speak, groping towards our goal.

However, the formation of these combinations does not necessitate the measurement of the effectiveness of investments: in selecting the variants from the formula $C + Kr$ – min we are selecting them according to the minimum labour outlays. The measurement of the effectiveness of investment is replaced by the measurement of labour outlays: those investments for which the labour outlays on the output prove to be the smallest are considered to be the most effective. This method of comparing variants (according to the labour outlays) is more in accord with the content of the problem of the effectiveness of investment than is the comparison of the indicators of effectiveness, comparing the actual with the standard. For the effect of investment is measured by the economy of labour, while the sum $C + Kr$ expresses the labour outlays measured by a method which makes it easier to find its minimum. The next section is concerned with the proof of this statement.

10. Why the Standard Effectiveness of Investment cannot be the Average Level of its Effectiveness

It has already been widely accepted that there is a need to establish a standard effectiveness of investment. This is expressed in the 'Recommendations to the All-Union Scientific-Technical Conference on Problems of Determining the Economic Effectiveness of Capital Investments and of New Techniques in the National Economy of the USSR'. In Point 13 we read:

'When calculating effectiveness in order to select the most suitable variants of capital investment, it is necessary to compare the pay-off periods obtained (or their reciprocal, the coefficients of effectiveness) with standard values of these indicators. These standard indicators must be established for the economy as a whole and for the sectors, so as to obtain the greatest effect of capital investment for the economy as a whole. The maximum permissible (standard) pay-off periods for the selection of variants of capital investment and new techniques must be determined on the basis both of the replacement of one technique by a newer one, and of the extent of capital investment allocated to the given sector.'[1]

This is a correct definition of the purpose of the standard effectiveness of investment ('to obtain the greatest effect of capital investment for the economy as a whole'), of its value as the maximum permissible quantity and the basic conditions for the determination of its magnitude. The function of standards of effectiveness (pay-off periods) for the individual sectors remains in dispute: it is unclear how they can be a basis for attaining the maximum effect of investment for the economy as a whole. However, they can at least be used as steps on the way to determining the overall economic standards.

Not all Soviet economists would agree with this definition of standard effectiveness as a minimum quantity (and correspondingly of the standard pay-off period as the maximum permissible quantity). Some colleagues suggest that the standard effectiveness of investment should be an average—the average level of their effectiveness. This is the opinion expressed by Acad. S. G. Strumilin,[2] Reader L. A. Vaag[3] and others.

It is clear that those who hold this point of view overlook that the standard effectiveness of investment cannot be an average because whatever method we use to compare prime costs and investment with the help of a standard effectiveness, it is always those investment variants whose effectiveness is not lower than the standard which prove to be the most advantageous. This happens whether we use the formula

[1] See *Voprosy Ekonomiki*, 1958, No. 9, p. 157.

[2] See S. G. Strumilin, On the Economic Effectiveness of New Techniques, *USSR Academy of Sciences, VSNTO*, pp. 14-15, Moscow, 1958.

[3] L. A. Vaag, General Problems of Evaluating the Economic Effectiveness of Capital Investment, *USSR Academy of Sciences, VSNTO*, p. 36, Moscow, 1958.

$$\frac{C_1 - C_2}{K_2 - K_1} - r = \min \geqq 0,$$

or the formula $C + Kr = \min.$[1]

This means that in equating the standard effectiveness of investment to the average effectiveness we are equating the minimum effectiveness of the planned investment to its average effectiveness, which is conceivable only when the effectiveness of all the investments is identical.

It is possible to equate the minimum investment effectiveness to the average only when the latter refers to a different aggregate of investments.

It could, for example, refer to all possible future investment, and this is clearly how Strumilin should be understood. Or it could refer to past investment by expressing the average profitability of productive capital, as Vaag and others have suggested.

However, neither conception of an average as the standard effectiveness of investment gives us a suitable tool for forming optimal balances of investments. The average effectiveness of all possible investment in no way ensures that the investment plan based on it will comply with the investment limit. Such an average could be used only as a first approximation to the standard effectiveness of investment.

Thus if it was found that the investment plan based on this mean did not comply with the accumulation plan, we would have to establish another standard; and if, after attempting several trial standards, we succeeded in balancing the investment plan with the accumulation plan, then the final standard effectiveness of investment would be not the average effectiveness of the planned investments, but their minimum effectiveness. Therefore it is hardly worth starting from the average effectiveness of possible investment as the standard effectiveness (even as a first approximation).

The use of the average profitability of productive capital as the standard effectiveness of investment leads to different results. Selecting variants of new investment on the basis of the average effectiveness of past investment is equivalent to raising the lower limit of the effectiveness of investment; for the average effectiveness of investment of each period becomes the lower limit of effectiveness of investment of the next. This is equivalent to the systematic narrowing of the possibilities for the growth of labour productivity. Those who defend this method certainly do not anticipate this result. Yet it is inevitable, because the past average effectiveness is used to select investments with an effectiveness which is not lower than this average.

[1] Strumilin's method is not formally identical with either of these methods. It can be put in the form of the following inequality: $(C_0 - C_1) + (K_2 - K_1)r_{cp} < (C_0 - C_2)$ where C_0 is the standard prime cost of output of the standard variant and C_1 and C_2 are the prime costs of the two investment variants; K_1, K_2 are the investments, and r_{cp} is the average of their standard effectiveness. However this inequality can be simplified: $C_1 + K_1 r_{cp} > C_2 + K_2 r_{cp}$. Thus, Strumilin's method of comparing variants is essentially equivalent to the formula: $C + K r_{cp} = \min$.

But this selection is governed by the same formula $C+K_{cp}$ = min which the defenders of the use of average effectiveness as the standard recommend.[1]

However, it is necessary in some way to make the conception of the standard effectiveness as the minimum permissible quantity more precise.

First, it would be incorrect to calculate this quantity from the statistics of actual effectiveness of investment. For with a non-optimal balance of investments the minimum effectiveness of the accepted variants will be lower than in the optimal one, and also lower than the maximum effectiveness of the rejected investment variants. This means that when we say that the standard effectiveness of investment is equal to the minimum effectiveness of the accepted variants, we are not even defining this standard completely: there can be as many such minima as there can be different sets of investment selected.

But when the accepted set gives the total maximum effect of investment, then

(1) the minimum effectiveness of the accepted variants will be a maximum;
(2) the maximum effectiveness of the rejected variants will be a minimum;
(3) the first quantity will be greater than, or equal to, the second.

Thus the standard effectiveness investment is a limit of a special kind, called a *minimax*.

11. The Reduction of Outlays at Different Periods to one Moment of Time

In our discussion of the maximum effect of investment we did not take account of when the investment was made, and so implicitly referred the investments of the different variants to one moment of time. In fact, however, the construction periods can vary a good deal, both in their total duration and in the times at which the separate outlays are made.

How then can we measure the economic consequences of construction periods?

These consequences depend on several factors. It is fairly clear that the greater the labour outlays on the construction and the greater the time which separates the outlay from the moment of actual output, the greater the consequences will be.

The product of these two quantities gives an index of association between the outlays: it reflects both the outlay of labour, and the time during which it is associated with production. Its dimensions are man-hours per year, or roubles per year (if a value measurement is used for the outlay).

Let the sums of investment made at different times be $k_1, k_2, \ldots, k_s$ and the time separating each of these sums be $t_1, t_2, \ldots, t_s$. Then the degree of association is expressed by the sum of the products $\sum_{j=1}^{s} k_j t_j$ where s is the number of outlays at different times.

[1] See L. A. Vaag, op. cit., p. 9, pp. 36-37 *et al.*

However, this quantity still does not give the 'weighted' characteristics of the construction periods, which express the lost minimum effect (i.e. economy of labour) which the corresponding outlay (investment) could have given over the time during which it is not giving any effect. The calculation of this lost effect must be based on the overall standard effectiveness of investment, and it must be added to the investment in order to reduce it to the moment when output first begins.

Correspondingly, the outlays of later years must also be reduced to this moment of time, using the standard effectiveness of investment and starting from the compound interest formula.

This method of reducing outlays at different periods to one moment of time was suggested by the All-Union Scientific-Technical Conference on Problems of Determining the Economic Effectiveness of Capital Investment and of New Techniques.[1]

12. Conclusions

Let us summarise this chapter. The fact that accumulation is limited poses the problem of its most effective use. If the volume of accumulation is too small for all the potential investments which would economise labour to be used, it is necessary to select those investments for which, firstly, the production programme of the final output will be fulfilled and secondly, the total effect of all investment will be as large as possible. This requirement follows from the principle of the economy of labour.

However, it is impossible to solve this problem without considering the problem of the best use of all means of production. It is impossible to construct the optimal (most effective) balance of accumulation and investments without considering the most effective balances of all means of production. The optimal balance of investments can be drawn up only as part of the system of optimal balances of all means of production.

The optimal balance of accumulation and investments drawn up by the method of direct selection will be unrealisable in so far as there is a shortage in the best means of production, since it is not only investment that is limited, but also many means of production, and the principle of the economy of labour requires the most effective use of all generally limited means of production as well as of investment. Hence the maximum total effect from the use of investment and limited means of production must be found.

Nor is this all. The dividing line between the relatively best (limited) means of production and those which are not scarce but are still suitable for use can be found only by constructing the most effective balances of all means of production. Thus the best use of investment can be determined only by preparing the whole system of most effective material balances, together with the investment balance. This means that there is no special problem of the effectiveness of capital investment which can be stated and solved apart from

[1] See *Voprosy Ekonomiki*, 1958, No. 9, p. 158.

the more general problem of the most effective use of all means of production.

This is the first conclusion drawn from this chapter. Although it is a negative one it is important, because in textbooks and in practice the problem of the effectiveness of investment has been stated in isolation from the problem of the greatest total effect of the use of all means of production.

Nevertheless this negative conclusion has its positive side too. Once it has been established that it is impossible to solve the problem of the effectiveness of capital investment in isolation from the wider problem, not only the essence of this problem, but also the basic method for solving it is defined.

Essentially, this problem, which includes the problem of the effectiveness of investment, consists in finding the minimum total outlays of labour. The method of solution involves the preparation of a system of optimal balances of the means of production (including the balance of investments).

This system of balances cannot be constructed by the method of direct selection of the most effective uses of each separate means of production. For when several heterogeneous means are used jointly to produce a product, it is not possible to single out the economy of labour that each of them affords.

However, the direct selection of the most effective uses of limited means can be replaced by selection based on the minimum outlays, if we include in the total outlays the standard economy of labour from the use of the given means. We have discussed this for the case when only one means was limited, and have established that the standard effectiveness of the given limited means can be found by constructing several trial balances. The outlays side of each of these balances is the requirement in the given means for all uses which give the planned output with the least total costs of production and with the standard economy of labour.

If the standard effectiveness has been determined correctly, the balance does away with shortage or surplus of limited means. If the standard is too high, then there is a surplus, while if it is too low, a shortage occurs. Having found the correct value of the standard effectiveness, we have at the same time determined the combination of variants which will give a final output that corresponds to the plan, and for which the limited means are used with the maximum total effect, and the costs of production of the whole final output are the least.

Thus, when only one means is limited, direct selection of its most effective use can be replaced by selection based on minimum outlays, measured in a special way.

Chapter IV thus posed the two questions:

1. What is the economic meaning of the measurement of outlay according to the formula $C+Kr = \min$?

2. Is it possible to use this method in practice and can optimal balances of all means of production be constructed with the help of it?

CHAPTER V

PRINCIPLES FOR MEASUREMENT OF OUTLAY

1. Differential Outlays

It is widely believed that the labour outlays on a product should always be measured only by the expenditure on the production of this product. There are different views about the composition of this expenditure, but no doubts have been expressed about measuring the labour expended on the product in terms of the labour used for its production.

This common practice is a barrier to the further development of the theory of value and to an advance in the use of the law of value in planning. In fact it is the basis of the divergence between practice and theory which has already been noted. It is also the basis of the superficial 'critique' of the Marxist theory of value.

Yet the measurement of the labour outlays on a product in terms of the labour directly involved in its production is not the only method of measurement. It is an elementary method using elementary mathematics, but it is quite possible, and under certain conditions necessary, to use other methods involving higher mathematics.

The measurement of outlays is not an end in itself. It is subordinate to both the general and the specific laws of economics at each stage of economic development. These and other laws direct the measurement of expenditure to the solution of definite extremal problems.[1] Thus the general law of the economy of labour stipulates that labour shall be measured in such a way that it can be minimised. Under capitalism the specific law of surplus value subordinates this measurement to the goal of maximising profits; the law of the economy of labour being satisfied only in so far as it is consistent with this goal.

The specific economic laws of socialism—the basic law, the law of the continuous growth of labour productivity, the law of planned (proportional) development—require the measurement of outlays in order to maximise the rate of growth of labour productivity, i.e. to maximise the rate of decrease of labour outlays per unit of final output.

These extremal problems which the measurement of outlays helps to solve require (under definite conditions) the use of other methods of measurement apart from the elementary calculation of production costs. These methods

[1] An extremal problem in mathematics is a problem concerned with finding the greatest or least values of some variable.

are not required only where labour outlays are expressed in value terms: there are several general principles for measuring expenditure in a developed socialised economy that would include measurement in terms both of value and of labour in a communist society.

The features of the measurement of the expenditure of labour which are peculiar to a certain economic system can be specified only by studying the general principles of this measurement. Therefore we shall first ignore the value problem and assume that we are already measuring outlays in labour time. Then we shall return to measurement in value terms. In this way we can elucidate both the general principles of the measurement of outlays and the specific features appertaining to different types of social relations in production.

It is a common assumption that the measurement of outlays does not require higher mathematics. Usually it does not even occur to economists that the method used to measure outlay when finding its minimum must be different from that used when this problem does not exist. In order to find the minimum outlay on some product or other, it is considered quite sufficient to calculate the outlay on its production for the different variants and to compare the totals. However, the problem could be satisfactorily solved in this way only at the lowest stages of economic development, no higher than simple commodity production, when the commodities exchanged were almost entirely the product of the individual labour of the peasant or artisan.

'What had they expended in making these products? Labour and labour alone: to replace tools, to produce the raw material, and to process it they spent nothing but their own labour-power; how then could they exchange these products of theirs for those of other labouring producers otherwise than in the ratio of the labour expended on them?'[1]

Under such conditions it was possible to determine the least labour-intensive processes of production for each product by a direct comparison of the requisite expenditure of labour. However, under socialism, it is impossible to solve the problem in this way. For the problem itself has essentially changed. Instead of determining the minimum labour required to produce each separate product, the problem becomes one of finding the least total outlay.

The reason for this is not only the conscious preference for general interests above individual interests, or for the least total outlay above the particular minima of outlays, but also (and above all!) the objective impossibility of using particular minima of outlays as a guide. The point is that in a socialist economy the individual minimum costs of production (for each product separately, for each enterprise separately) are incompatible. This means that while each particular minimum could be attained on its own, together they are unattainable. For an illustration let us return once more

[1] K. MARX, *Capital*, Vol. III, p. 874, Moscow, 1959 (English edition), (Supplement of F. Engels).

to Table 23 (see p. 85). Suppose that we can spend not more than 400 million roubles on all five investment projects. As we can see from the table, for the variant of each project with the least prime cost of output to be realised, 100 million roubles must be invested in each. Clearly each variant is realisable on its own, but together they are not; for 500 million roubles would be required and only 400 million roubles are available.

Every experienced project-maker knows that he cannot be guided by the minimum prime cost of output in his selection of variants, since this minimum is impracticable because of the restriction on investment, the limit on scarce means of production, the shortages of the best natural resources, and so on. It is no different if, instead of calculating prime cost, he calculates the individual value of the product. For the least possible individual values of the separate products also assume the use of only the best conditions of application of labour, and are therefore incompatible. Thus, in a socialist economy, the principle of particular minima of costs of production does not hold, whatever one's wishes in the matter: it becomes objectively unrealisable.

The principle of the economy of labour under socialism can be realised only as the principle of the least total outlay on the entire output of the economy.

The pre-eminence of the least total outlay over the particular minima is an objective necessity in a socialist economy.

This means that the most effective variant of production of any product is not the one requiring the least outlay on its production, but that which corresponds to the least total outlays for the economy as a whole. It is impossible to find this variant by an elementary method (by calculating outlays, and comparing totals). For it would be necessary to calculate the costs of production for the final output of the whole economy for all possible combinations of variants of the individual products. There is an enormous number of such combinations, the overwhelming majority of which will be ineffective. This method of solution is extremely irrational, as it requires many unnecessary calculations. In fact there is no need at all to calculate the total outlay of the economy in order to find the variant corresponding to its minimum.

It is sufficient to calculate the increase in the cost of production of the final output of the economy attributable to the production of the given product. That variant which requires the least additional cost of production for the whole final output is the one with the least total outlay. Since outlay will then be measured by the increments of a variable, we can call it the 'differential outlay' on the given product for the economy as a whole.

If the selection of the variant did not affect the costs of production of other products, then its differential outlay would be the same as its costs of production. In fact, however, it is not so. As we shall show below, the selection of a variant is usually associated with some increments in the costs of production of other products. Therefore, as a rule, the differential outlay for the production of an individual product is not equal to its costs of production.

The concept of differential outlay is most easily understood as the difference between the labour required to produce the total output of the economy once including, and then excluding the given product.

However this definition of differential outlay does not suggest the method for calculating it, which is based on the calculation of the labour expended on the production of the given product and the consequent increments in costs of production of other products.

2. The Feedback between Outlays for Different Purposes

The relation between the outlays on different products is of two kinds:

1. Direct: an increase in the outlay on a given product causes an increase in that on other products;

2. Indirect: an increase in the outlay on a given product causes a decrease in that on other products.

The direct relation between outlays is usually appreciated. It is based on the fact that outlays on the means of production are part of the outlays on the products manufactured from these means.

If there were only a direct relation between the outlays on different products (larger—larger, smaller—smaller) than the particular minimum outlays would be quite compatible, and the least total outlay could be found by finding the minimum outlay on each product separately.

But the indirect relation, or feedback, between outlays complicates the matter. A project variant requiring less outlay on the given product can entail an increase in the outlay on other products which makes up for any economy in prime cost which it yields. Because of the existence of feedback between outlays on different products, the sum of the individual minimum outlays does not equal the minimum total outlay of the whole economy. For this reason we cannot find the least total outlay by finding the minimum outlay on each product separately.

Feedback between outlays always occurs when the following three conditions are satisfied:

1. the means of production can be replaced by different ones, i.e. different means of production can serve the same purpose;

2. the different substitutes have unequal effectiveness;

3. there is a shortage of the more effective means of production in comparison with the requirements in them (or, more exactly, with the extent of their effective uses).

All three conditions are necessary for feedback to exist between outlays. While the significance of the first two is obvious enough, the third might need some clarification.

The unequal effectiveness of the means of production would be of no economic importance if there were not less of the most effective means of production than is required for all purposes. But a shortage of these means of production forces us to use less effective means as well, which necessarily causes feedback between the outlays on products which could use more effective means of production. For the use of the best means of production (best sources of raw materials or power, best machinery, etc.) for one purpose always involves the need to use worse means of production (worse sources of raw materials or power, less perfect machinery) for other purposes.

Therefore the economy of labour which can be derived from the use of the best but limited means of production always involves an increase in the labour outlays for other purposes: economy of labour in one place sets off over-expenditure of labour in another place. The economy achieved might be either larger or smaller than the over-expenditure, for the various uses of the best means of production are not equally effective: some afford a greater and others a smaller economy of labour compared with the use for the same purpose of less effective means of production necessary to satisfy the requirements in it.

Let us give some examples of feedback between outlays.

Given the total accumulation of the economy, a project variant which requires greater investment in comparison with another variant of the same project involves a corresponding reduction in the investment in other projects. To select the variants of the other projects according to the minimum investment required may entail the use of less perfect machinery, or the renunciation of costly, but effective, structures (tunnels, thicker walls, embankments, etc.) or an increase in the life of obsolete machinery, or a quicker rate of felling forests, or a decrease in the batch size of articles manufactured serially, or with other consequences of cutting down investment without reducing annual output. All these consequences are associated, usually, with increased prime cost of the corresponding products.

This means that the selection of a variant requiring greater investment for a given project lowers the prime cost of output for this project, but raises that of others whose investment must be curtailed.

Here is another example. The number of uses of oil which economise labour compared with other forms of fuel is much greater than the supply of oil. Therefore, in deciding on how oil should be used, it is wrong to be guided solely by the expected economies in prime cost and investment in any one particular use. For this use will rule out another effective use which could also economise prime cost and investment.

This means that the selection of a variant requiring expenditure of oil lowers its own prime cost and investment at the cost of increasing that of other projects where the use of oil would be effective, but is incompatible with the given use.

3. Feedback and Differential Outlays

Therefore to find a project variant which corresponds to the least total outlay for the whole economy, it is also necessary to measure not only the costs of production for the different variants of the project but also the increases in outlays on other products which are caused by the more effective means of production being used for a given purpose rather than for the others. We call these increases in outlays on other products 'feedback outlays', since they express the indirect relation or feedback between the costs of production of different products.

Then we can say that the differential outlays on each individual product are made up of

1. its costs of production; and
2. its feedback outlay.[1]

The calculation of feedback outlays is an objective necessity in a socialist economy. Hence it makes itself felt even in spite of an ignorance about the essence and correct methods of measuring these outlays, despite the disinclination to consider them, and even a condemnation of them.

This happens first of all because the fact that feedback outlays have not been accounted for is revealed in the same convincing way as any other unaccounted outlays—the purpose for which these outlays were made is seen to be unrealised through lack of means.

However the consequences of not accounting for feedback outlays are of a more general nature than those of not accounting for costs of production. If some of the costs of production of a product are not taken into account (such as, say, the outlay of fuel) then the object of this outlay remains unrealised (either in part or wholly). But if feedback outlay resulting from the use of some scarce means (such as a scarce type of fuel) is not taken into account, then all the uses of these means which economise costs of production in comparison with other types of fuel turn out to be incompatible.

Yet in current project-making practice there is no scientific method of calculating feedback outlays. Instead, the project-makers consider the sizes of investment, the outlay of scarce raw materials, fuel, and other elements of production that are qualitatively quite different and have different dimensions from the feedback outlays which depend on them. As a result a heterogeneous non-additive composition of outlays is obtained, and it becomes impossible even to pose the problem of the minimum total outlay.

[1] The term 'feedback' is used also in another sense in economics, to denote the fact that the output of goods (for example, of steel) is used as an outlay on the production of the same goods (see Nemchinov's article in this collection, 'The Use of Mathematical Methods in Economics'). This form of feedback must be taken into account when measuring costs of production. Thus the measurement of differential outlays assumes that both kinds of feedback are taken into account, viz.

(*a*) feedback in the sense of the transformation of a product into an input for its own production;

(*b*) feedback in the sense that a decrease in outlay on one project involves an increase in outlay on others.

Feedback of the first kind can be taken into account only by using successive approximations, or by solving a system of linear equations. Feedback outlays of the second kind can be determined by using standard effectiveness of use, relative to the best means of production (see below).

Of course, it is possible to balance the total outlay of limited means with their supply without comparing prime cost with these outlays, i.e. without considering the feedback outlays. All that is necessary is to reduce demand according to some simple rule (such as proportionally). The plan thus equalised can be considered to have been ensured of fulfilment with the material resources. But it does not enable them to be used in the best way: it will be feasible, but not optimal.

Certainly under socialism there is no place for such a purely mechanistic curtailment of the requirements of limited means. When the balances of these means are constructed, the importance of the different requirements, and also, as far as is possible, the effectiveness of different uses of these means are taken into account. When any means is in short supply, compared with the requirements in it, the less important uses are rejected or cut, while the more important ones are retained.

In their turn, the consumers of limited means too must somehow or other compare the prime cost of output with the outlay of the limited means when selecting variants of its use. For without such a comparison (however implicit) it would in many cases be impossible to decide even approximately which variant is the most effective and what is more important—the economy in prime cost (in roubles per year) or the additional investment (in roubles) plus the additional outlay of scarce means of production (in tons) and so on.

Therefore in practice various methods are used to compare prime cost with the outlay of limited means (such as pay-off periods, increased prices of scarce materials, and so on) despite their vagueness, despite the ignorance of methods for calculating the standards of comparison, despite the severe criticism of these made by some economists. However, these various coefficients of comparison do no more than conceal the imperfection of standards for calculating feedback outlays.

Thus the need for taking account of feedback outlays manifests itself both in the need for constructing balances of the means of production with regard to the effectiveness of their use, and in the need for comparing costs of production with the outlay of limited means. Yet, there is still insufficient recognition of this need. It is true that high prices are fixed for scarce raw materials and fuel, but obviously they only partly reflect feedback outlays. We can see this from the fact that it is impossible to rely only on the minimum prime cost of output obtained with the use of scarce materials when deciding on this use.

The problem of the allocation of investment is also solved, as a rule, without due regard for feedback outlays, by comparing indicators of effectiveness (or their reciprocals, pay-off periods) with some standard or other. However, as we saw above, it is impossible to solve the problem in this way. It can only be solved as part of the whole problem of the most effective utilisation of all means of production. Therefore the feedback outlays stipulated not only by investments but also by other limited means of production must be taken into account when selecting an investment variant.

4. The Range of Feedback Outlays

Let us try to establish which means of production are associated with feedback outlays. To do this we must specify which of them satisfy all three conditions for the existence of feedback between outlays.

First of all there are the many irreproducible means of production, such as land, deposits of useful minerals suitable for making lead piping, etc. The use of the relatively good means of production of this kind will be loaded with feedback outlays, since it involves more than just the use of least effective means of production, i.e. the worst of those needed to satisfy the requirements.

Then there is the multiplicity of reproducible means of production which are replaceable but not equally effective, the reproduction of the best of them being limited by the volume of accumulation of the whole economy. It is true that each reproducible means of production taken separately can be produced in as large a quantity as is required for all effective uses, i.e. for all uses where it is required and where it affords an economy of labour in comparison with other means of production. However, the production of all reproducible means of production depends on the limited volume of accumulation of the whole economy. (In stressing that it is limited we do not wish to imply that its absolute size is small, but that it is less than the possible volume of effective investments.) This restricted nature of the best reproducible means of production causes the exceptionally wide range of the feedback outlays of labour on these means. Every sector is included in the feedback, for every sector uses reproducible means of production and the outlay of these means depends everywhere on the same common limit of accumulation in the economy as a whole.

Further, a great number of previously produced means of production satisfy all three conditions of existence of feedback outlays. To this group belongs almost all the fixed and circulating capital of the economy.

This statement might seem paradoxical, for as a rule old means of production are not as good as new ones, being technically inferior and subject to wear and tear.

However, the relative effectiveness of the existing old and the new, but not yet produced, means of production will appear in a different light if, instead of looking for the least total sum of past and present outlay, we look for the least total sum of present outlay of labour alone. When the problem is put in this way it corresponds to the problem of obtaining the maximum output per worker. In the calculation of present outlay, previously-produced means of production have the great advantage that they do not require any outlay of labour on their production, but require only outlay on their use, while means of production which are not yet produced require labour both for their production and for their use.

Due to this advantage, instruments of labour which are obsolete for production can be more effective in use than the most effective of the new, but not yet produced, instruments of labour.

This is the usual relation between the effectiveness of old and new instruments of labour. Old instruments of labour are usually produced in a new form, instead of in their previous form. This is not an enormous accounting error: it is just that it would be ineffective to produce them in their previous form.

Yet many instruments of labour which are out-of-date are used nevertheless. It is unlikely that there has been a universal accounting error. On the contrary, it is more probable that by using partially obsolete means of labour we obtain output with less outlay of present labour than we would by using new, but still unproduced, machinery and instruments.

It follows that it is necessary to make a strict distinction between obsolescence for production and obsolescence for use. Obsolescence for production depends on whether the means of production should be produced—in the previous form or a new form; what should the new means of production be like? Obsolescence for use depends on how long the old means of production should be used.

Of course, this advantage of using old means of production will only compensate for their defects up to a certain point. They can become too old for use as well as for production. This would be the case if the costs of reproduction of output using the old instruments of labour, excluding past outlays on them, no longer corresponded to the least total outlay, i.e. when the prime cost of output using the old instruments of labour without proper amortisation of past investments exceeds the total cost of output using new instruments of labour and the feedback outlay associated with investment in these instruments.[1]

Until this limit is reached, however, almost all old means of production give an economy of labour in comparison with the best non-existent means of production. The only exceptions are those which are bordering on the obsolete. Hence, the use of almost every old means of production for any purpose makes for an increase in the future labour for other possible purposes, i.e. causes feedback outlays.

These outlays must be taken into account when calculating the effectiveness of production from old means of production, since otherwise it would be impossible to determine which variants using the old means of production are the most effective, i.e. correspond to the least total outlay of labour on the fulfilment of the given production programme.

At the same time, the magnitude of the feedback outlays indicates how suitable (effective) the old means of production are. If it is equal to zero, this means that these means of production have reached the limit of their effective use and must be replaced by new ones as soon as the indicators become worse.

The great majority of the instruments of labour used have an effectiveness

[1] Here we have given an abbreviated formula for the limits of use of old instruments of labour. In addition to the elements we have noted, it will still be necessary to consider the feedback outlays caused by the use of scarce irreproducible means of production.

equal to zero. In other words, most available instruments of labour enable output to be produced with less outlay of future labour than better, unproduced, machinery and tools can. Hence from the point of view of the economy of future labour, feedback outlays are involved in the use of the great majority of existing means of production.

This principle of the economy of future labour takes past outlays into account only to the extent of the future feedback outlays associated with the use of the product of these past outlays. This is a generalisation of the indisputable principle that existing means of production must be priced according to their costs of production.

Formulated in this way, this statement is only relevant when the old and the most effective of the new (not yet produced) means of production are identical, so that the feedback outlays associated with the use of the old means are equal to their costs of production. The most typical example of this is afforded by raw materials and fuel, which are usually stocked in the same form as they will be produced in future. As a result, the feedback outlays involved in the use of these stocks are usually the same as their costs of production.

However, another case, no less important, presents itself when the means of production are produced in another form, either different in quality or design. This is usually the case with instruments of labour. Here, the valuation of the old means of production cannot be equal either to the cost of their reproduction in the previous form, or to the cost of their reproduction in the new form. For example, suppose that the new machine is cheaper and more effective than the old. Then neither the costs of reproduction of the old machine nor those of the new one can be used for valuation of the former, as they will both be too high.

We can say, though, that the costs of reproduction of the old instruments of labour can be determined by the costs of reproduction of the new, taking differences in quality into account. However, in order that differences in quality may be reflected in differences in outlays, the principle of valuation according to costs of production must be given a wider meaning; that is, existing means of production must be costed in so far as their use involves increased labour for the reproduction of other products. This can be put in another way: the valuation of old means of production must be according to the economy of future labour which they provide, taking past labour to be equal to zero. But this economy of future labour is no more than the feedback outlays.

Thus, valuation in accordance with feedback outlays is the general rule in the valuation of existing means of production, both when the qualities of the old and new means of production are different and when they are the same.

We must mention yet another case where feedback outlays arise. The use of accumulation can be associated not only with the feedback outlays resulting from its scarcity, but also with additional feedback outlays over and above this.

This happens when the reproduction of some means of production is limited to a greater extent than follows from the overall balance of accumulation and capital investment of the whole economy. The use of such means of production will involve additional feedback outlays caused by its especial scarcity, unwarranted by restrictions on accumulation.

It is easily seen that feedback outlays here are a consequence of the removal of scarcity of a certain means of production, and clearly a case such as this contradicts the principle of the economy of labour, since feedback outlays represent the unexploited potential economy of labour. This means that they must be reduced, i.e. every possible and practicable economy of labour must be exploited. With short-term planning the scarcity of several reproducible means of production can be the result either of a lack of balance in the past or of an abrupt change in the production programme.

Production cannot immediately eliminate an inherited lack of balance; it cannot instantaneously adapt itself to abrupt changes in the production programme. In such cases, the scarcity of several reproducible means of production will be a temporarily unavoidable factor, and so must be allowed for beforehand in the plan, together with the consequent additional feedback outlay.

Thus, reproducible means of production can in some cases involve feedback outlays of two kinds owing, firstly, to capital investment, and secondly, to temporary shortages in the production of the given means of production.

Thus the use of the large majority of means of production is accompanied by feedback outlays, owing to the fairly obvious fact that there are not enough of best types of natural resources or previously produced means of production or planned accumulation to realise the best conditions of production in all existing and projected enterprises. The range of feedback outlays reflects the no less obvious fact that for each type of the means of production there are always many which are more effective than the worst of those required to complete the programme.

As a result, feedback outlays are not a rare exception, but are the general rule. Conversely, their absence is the exception. Therefore it will not be stretching a point if we say that in order to find a planning variant which accords with the least total outlay of labour it is necessary to look for the variant which requires the least sum of the costs of reproduction and feedback outlays, i.e. the least differential outlay. The feedback outlays might in some cases be equal to zero.

5. The Measurement of Differential Outlays as the Application of the Mathematics of the Variable to the Calculation of Outlays

Differential outlays are distinguished by important features which result from the fact that they are used to solve the extremal problem of finding the minimum outlays.

The first feature is that the measurement of outlays must be the measurement of their movement, i.e. of the increments in the outlays of social labour associated with the production of each product.

The second feature is that the measurement of outlay must take into account its interconnexions in the economy as a whole.

We have seen that differential outlay includes feedback outlays. But feedback outlays can be measured only if we calculate the outlay on each product not as a part of, but as an increment in, the labour expended on the total output of society. Only by comparing the outlays on the whole social product before and after the introduction of the given output can we determine the resultant increase in costs of production of other products. A method which considers the outlays on the specific output as part of the outlays on the whole social product will not enable us to determine the feedback outlays.

Thus the first condition for the measurement of differential outlays is to measure it in terms of the increments of a variable and not as part of a constant. Only in this way will its movement in the production process be expressed.

However, we could measure outlays as the increments in the costs of production in those sectors of the economy concerned with the production of the given product and of the means of production for it. This would mean ignoring those increments in the other economic sectors which are caused by the production of this product, i.e. the feedback outlays. Thus the second necessary condition for the measurement of differential outlays is that the interaction of the outlays in all sectors is taken into account; and in order to do this it is necessary to measure the outlays on each individual product as the increment in the outlays on the total output of the economy.

The measurement of differential outlays is an application of dialectics to the measurement of labour outlay, and can be used to find the least total outlay. But finding the maximum or minimum of a variable quantity is one of the specific problems of the mathematics of variables which, according to Engels' definition 'is in essence nothing other than the application of dialectics to mathematical relations'.[1] 'The relation between the mathematics of variable and the mathematics of constant magnitudes is in general the same as the relation of dialectical to metaphysical thought.'[2]

6. The Measurement of Differential Outlays when only One Means of Production is Scarce

If only one means of production is restricted, then the optimal balance of these means can be constructed by the direct selection of the most effective variants (see Chapter IV), and the measurement of differential outlays is unnecessary. However, it is simplest to illustrate the essentials of differential outlays by using this case as an example.

[1] F. Engels, *Anti-Dühring*, p. 127.
[2] op. cit., p. 115.

How should differential outlays be measured? How can we measure the increments in outlays on the whole final output of the economy which are caused by the production of the given product, if, in order to do this, we have to know just what other uses of the limited means will be prevented by this use?

A definite answer to this question might at first seem impossible. The uses which are prevented will depend on the system of allocating the limited means. However, this vagueness vanishes if we make the allocation of limited means subject to the law of economy of labour. Then the question has a definite answer, and in calculating the differential outlays it is necessary to count each use of the limited means as excluding a use whose effectiveness is equal to the standard effectiveness required in the construction of the optimal balance of the limited means.

Hence the standard effectiveness of limited means is at the same time the standard for calculating the feedback outlay. It represents not only the minimum effectiveness of those variants of the use of this means which must be accepted, but also the maximum effectiveness of those variants which must be rejected. This means that it represents the maximum feedback outlay associated with the use of a unit of limited means.

Thus, in comparing investment variants using the formula

$$\frac{C_1-C_2}{K_2-K_1}-r = \min \geqq 0,$$

r expresses the standard effectiveness of investment, while in comparing investment variants using the formula

$$C+Kr = \min$$

r expresses the standard feedback outlays associated with an investment of one rouble. Correspondingly Kr expresses the feedback outlays involved in the investment K, and the sum $C+Kr$ is the differential outlays.

This sum $C+Kr$ is just that increase in the costs of production of the whole final output of the economy which is caused by the production of an extra product requiring a cost of production C and investment K.

Let us demonstrate the formulation of the optimal balance of investments by calculating the differential outlays for Problem 2 (see p. 85). Since in this chapter we are at first ignoring the monetary form of outlay, we must change the unit of measurement and instead of 'prime cost' put 'production outlays' and instead of 'roubles' put 'man-hours'. Then with a limit of investment equal to 400 million man-hours, the standard effectiveness of investment is 0·067 man-hours per year per man-hour of investment.

With these conditions, the differential outlays are calculated in Table 33.

From this table we can draw the following conclusions:

1. The minima of differential outlays correspond to those variants which are part of the optimal balance of investments chosen directly (IV_A, III_B, IV_C, II_D, II_E).

TABLE 33

1	2	3	4	5 (2+4)
Variant	Costs of Production of Output (in million man-hours/year)	Investment of Labour in Productive Capital (in million man-hours)	Feedback Outlays (in million man-hours/year)	Differential Outlays (in million man-hours/year)
I_A	91	50	3·3	94·3
II_A	90	60	4·0	94·0
III_A	88	70	4·7	92·7
IV_A	81·2	80	5·3	**86·5**
V_A	80	100	6·7	86·7
I_B	76	50	3·3	79·3
II_B	72·8	70	4·7	77·3
III_B	71	80	5·3	**76·36**
IV_B	70	100	6·7	76·7
I_C	64	50	3·3	67·3
II_C	63·5	60	4·0	67·5
III_C	62·9	70	4·7	67·6
IV_C	60·8	80	5·3	**66·1**
V_C	60	100	6·7	66·7
I_D	53·2	50	3·3	56·5
II_D	50·7	80	5·3	**56·0**
III_D	50	100	6·7	56·7
I_E	42·6	50	3·3	**45·9**
II_E	40·6	80	5·3	**45·9**
III_E	40	100	6·7	46·7

For the production of E the minimum differential outlays occur in the two variants I_E and II_E, since the effectiveness of additional investment for II_E is equal to the standard effectiveness. The investment limit allows us to accept variant II_E, which is to be preferred on the grounds of its costs of production.

2. The minimum differential outlays are compatible, for the total investment of the variants to which they belong does not exceed the limit.

3. Finally, from this table we can see that a relatively small increase in the production of any product contrary to the optimal plan will raise the costs of production of the total output by an amount equal to the differential outlays.

From Table 33 we find that the differential outlays for the production of A (variant II_A) are 86·5 million man-hours per year. Suppose that the production plan for A is increased by three-eighths with the same total investment limit. The differential outlays for the additional output are

$$86{\cdot}5 \times \tfrac{3}{8} = 32{\cdot}4 \text{ million man-hours/year}$$

(This calculation assumes that an increase of $\frac{3}{8}$ in the production of A causes a proportional increase both in its costs of production and its investment.)

Now let us see to what extent the cost of production of all five products A, B, C, D and E increases.

The expansion of the production plan for A by $\frac{3}{8}$ involves 30 million man-hours of extra investment. Therefore we must reduce the investment in the production of E correspondingly, since this is the least effective: instead of the variant II_E we must take the variant I_E, which requires 30 million man-hours less of investment. Then the adjusted optimal balance of investments is composed of the variants IV_A, III_B, IV_C, II_D, I_E. The total costs of production of the annual output for these variants is

$$81{\cdot}2 \times \frac{11}{8} + 71 + 60{\cdot}8 + 50{\cdot}7 + 42{\cdot}6 = 336{\cdot}7 \text{ million man-hours/year}$$

The costs of production of the annual output in the same production units before the production of A was expanded was

$$81{\cdot}2 + 71 + 60{\cdot}8 + 50{\cdot}7 + 40{\cdot}6 = 304{\cdot}3 \text{ million man-hours/year}$$

Comparing the two we find that the increment in total costs of production caused by an increase in the production of A by $\frac{3}{8}$ is

Costs of Production of $A+B+C+D+E+\frac{3}{8}A$	$=$ 336·7 million man-hours/yr.
Costs of Production of $A+B+C+D+E$	$=$ 304·3 million man-hours/yr.
Difference:	32·4 million man-hours/yr.

But this increment is the differential outlays for $\frac{3}{8}A$.

Thus in calculating the differential outlays on the basis of the costs of production of the total final output we have arrived at the same result as when calculating it according to the formula $C+Kr = \min$.

Let us use this example to illustrate some more distinctive features of differential outlays.

1. Clearly, if we had increased the production of A by more than $\frac{3}{8}$ then the formula $C+Kr = \min$ would give a somewhat smaller result than the increment in the costs of production of all five products. For example, in order to increase the production of A by $\frac{3}{4}$ we would have to curtail investment with an effectiveness greater than the standard one: the variant II_D would be replaced by the variant I_D. This means that the calculation of differential outlays on the basis of standards of effectiveness is intended for the calculation of outlays on output comprising a small fraction of the total social product. But, in this connexion, the calculation of differential outlays on the basis of the standard effectiveness enables us to use the minimum differential outlays on each small part of the social product separately, i.e. the individual minima, when looking for the least total cost of production. This property of differential outlays is exceptionally valuable from the point of view of the organisation of management of a socialist economy.

2. It is clear too that the calculation of differential outlays will best serve the law of the economy of labour if, instead of being used to measure variants which have already been put into effect, it is used to find the best of the possible (but not yet realised) variants. Indeed, let us change our example and assume that the production of A is increased by $\frac{3}{8}$ after the limited investment has been

allocated and the production of E has already been put into effect according to variant II_E. Then it would be difficult, if not impossible, to replace variant II_E by the variant I_E. It would be possible to have unlimited possibilities of replacing some variants by others in each production unit only if there were still some variants which had not yet been implemented. But if this were so, then the differential outlays would reflect the comparison of potential rather than actual costs of production of the total final output of the economy. Thus, in our example, the cost of production of $A+B+C+D+E+\frac{3}{8}A$ is compared with the cost of production of each planning variant, i.e. with the production of A, B, C, D, E. We obtain the result that the production of the additional $\frac{3}{8}A$ entails for the economy as a whole 32·4 million additional man-hours per year in costs of production compared with another possibility of producing A, B, C, D, E. But if this other possibility has already been implemented, this calculation might prove to be unrealistic.

3. One property of differential outlays must inevitably cause difficulties for those who are unaccustomed to dialectics in quantitative analysis. This is the property that, when the differential outlays for different products are added together, they include the same costs of production more than once. The sum of the differential outlays for all the individual elements of the social product is greater than the costs of production of the whole by the sum of feedback outlays. This is at variance with the requirement that the sum of the outlays in all parts of the social production should be equal to the costs of production of the whole. However, the importance of differential outlays lies not in their absolute magnitude, but in their relative magnitude. It is needed for the comparison of variants, and therefore this difference can be removed by an appropriate change in the unit of measurement of differential outlays. For example, if the total sum of differential outlays is $\frac{1}{3}$ larger than the sum of costs of production, all we need to do in order to make these sums equal is to take one man-hour of differential outlays equal to $\frac{3}{4}$ hour. A change in the unit of measurement does not alter the ratios between differential outlays of different variants, and the minimum of outlays remains as before. This being so, it is possible for the prices of the means of production to be proportional to the differential outlays, while the total price of the final output equals its value.

As an example we calculate the reduced differential outlays for the data of Table 34.

In this table, the total sum of the reduced differential outiay (304·5) is practically equal to the total sum of costs of production (304·3). Costs of production have at the same time been transformed in differential outlays, simply by multiplying them by $\frac{304}{331} = 0{\cdot}92$ (for each variant). Thus each man-hour of differential outlays has been equated to 0·92 man-hours. This recalculation has not changed the relations between the differential outlays for the different variants, and therefore the reduced differential outlays for

TABLE 34

Variant of Optimal Balance	Costs of Production (in million man-hours/year)	Differential Outlays (in million man-hours/year)	Differential Outlays Reduced to Overall Equality with Costs of Reproduction
IV_A	81·2	86·5	79·6
III_B	71·0	76·3	70·3
IV_C	60·8	66·1	60·8
II_D	50·7	56·0	51·6
II_E	40·6	45·9	42·2
	304·3	330·8	304·5

the individual products largely diverge from their costs of production. This is due to the differences in the ratios of the investment to the costs of production: i.e. to the difference in $\frac{K}{C}$ where the K are the investments and the C the costs of production. When this ratio is equal to the average of all production units $\left(\frac{\Sigma K}{\Sigma C}\right)$ the reduced differential outlays are equal to the costs of production (variant IV_C). When $\frac{K}{C} < \frac{\Sigma K}{\Sigma C}$, then the reduced differential outlay is less than the costs of production (variants IV_A, III_B). When $\frac{K}{C} > \frac{\Sigma K}{\Sigma C}$ the reduced differential outlays are greater than the costs of production (variants II_D, II_E).[1]

As an illustration, we return to Problem 2.

TABLE 35

1	2	3	4	5	6	7 (6 : 3)
Variant	K	C	$\frac{K}{C}$	$\frac{K}{C} \div \frac{\Sigma K}{\Sigma C}$	$\frac{(C+Kr) \times \Sigma C}{\Sigma(C+Kr)}$	Ratio of Reduced Differential Outlays to Cost of Production
IV_A	80	81·2	0·98	0·75	79·6	0·98
III_B	80	71	1·13	0·86	70·2	0·99
IV_C	80	60·8	1·32	1·00	60·8	1·0
II_D	80	50·7	1·58	1·20	51·6	1·02
II_E	80	40·6	1·97	1·5	42·2	1·04
	$\Sigma K = 400$	$\Sigma C = 304{\cdot}3$	$\frac{\Sigma K}{\Sigma C} = 1{\cdot}32$			

[1] This can be expressed in general terms by transforming the inequality

$$(C+Kr)\frac{\Sigma C}{\Sigma(C+Kr)} \lesseqgtr C$$

The left-hand side represents the reduced differential outlays, and the right-hand side represents the cost of production. This inequality becomes

$$\frac{C+Kr}{C} \lesseqgtr \frac{\Sigma(C+Kr)}{\Sigma C}$$

giving

$$\frac{K}{C} \lesseqgtr \frac{\Sigma K}{\Sigma C}$$

(since $r > 0$).

7. The Measurement of Differential Outlays when Many Means of Production are Scarce

Our example showed us that by calculating the differential outlays we can find the variants which correspond to the least total cost of production, but it still did not prove that the measurement of differential outlay was necessary for this purpose. Our example would have been more easily solved by the direct selection of the most effective uses of the scarce means.

However, a direct selection of the most effective variants can only be made when only one means is limited. When two or more different means of production are limited, the problem cannot be solved by a direct selection, since this method presupposes the calculation of the indicators of the effectiveness of use of each means, and in the case of the joint outlays of two or more limited means, the economy of labour which one variant of production gives compared with another turns out to be the combined and indivisible effect of several limited means, such as investment, oil, copper, tin and so on.

Therefore it is not possible in this case to calculate the necessary indicators of effectiveness of each of the limited means for the direct selection of their most effective uses. In other words, if there are several conditions restricting the least total outlay, such as the limit on accumulation, restricted supplies of various natural resources, and so on, then it is not possible to look for the conditional minimum outlays for each of these conditions separately; the minimum outlays can only be found by taking all the limits into account at once.

But it is possible to measure differential outlays, however many limited means there are, since the calculation and comparison of differential outlays do not require the determination of indicators of the actual effectiveness of each expended means, but only their standard effectiveness.

For example, the calculation and comparison of differential outlays using the formula $C+Kr = \min$ did not involve the determination of the actual effectiveness of the corresponding investment. But this formula can be generalised by extending its effect to the case of the joint outlays of any number of different means.

Suppose that we have m limited means, that their outlay for the annual final output of the economy is $q_1, q_2, \ldots, q_m$ and that their standard effectiveness (assuming that we know them) are equal to $r_1, r_2, \ldots, r_m$ respectively. Then the total maximum effect of the use of all m means of production (i.e. the least total costs of production will be afforded by that variant of each product for which $c+q_1r_1+q_2r_2+\ldots+q_mr_m = \min$ or, more shortly, $c+\sum_{h=1}^{m} q_hr_h = \min\ (h = 1, 2, \ldots, m)$.

This is the general formula for differential outlays[1] and the rule for the

[1] In this formula all the products qr have the same dimensions, being those of the costs of production (C).

The standard effectiveness of any means has the dimension—man-hours per unit of selection of variants. It shows that if we know the standard effectiveness of each limited means, we can calculate the differential outlays for any number of jointly expended means. To do this we must (1) multiply the outlay of each means by its corresponding standard; (2) add these products; (3) add the resulting sum of feedback outlays to the cost of production of the given output. The only question is how to determine the standard effectiveness.

Differential outlays possess a remarkable property which reveals how the required standards can be determined: for any non-negative standard effectiveness the variants requiring the least differential outlays form a potentially-optimal combination. Even with incorrect standards of effectiveness, the variants requiring the least differential outlays still correspond to the least total outlay which can be realised with the necessary limits for the given variants of means of production and investment.[1]

This has already been proved for the case when only one means is limited, and the final output consists of only two products. Let us now prove this statement for the more realistic case when a number of means are limited and the final output consists of several different products.

If we select the variants requiring the least differential outlays for the production of each final product, then whatever the standards of effectiveness be, we shall have formed a combination of plan- (project-) variants which, first, is intended for the given production programme, and second, has the least total sum of differential outlays (for the whole programme).

But differential outlays consist of the two different terms: cost of production and feedback outlays. Let us find which of these determines the minimum total sum of differential outlays for the whole final output of the economy.

Given the standards of effectiveness and constant quantities of each means, the total sum of all feedback outlays calculated according to these standards

means of production; the outlay of means of production (q) is expressed either in natural units per unit of output, or has the dimension—unit of measurement of the means per year. The selection of the unit of measurement of means is clearly associated with the unit of measurement of cost of production (C). If q relates to the unit of output, then the costs of production must be expressed in man-hours per unit of output. If q relates to the annual production of output, then the cost of production must also relate to the annual production. In the first case, all the products qr will be expressed in man-hours per unit of output:

$$\frac{\text{man-hours}}{\text{unit of means}} \times \frac{\text{amount of means}}{\text{unit of output}} = \frac{\text{man-hours}}{\text{unit of output}}$$

In the second case all the products qr will have the dimensions

$$\frac{\text{man-hours}}{\text{unit of means}} \times \frac{\text{amount of means}}{\text{year}} = \frac{\text{man-hours}}{\text{year}}$$

This shows that in both cases we can add together all the products qr and add them to the costs of production.

[1] This is true for any values of the standard effectiveness, provided that they are not less than zero. Negative standards of effectiveness are at variance with the principle of economy of labour: they mean that the given means of production can be used even when this use is associated with additional costs compared with the use of non-scarce means of production.

will be a constant quantity, in whatever way the destinations of the limited means are rearranged. But the total sum of costs of production depends on how the means of production are used, since different uses of each give different economies.

Hence the least total sum of differential outlays is determined by the least total sum of the costs of production of the final product. More exactly: the combination of variants for which the sum of differential outlays is minimal will have a smaller cost of production for the final product than all the other possible combinations of variants requiring the same quantities of each means of production available at the beginning of the planning period.

This statement holds good for all non-negative standards of effectiveness, but only one definite system of these standards gives the least total cost of production which can be realised with the actual available means. This system can be found by forming trial balances of the means of production with different trial values of the standards of effectiveness. The values of the standards for which the balances of all means of production are in balance give the solution of the problem, on condition that the individual least differential outlays are consistent and all the relatively best means of production are used in their entirety.

The first condition implies that the requirement in each means for the variants having least differential outlays should not exceed its supply or limit.

The second condition implies that all the means whose standards of effectiveness are greater than zero shall be fully used. The means of production whose standards of effectiveness are equal to zero may be used only partly, or not at all.

If the standards of effectiveness are too low, then the requirement in the limited means will exceed their limit. The individual least differential outlays will be inconsistent due to shortage of the better means. If the standards of effectiveness are too high, the requirement in the limited means will turn out to be less than their limit, which corresponds to a combination of variants requiring a greater outlay of labour than is necessary when the available means are fully used.

As an illustration, let us solve Problem 3 (p. 100) by this method.

TABLE 36

A				B				C			
Variant	Cost of Production (in thousands of man-hours)	Investment (in thousands of man-hours)	Outlays of Scarce Raw Material (in tons/year)	Variant	Cost of Production (in thousands of man-hours)	Investment (in thousands of man-hours)	Outlays of Scarce Raw Material (in tons/year)	Variant	Cost of Production (in thousands of man-hours)	Investment (in thousands of man-hours)	Outlays of Scarce Raw Material (in tons/year)
I_A	102	80	0	I_B	200	100	0	I_C	130	110	0
II_A	96	70	10	II_B	180	80	20	II_C	100	100	20
III_A	90	120	10	III_B	175	120	20	III_C	95	110	30

As we are ignoring the law of value for the time being, we replace the monetary unit of measurement of outlay in this problem by man-hour. Then Table 29 is replaced by Table 36.

As a first approximation we set the following standards of effectiveness: for investments—0·1 man-hours per year per man-hour of investment; for scarce raw materials—2·0 thousand man-hours per ton.

We then calculate the trial differential outlays for these standards (in thousands of man-hours per year). (The minima are in darker print.)

TABLE 37

Variant	Differential Outlays	Variant	Differential Outlays	Variant	Differential Outlays
I_A	**110**	I_B	**210**	I_C	**141**
II_A	123	II_B	228	II_C	150
III_A	122	III_B	227	III_C	166

The requirement in investment and scarce raw materials for the variants I_A, I_B and I_C with the least sums are

290 thousand man-hours of investment

0 tons/year of scarce raw materials.

Comparing these quantities with their limits (260 thousand man-hours and 40 tons) we see that our provisional standards are incorrect: the standard for investment must be increased, and that for scarce raw material reduced. As a second approximation we set the investment standard at 0·2 man-hours per year per man-hour of investment, and that of scarce raw materials at 1·0 thousand man-hours per ton.

We then calculate the differential outlays for these standards (in thousands of man-hours per year):

TABLE 38

Variant	Differential Outlays	Variant	Differential Outlays	Variant	Differential Outlays
I_A	**118**	I_B	220	I_C	152
II_A	120	II_B	**216**	II_C	**140**
III_A	124	III_B	219	III_C	147

The requirement in limited means for the variants with the least differential outlays is now

260 thousand man-hours of investment

40 tons per year of scarce raw materials

which is in accordance with the limits.

Thus, the optimal balances of investments and scarce raw materials are obtained with the variants I_A, II_B and II_C.

We must emphasise that this will give the maximum total effect of investment and scarce raw material taken together. This is not the maximum effect of investment nor the maximum effect of the use of scarce materials; instead, by using this method we have found the maximum effect of the use of all limited means. We therefore call it the maximum total effect of all means.

It is clearly this maximum which meets the requirements of the principle of the economy of labour, for it gives the total maximum economy in the costs of production of all the given output, i.e. the least total cost of production of all those combinations of variants in Table 36 which conform to the limits of investment and scarce raw materials.

8. The Mathematical Interpretation of the Measurement of Differential Outlays

This law for measuring differential outlays is so simple that the reader might ask why the mathematics of variables has to be used.

This is a fair question, for the mathematics of variables is often represented as the analysis of indefinitely small quantities. Let us therefore spend some time on the mathematical side of the matter, and see to what class of extremal problem belong those whose solution requires the measurement of differential outlays, and what is the mathematical meaning of the standards of effectiveness which are needed for calculating these outlays.

The mathematics of variables distinguishes between problems of unconditional and conditional extrema. An unconditional extremum is the extremum of a quantity which depends on independent variables. If the variables determining the quantity whose minimum or maximum we are looking for are connected by some relationship, then we have a conditional extremum problem. The problem of finding minimum cost of production is of this kind, for it must be solved with a fixed supply of producer goods and fixed ceiling to investment.

The conditional character of the minimum outlay of labour has been overlooked by our economists. Yet it is this which causes the greatest difficulties, both for an understanding of the laws of measurement of outlays, and for the use of them in planning. These constraints complicate the problem of finding the minimum outlays. They cause the incompatibility of the individual minima of outlays, and the feedback between costs of production. If they did not exist, then the individual minima of costs of production would be quite consistent with one another and with the minimum total outlay.

From a mathematical point of view, the standards of effectiveness are auxiliary multipliers, which we can use to find the conditional extremum just as if the constraints were removed, as if we were finding the unconditional extremum. Applied to the problem of the minimum outlay this means that by using the standards of effectiveness we are overcoming the incompatibility of the individual minima of outlays: they become compatible and belong to the variants corresponding to the minimum total costs of production. However, this use of auxiliary multipliers in the problem of finding minimum outlays was suggested only a short time ago.

First, therefore, we consider the function of these multipliers in the classical methods of finding the conditional extremum, the Lagrange method, and then we shall show how this method can be applied to the measurement of differential outlays. Thus we consider two variants of the method of multipliers:

(1) in the context of the infinitesimal calculus;

(2) for finite numbers.

We have m different conditions of the application of labour (means of production, investment etc.). The supply of each is denoted by Q_h where $h = 1, 2, \ldots, m$.[1]

The planning period is long enough to include the time during which the investment is converted into productive capital and used.

The production programme of the final output stipulates the output of n different products, which together make up the national income. We denote the labour outlay (in physical or money terms) on each by c_i where $i = 1, 2, \ldots, n$.

The value of the c_i will depend on the means of production used.

We denote the outlay of the hth means of production on the ith product by q_{hi}.

It is required to find the distribution of the means of production and investment between the various purposes (i.e. the q_{hi}) for which $\sum_{i=1}^{n} c_i = \min$ with the condition that the use of each means of production is equal to its supply:

$$\sum_{i=1}^{n} q_{hi} - Q_h = 0 \qquad \ldots \quad [5.1]$$

Adding conditions [5.1], multiplied by some as yet undetermined multipliers λ_h, to the function whose minimum we are seeking $\left(\sum_{i=1}^{n} c_i\right)$, we obtain the more complicated function:

$$\Phi = \sum_{i=1}^{n} c_i + \sum_{h=1}^{m} \lambda_h \left(\sum_{i=1}^{n} q_{hi} - Q_h \right)$$

This function is obviously equal to $\sum_{i=1}^{n} c_i$. However, we can determine its minimum as if the restricting conditions [5.1] did not exist. Equating the partial derivatives of the first order with respect to q_{hi} in this function to zero (taking the λ_h as constants) we obtain mn equations of the form:

[1] To avoid increasing the number of different notations, we assume that the Q_h include:

(1) reproducible objects of labour;

(2) reproducible instruments of labour;

(3) natural resources;

(4) planned investment.

The supply of instruments of labour is conveniently expressed in units of their possible use—machine-hours, etc. Correspondingly, investment can be expressed more accurately in the units of its utilisable capacity over the course of the planning period.

$$\frac{\partial \Phi}{\partial q_{hi}} = \frac{\partial}{\partial q_{hi}} \left(c_i + \sum_{h=1}^{m} \lambda_h q_{hi} \right) = 0 \qquad \ldots \quad [5.2]$$

Together with the m conditions [*5.1*] expressing the equality of the outlay of each means of production and its supply, we obtain $nm+m$ equations, whose solution gives the nm unknowns q_{hi} and the m multipliers λ_h.

This is how the minimum outlay is found by the Lagrange method. In planning practice this method is not applicable now, nor in all probability will it be under communism. For it is not only necessary to know the functions expressing the dependence of the expenditure of labour for each final product on the use of each means of production, but it is also necessary for all these functions to have derivatives.

However, if we try to solve this problem by the multiplier method in finite numbers, it appears to be soluble not only under communism, but under socialism too.

It is not difficult to show that the multipliers λ_h not only allow us to solve the problem as if the constraints were absent, but they also eliminate the inconsistency of the individual minima of outlays (c_i) arising due to these constraints. To prove this, let us consider what finite numbers correspond to equations [*5.2*].

Of course a necessary condition for a function to take an extremal value is that its first derivative is equal to zero.

This means that we can assume that the equality [*5.2*] can be replaced by the relations:

$$c_i + \sum_{h=1}^{m} q_{hi} \lambda_h = \text{extremum} \qquad \ldots \quad [5.3]$$

Let us verify this assumption.

By summing expression [*5.3*] over i we obtain:

$$\sum_{i=1}^{n} c_i + \sum_{i=1}^{n} \sum_{h=1}^{m} \lambda_h q_{hi} \qquad \ldots \quad [5.4]$$

Here the repeated sum is constant (for given λ_h) and independent of the distribution of Q_n among the different destinations:

$$\sum_{i=1}^{n} \sum_{h=1}^{m} \lambda_h q_{hi} = \sum_{h=1}^{m} \sum_{i=1}^{n} \lambda_h q_{hi} = \sum_{h=1}^{m} \lambda_h \sum_{i=1}^{n} q_{hi} = \sum_{h=1}^{m} \lambda_h \cdot Q_h = \text{const.}$$

This means that if the sum [*5.4*] is a minimum, then

$$\sum_{i=1}^{n} c_i = \min$$

Thus, the solution of our problem by the Lagrange method gives us multipliers for the means of production such that

$$S_i = c_i + \sum_{h=1}^{m} \lambda_h q_{hi} = \min \qquad \ldots [5.5]$$

and

$$\sum_{i=1}^{n} q_{hi} = Q_h, \qquad \ldots [5.1a]$$

which means that the individual minima of S_i are consistent. But S_i represents nothing less than the differential outlay of the ith product. This means that the Lagrange method gives us the necessary multipliers for the calculation of differential outlays: the λ_h are the standards of effectiveness of Q_h analogous to the r_h in our formula for differential outlays. It follows from [*5.5*] and [*5.1a*] that

1. once we have found the multipliers λ_h we have solved the problem: knowing them, we can determine all the required variants of use of the means of production with minimum values of S_i;

2. the values of the multipliers can be found by approximation. If they are incorrect, then the variants of the plan which satisfy condition [*5.5*] will not satisfy [*5.1a*]. The same thing can be put in other words: if, for given values of the multipliers, the requirement in each means of production is not equal to its supply, these multipliers are incorrect.

However, the construction of optimal balances by the Lagrange method (assuming for the time being that it is possible) has the disadvantage that it introduces several unknowns into the initial conditions of the problem.

In fact, with this method the restrictions on the available means of production must be expressed by the equalities [*5.1*], [*5.1a*], as otherwise the necessary system of equations cannot be obtained. This means that the quantity of used means of production must be determined even before the problem is solved. This is easily done for the best means of production, since they must be fully used, but the requirement in those means of production whose standards of effectiveness are equal to (or nearly equal to) zero can be determined only by constructing the system of optimal balances.

Only then are all the available means of production divided clearly into those which are to be used, and those which are not. This means that the restrictions [*5.1*] and [*5.1a*] must themselves include a provisional solution of one of the problems concerned in the system of optimal balances. Therefore the solution of the problem based on these restrictions might turn out to be non-optimal, some standards of effectiveness (λ_h) and also some q_{hi} (expenditures of the means of production) taking negative values.

In solving the problem in finite numbers, the equation relating the requirement in each means of production to its supply can be replaced by inequalities stipulating that the requirement in each means of production must not exceed its supply:

$$\sum_{i=1}^{n} q_{hi} \leqq Q_h \qquad \ldots [5.6]$$

This expression of the constraints is better than [5.1], [5.1a] for it does not anticipate the solution of the problem and is relevant both to those means of production whose standards of effectiveness are greater than zero and to those with zero standards:

$$\text{if } \lambda_h > 0, \text{ then } \sum_{i=1}^{n} q_{hi} = Q_h,$$

$$\text{while if } \lambda_h = 0, \text{ then } \sum_{i=1}^{n} q_{hi} \leqq Q_h.$$

If we add the conditions that λ_h and q_{hi} shall not be negative to those in [5.5] and [5.6], we obtain a variant of the multiplier method which in general terms was suggested by L. V. Kantorovich, who called it the method of solution multipliers.[1]

Now we can very briefly explain the role of the conditions [5.1] to [5.6] which create the greatest difficulties in the measurement of outlays, in particular in the use of the law of value under socialism.

Conditions [5.1] to [5.6] reduce either (*a*) to the substitution of the function whose minimum we are looking for (costs of production of final output $\sum_{i=1}^{n} c_i$) by a more complicated function

$$\Phi = \sum_{i=1}^{n} c_i + \sum_{h=1}^{m} \left(\sum_{i=1}^{n} q_{hi} - Q_h \right),$$

or (*b*) to the substitution of the costs of production of individual products (c_i) by the more complicated differential outlays

$$S_i = c_i + \sum_{h=1}^{m} q_{hi} \lambda_h$$

The first complication arises in the solution of the problem by calculus of indefinitely small magnitudes, and the second in the use of finite quantities only. In both cases the complication of the outlays enables us to solve the problem of their minimum as if the constraints [5.1] to [5.6] were removed.

In practice, only the second method of solution is feasible. Hence the measurement of the outlay on each product in its complicated form, in the form of differential outlays, is necessary to achieve the maximum economy of labour.

9. The Problem of the Measurement of Outlay under Communism

The problem of measuring outlay under communism is not of theoretical

[1] L. V. Kantorovich, *Mathematical Methods of the Organisation and Planning of Production*, Leningrad, 1939 (see p. 225 of the present collection); see also his article An Effective Method of Solution of Some Classes of Extremal Problems, *USSR Academy of Sciences, Doklady*, Vol. xxviii, No. 3 (1940).

interest only, for it has great practical value in a socialist economy. It would be incorrect to look for the solution of this problem under socialism in the value form which exists in a lower type of productive relations. Higher forms must not be deduced from lower forms; on the contrary, lower forms can be better understood with a knowledge of higher forms.

'The anatomy of the human being is the key to the anatomy of the ape. But the intimations of a higher animal in lower ones can be understood only if the animal of the higher order is already known. The bourgeois economy furnishes a key to ancient economy, etc.'[1]

Accordingly, any hypothesis about the forms of measurement of outlay under communism will throw light on the principles of their measurement under socialism, showing the direction and final stage of development of the law of value in a socialist economy.

A study of the effect of the law of value under socialism will, in its turn, uncover those 'intimations of a higher animal' in a lower one (capitalist form of value), which 'can be understood only if the animal of the higher order is already known'.

Therefore let us try to look into the future and imagine a communist society with a much higher level of techniques, planning and economic organisation than that which we have so far achieved. There can be little doubt that in such a society the measurement of outlay will involve extremal problems to a greater extent than in any previous stage of economic development.

What, then, is the basic extremal problem of communist economics going to be?

The formulation of the extremal economic problem must reflect reality: it must be an expression of the effect of economic laws. Communism has not yet become a reality, but we know the general economic laws which will lead to it and which it will obey.

The most general extremal problem is the law of the economy of labour, a law which applies not only to the quantitative relations within each system of production (such as the relations of exchange, the structure of production, and so on) but also to the qualitative changes in the economic system. In the last analysis, it is this law which leads to the replacement of one social system by another, ensuring higher rates of growth and a higher level of labour productivity. Therefore the maximisation of the rate of growth of labour productivity is the general extremal problem of economic development.

Whichever system best solves it in the given historical conditions, solves it, naturally, not as a mathematical problem, but as an economic one.

This means that when a social system begins to hinder the further growth of labour productivity (which would be possible for the given level of development of the productive forces) it must be replaced by another system which

[1] K. MARX, *A Contribution to the Critique of Political Economy*, p. 300, New York, 1904.

corresponds to the higher productive forces, and therefore ensures a higher rate of growth of labour productivity.

This change in the relations of production is as necessary as the tendency for labour productivity to increase is inevitable. Sooner or later this tendency will break through the forms of social relations which obstruct it, and find new forms enabling it to develop.[1]

Of course this law applies under communism too. The maximisation of the growth of labour productivity under communism is at the same time a process of the maximum increase in time free from material production.

'... The realm of freedom actually begins only where labour which is determined by necessity and mundane considerations ceases; thus in the very nature of things it lies beyond the sphere of actual material production. ... Freedom in this field can only consist in socialised man, the associated producers, rationally regulating their interchange with Nature, bringing it under their common control, instead of being ruled by it as by the blind forces of Nature; and achieving this with the least expenditure of energy and under conditions most favourable to, and worthy of, this human nature. But it none the less still remains a realm of necessity. Beyond it begins that development of human energy which is an end in itself, the true realm of freedom, which, however, can blossom forth only with this realm of necessity as its basis. The shortening of the working day is its basic prerequisite.'[2]

Let us consider one part of the problem of the maximisation of the rate of growth of labour productivity, the problem of finding the minimum outlay of labour on final output of given composition and volume with a given volume of accumulation. In this problem, the quantity to be minimised is future labour, i.e. living labour considered from a social point of view rather than from that of an individual enterprise. Past labour is equated to zero, and the means of production produced by it are included in the outlay to the extent of the economy of future labour which their use affords, i.e. to the extent of the feedback outlays. This paradoxical feature of the measurement of differential outlays needs further clarification.

For society as a whole, past labour is at each given moment (at the beginning of the planning period, say) a constant quantity: it is as impossible to change it as it would be to change the past. But future (living) labour is a variable quantity: it will be greater or less depending on how the plan target of final output is to be produced. Thus for society as a whole the minimum

[1] This is the profound meaning of Lenin's well-known thesis: 'The productivity of labour is, in the last analysis, the most important, principal factor in the victory of a new social system. Capitalism brought about labour productivity unimaginable under serfdom. Capitalism can and will finally be overthrown due to the fact that socialism can create a new, much higher, productivity of labour.'

V. I. LENIN, *Collected Works*, Vol. 29, p. 394 (Russian edition).

Here Lenin is pointing out the law which lies at the root of the development of the productive forces and which restores the harmony between the relations of production and the character of the productive forces—the law of the economy of labour.

[2] K. MARX, *Capital*, Vol. III, p. 799f.

of all outlays of labour (past and living) on the production of the given output is determined by the minimum expenditure of living labour, since the minimum of the sum of a constant and variable quantity is determined by the minimum of the latter.

Thus, in the last analysis, the law of the economy of labour is the law of the economy of living labour, the law of the growth of productivity of living labour.

Past labour is equated to zero in a communist economy on the same basis as constant capital is equated to zero in a capitalist economy (as in the calculation of surplus value): past labour is a constant.[1]

In a communist economy there is no capital, and therefore no division of capital into constant and variable parts, but there is still the division of the labour outlays into constant and variable parts.

However, past labour is a constant quantity (at any given moment of time) only for society as a whole: for any part of the economy outlay of past labour is a variable quantity. Thus an individual sector of the economy can spend more or less past labour by changing its outlay in other sectors. Therefore the outlay on each product includes both living labour and material costs. The fact that the outlay of past labour is equated to zero in no way means that the product of this outlay should be considered as free, not costing labour. It means only that the products of past labour are included in outlay according to future outlays, instead of past ones, to the extent to which their use economises on the living labour of society. The measurement of the outlay of the products of past labour is made on the basis of which use will give the greatest economy of living labour.

The objective necessity for such a measurement of the expenditure of the products of past labour is dictated both by the law of economy of labour and by the laws of mathematics. It is therefore to be seen even under capitalism, in the definite value of costs of production, in the existence of obsolescence. Of course, if the means of production are reproduced in their previous form, then their value is determined by the labour time required to produce them.

When, however, the means are reproduced in a different form, the labour outlays on them are determined by the economy of future labour which the use of the given means of production will afford, taking past outlay equal to zero. From this point of view, the determination of the value of productive outlays is a particular case of accounting for the conditions of application of labour by the economy of future labour which the use of these conditions will give, taking past expenditure equal to zero.[2]

[1] See K. Marx, *Capital*, Vol. I, p. 215, Foreign Languages Publishing House, 1954.

[2] This enables us to remove an obvious contradiction which occurs in the current treatment of labour productivity.

On the one hand it is asserted that only living labour is productive. Therefore, it might seem, we can speak of the productivity only of living labour.

On the other hand it is asserted that labour productivity increases with the economy of labour, including here the economy of both living and materialised labour for the society

Will the measurement of differential outlays be necessary under communism?

In all probability it will. For the need to allow for feedback (and differential) outlays arises from differences in the conditions of application of labour, differences in the effectiveness of the means of production used. And it is unlikely that these differences will disappear with the advance of techniques.

First, differences in the effectiveness of natural resources used will remain.

Second, differences in the effectiveness of reproducible instruments of labour will also remain. Technical progress cannot remove them, because it engenders them. Differences in the effectiveness of used fixed capital could disappear only if technical progress stopped. But under communism the reverse is to be expected; there will be still higher rates of growth of technical advance than today.

Third, differences in the effectiveness of expenditure associated with differences in the period of production and circulation will remain. These differences are expressed in the indicator of 'investment'. The period of production (and also of construction) is not an expenditure, but is a property of the effect of expenditure which cannot be unrestricted. Therefore under communism too it will probably give the problem of the minimum outlay the character of a conditional extremum.

It follows that under communism the incompatibility of individual minima of costs of production and the resulting need for calculating differential outlays will still exist. This makes the essence of differential outlays and their role in the solution of the extremal problem much clearer. The distinction between outlays and the conditions of their use also becomes clearer. This distinction is an essential one: we attempt to reduce outlays to the minimum, while using the conditions of their use to the maximum.

The mathematical scheme of the conditional extremum permits any distribution of the roles of conditions and expenditure. For example, we can take the number of workers and the quantity of available means of production as given, and look for the minimum investment in the production of the plan targets of output. However, economics does not allow freedom in the choice of what to count as outlay. The law of the economy of labour determines that in reality it must be reduced to a minimum.

It is true that this is never seen by an unfamiliar eye. For example, where labour power is a commodity and the immediate aim of its use is profit, it is not easy to distinguish between outlays and the conditions of their application. To do so it is necessary to pass from the many daily facts to the laws by which they are ruled. However, when the working day is shortened, and the

as a whole. Thus it is not only living labour which is productive; so also is materialised labour.

The contradiction between these views will be resolved if the expenditure of the products of past labour is measured by the economy of living labour afforded by the use of these products, i.e. by feedback outlays.

investment and natural resources used are increased, then it becomes quite clear that investment and natural resources are not a special form of outlay, but are conditions of the application of labour which give the problem of the maximum economy of labour its conditional character.

Let us now give the essential features of the construction of the optimal plan and, in this connexion, of the measurement of differential outlay under communism.

The initial data are:

1. the amount of each means of production (reproducible and non-reproducible) available at the beginning of the planning period. We denote them by Q with a suffix indicating different types of these: for example, Q_h, where $h = 1, 2, \ldots, m$ (these are the 'available means of production');
2. the planned accumulation in the course of the same period, i.e. the labour outlays on the creation of new productive capital. We denote it by A;
3. the production programme of the final output during the planning period,[1] consisting of n final products;
4. the expenditure of each of the m means of production available at the beginning of the planning period for the annual production of each of the n final products. We denote these expenditures by q with two suffixes, indicating respectively the means of production and the final product on which this means is to be expended; thus, the expenditure of the hth means of production on the ith product is expressed by q_{hi} $(i = 1, 2, \ldots, n)$;
5. the future expenditure of social labour on the annual production of each final product. Thus, the expenditure of labour on the production of the ith product is expressed by c_i;
6. the investment k_i necessary for the production of each final product.

Each final product can be produced in various ways (using different variants). Therefore k_i, c_i and q_{hi} have various values, depending on the variant of production of the ith final product.

The question is how to find those variants of production of each final product for which the entire programme of final output can be completed with the least outlay of future labour, i.e. for which $\sum_{i=1}^{n} c_i = \min.$

Method of solution.

1. We remove the incompatibility of overall economic effects for those

[1] The assumption that the production programme is known at the beginning of the construction of the plan is, under communism, quite justified. Certainly at the present time the volume of requirements in each final product can be determined only if the outlay on it is known. But at a very high level of labour productivity, when distribution is made according to needs, then for many products their volume can be calculated from scientific standards of requirement.

planning (project) variants of individual objects of expenditure in which it occurs.[1]

2. We fix trial standards of effectiveness for each available means of production and for investment. We denote the former by r with a suffix indicating the means of production (for example r_h), and the latter by r_k. We take the standards of effectiveness of the available means of production which are the least effective of those required as equal to zero. This means that these means of production (plots of land, old machinery, etc.) do not give any economy of labour compared with any of the necessary means of production. The effectiveness of the remaining (relatively best) means of production must be greater than zero.

3. For each variant of production of each final product we calculate the differential outlay from the formula

$$S_i = c_i + k_i r_k + \sum_{h=1}^{m} q_{hi} r_h \qquad \ldots \quad [5.7]$$

4. For the production of each final product we select the variant with the least differential outlay (S_i) and obtain the potentially-optimal combination of variants. This means that this combination gives a final output with the least production cost $\left(\sum_{i=1}^{n} c_i\right)$ of all possible combinations using the same amount of each means of production $\left(\sum_{i=1}^{n} q_{hi}\right)$ and the same investment $\left(\sum_{i=1}^{n} k_i\right)$.

5. We calculate the requirement in each available means of production and in investment for all the variants selected in this way.

6. We compare the sums of these with the supply of the means of production and the planned investment limit. If the requirements differ from the limit, we adjust the trial standards for the corresponding means. If the requirement is greater than the supply, or the limit, then the standard must as a rule be increased. If the requirement is less than the limit, then the standard must be lowered.

Together with the adjustment of the standards, the supply side of the balances of the corresponding means of production must also be corrected. In some cases means of production with zero standards may be discarded if they are included in none of the variants with differential outlay. In other cases additional means of production—the best of those previously rejected—may be included. Once again, those means of production included in the balance are given zero or even positive standards of effectiveness, all the relatively best means of production with a standard greater than zero being fully used.

7. We calculate the differential outlay with the adjusted standards and

[1] Cf. Chapter II.

repeat operations 3, 4 and 5 for as long as the requirement in each means of production with a standard greater than zero, and in investment, is not equal to its supply and limit. For only when this condition is fulfilled can the minimum outlay of labour possible within the limits of planned total accumulation and supply of the best means of production be achieved.[1]

The effective requirement in those means of production for which $r_h = 0$ might be less than their supply. All those natural resources and previously-produced means of labour which, even for a zero standard of effectiveness, would not be included in any of the variants with least differential expenditure, must remain outside the balance.

We denote those standards of effectiveness for which a balance of the requirements in each available means of production and in investment is attained by r'_h and r'_k.

Thus, we obtain m material balances and a balance of investment of the form

$$\left.\begin{aligned} \sum_{i=1}^{n} q'_{hi} &\leqq Q_h \\ \sum_{i=1}^{n} k'_i &= A \end{aligned}\right\} \quad \ldots \quad [5.8]$$

The dash shows that these values of q_{hi}, k_i (and also of c_i and S_i) refer to variants satisfying both [*5.7*] and [*5.8*], i.e. variants of the production of the ith product which are distinguished by the least differential outlay for the final values of the standards of effectiveness r'_h and r'_k. Once these variants have been found, the problem is solved.

Thus the standards of effectiveness are determined by the balance method together with the construction of a system of optimal balances of the available means of production and of investments: we look for the potentially-optimal combination for which the total requirement in each of the available means of production and in investment is equal to, or does not exceed, their planned supply and limits.

The resulting balances of the means of production and of investments determine those variants of production of the final products which give the minimum outlay of future labour on the production of all these products:

$$\sum_{i=1}^{n} c'_i = \min$$

At the same time the forms, types and quantities of those means of production which must be produced during the planning period in order to fulfil the final output programme are determined. Just as in a factory the quantity of intermediate goods is determined according to the production

[1] We are assuming here that the planned limit of investment has been correctly determined. The question of planning the volume of accumulation will be considered in the next chapter.

programme of consumer goods and the indicator of effectiveness of the various technological processes, so in the economy as a whole the production programme of means of production is derived from the final output programme and the expenditure required to produce it by the selected process.[1]

Essentially we have already proved that this method works. We first proved it by argument, and then, very briefly, by showing the connexion between this method and the Lagrange method. The basic proof in the simplest case was given while we established the properties of potentially-optimal combinations of investment variants. For this method of constructing the optimal plan is no more than an approximation to the optimal combination of variants by means of successive formulation of a number of potentially-optimal combinations.

This means that we need only extend this proof to the case of the production of n final products using m available means of production in addition to investment.

1. First we have to prove that for any uses of the same available means of production and the same sum of investments apart from those accepted according to the balances [*5.8*], the production cost of the final output will be greater than $\sum_{i=1}^{n} c'_i$.

Let us take different production variants for some (or all) of the final products from those given by [*5.8*] (for example, different machinery producing the raw materials for several final products); and in doing so let us select the new variants so that the requirement in each available means of production and in accumulation for the new combination is equal to the corresponding requirement for the previous one.

$$\sum_{i=1}^{n} q_{hi} = \sum_{i=1}^{n} q'_{hi}; \quad \sum_{i=1}^{n} k_i = \sum_{i=1}^{n} k'_i \qquad \ldots \; [5.9]$$

This change in the use of the available means of production and investment introduces variants which, for the same system of standards of effectiveness $r_h = r'_h$ and $r_k = r'_k$, will require greater sums S_i (i.e. larger trial differential expenditures) than the discarded variants. For the previous variants had the least sums S_i.

Hence, the sum of the differential outlay on all the final output of the whole economy is increased:

$$\sum_{i=1}^{a} S_i > \sum_{i=1}^{n} S'_i \qquad \ldots \; [5.10]$$

But the total sum of standard feedback outlays for the total final output is

[1] It is not the entire product-mix of the means of production which is determined by this method, but only the composition of those elements which are necessary to fulfil the final output programme. This is because only a certain part of the production of the means of production is included in the final output programme of the overall economic plan.

unaltered, since with these changes in the use of the means of production and investment the following remain unchanged:

(*a*) the amount of each available means of production;
(*b*) the accumulation of the whole economy;
(*c*) the standards of effectiveness of the means of production and investment.

Symbolically, this can be expressed as follows. We expand the inequality [*5.10*]. To do this we sum over *i* (from 1 to *n*) the *n* inequalities of the form

$$c_i + k_i r'_k + \sum_{h=1}^{m} q_{hi} r'_h > c'_i + k'_i r'_k + \sum_{h=1}^{m} q'_{hi} r'_h$$

giving the total

$$\sum_{i=1}^{n} c_i + \sum_{i=1}^{n} k_i r'_k + \sum_{i=1}^{n} \sum_{h=1}^{m} q_{hi} r'_h > \sum_{i=1}^{n} c'_i + \sum_{i=1}^{n} k'_i r'_k + \sum_{i=1}^{n} \sum_{h=1}^{m} q'_{hi} r'_h \quad \ldots [5.11]$$

But from condition [*5.9*] it follows immediately that

$$\sum_{i=1}^{n} k_i r'_k = \sum_{i=1}^{n} k'_i r'_k; \quad \ldots [5.12]$$

$$\sum_{i=1}^{n} q_{hi} r'_h = \sum_{i=1}^{n} q'_{hi} r'_h \quad \ldots [5.13]$$

Summing the system of equalities of the form [*5.13*] over *h* (from 1 to *m*), we obtain the result

$$\sum_{h=1}^{m} \sum_{i=1}^{n} q_{hi} r'_h = \sum_{h=1}^{m} \sum_{i=1}^{n} q'_{hi} r'_h \quad \ldots [5.14]$$

Summing equalities [*5.12*] and [*5.14*] we obtain the total sum of feedback outlay: on the right-hand side for the variants entering in the balance [*5.8*], and on the left-hand side for the other variants of use of the same available means of production and the same accumulation. But if the feedback outlay remains unchanged when there is an increase in the sum of differential outlays, this increase is attributable to an increase in the cost of production.

Symbolically, subtracting equality [*5.12*] and [*5.14*] from the inequality [*5.11*] we have:

$$\sum_{i=1}^{n} c_i > \sum_{i=1}^{n} c'_i$$

which is what we set out to prove.

2. It remains to prove that by drawing in other available means of production not in the optimal balances [*5.8*] the production cost of final output is increased (provided that there is no increase in accumulation).

We recall that the standards of effectiveness for each available means of production must begin at zero, and that all the means of production whose standards are greater than zero must be fully used. It follows that only those available means of production which even for a zero standard are not included in any of the variants with the least sum S_i will remain outside the balance. Therefore the introduction into these balances of any of the available means of production not already included will at the very least not lower, but most probably will increase, the production cost of the final output.

Thus we have proved that the problem of the maximisation of labour productivity under communism can be solved by measuring differential outlay. The balances of the means of production and the balance of investment constructed in this way ensure the production of the given final output of the whole economy with less outlay of labour than all those which are possible using all available natural resources, previously-produced means of production and planned accumulation.

If this outlay is so small that it is advisable to increase the production programme, this programme can be revised. And then, by finding the minimum outlay on the new production programme of the final output, we can determine the optimal production programme with regard both to requirements and to possible outlay.

However, the fact that it is possible to find the minimum outlay of labour by means of measuring the differential outlay does not prove that it is necessary to use this method. For there exist other methods of finding the conditional extremum in addition to the multiplier method. Thus, several linear programming methods will solve the problem without the use of auxiliary multipliers, but they assume the complete centralisation of economic decision-making, right down to the smallest details. Therefore they are applicable to particular problems but not to the problem of the least total outlay.

A communist economy assumes a very high level of both centralisation and democratisation of management of the economy, i.e. the full development of both aspects of democratic centralism. The more perfected planning is and the greater the creative activity of the people is, the higher will be the rate of growth of labour productivity.

At first glance the combination of these two trends, centralisation and democratisation, might seem incompatible. It might appear that the greater the scope of the planning centre is, the less will be the scope of the local organisations. However, it is shown in practice that these trends are already compatible under socialism, as an increasing number of problems are solved by the centre and the provincial organisations jointly.

Moreover, not only are democratisation and centralisation compatible; they are linked with one another. This has been demonstrated by the experience of socialist construction. There cannot be effective centralisation without democratisation, nor can there be effective democratisation of management without centralisation. In the development of joint organisational operation, the cooperation of the centre and the provinces is the whole essence of progress in the organisation of the socialist economy. The more economic questions are solved by the joint efforts of both, the more concretely and exactly will the plans reflect both the whole economy and the local conditions, and the higher will be the level of planned management and the more effective will local initiative be.

The ultimate aim in the organisation of management in a socialist economy is that all questions without exception, from the biggest to the very smallest, shall be solved jointly by the centre and the provinces. For with the present division of labour and means of communication, the economic links between the various parts of the whole economy are very close, complex and heterogeneous. Therefore, in a socialist economy, and even more in a communist economy, all problems must be solved with regard to the conditions and interests of the entire social economy.

For example, the question of whether to make a machine part from a scarce or non-scarce material is not a question for the whole state. Yet in answering it, the overall economic balance of all metals must be taken into account. This the local organisations cannot do in every case where the question arises. Therefore the planning centre must assist to a definite extent in answering such tiny questions.

The centralised management of the economy can be realised in two basic forms: direct and indirect. For example, the requirement in a scarce metal can be regulated either by limiting its outlay or by fixing a higher price.

Indirect centralisation consists in fixing standards for the calculation of outlay and results with the help of which the 'provinces' can themselves find the best variants of use of their efforts and means—the best from the point of view of the whole economy, corresponding to its optimal development plan.

Planning includes both forms of centralisation, the experience of socialist construction having shown both to be necessary. Direct centralisation is a basic form of planning; it is essential also to indirect centralisation, for a scientifically based system of standards for the calculation of outlay and results can be developed only from the plan as a whole. Thus, with indirect centralisation each question (even the smallest) is answered jointly by the centre and the 'provinces'. The centre works out the general standards for its solution, the 'province' applies these standards to each particular case.

Only by the combination of these two forms of centralisation can there be the greatest development of the planning principle and the widest democracy in economic construction. For example, in the direct limiting of requirements of a scarce metal, centralisation is restricted to the allocation of the metal according to users, and not according to its particular uses. When the metal is limited, the less important its price is in restricting their requirements, the less the metal-users will feel the guiding role of the centre. In this case they usually overestimate their requirement, and this makes all economic planning more difficult. The indirect limitation by means of prices (or, under communism, by means of standards of effectiveness) affects all decisions involving the requirement in metal, provided these decisions are dictated by a calculation of outlay. At the same time, the metal-users will here take a more effective part in the formation of the allocation plan than when requirements are directly limited, since they will set the standards for the correct calculation of their requirements on the basis of the relative effectiveness of use of the various metals.

The scheme we have given for constructing the optimal plan on the basis of the measurement of differential outlays assumes an exceptionally high level of centralisation. The working out of many standards of effectiveness is bound up with the centralisation of information concerning a large number of project variants.

However, these standards enable a greater development of independence and initiative of the provinces than has yet been dreamed of. For not only are the individual minima of differential outlays consistent, but also they point to the variants corresponding to the least total outlay of labour. Therefore the standards of effectiveness computed by the planning centre can be used not only to incorporate small changes in the existing plan but also for operational control of plan fulfilment and for the elaboration of the new plan project in the 'provinces'.

Guided by the minimum differential outlay, each production unit can find the variants corresponding to the least total outlay of labour. In the same way the standards of effectiveness of the means of production can subordinate local decisions to the goals of formulating and fulfilling the optimal plan of the social economy to a greater extent than is possible with the present system of economic accounting, thus leaving much more room for local initiative.

It is clear that the measurement of differential outlays not only conforms to the law of economy of labour, but also complies with the other economic laws of communist society. There are no other methods of measuring outlay which could serve all these laws simultaneously. It is for this reason that the measurement of differential outlays can be thought of as being an objective necessity in a communist economy.

10. The Principles of the Measurement of Outlay in a Socialist Economy

There is much in common between socialism and communism: they are two phases of the same social system. However, under socialism the law of value and the law of distribution according to labour still apply. The question is what effect these laws have on the measurement of outlay.

Let us begin with the law of value, whose operation is undoubtedly subject to the specific economic laws of socialism. The basic economic law of socialism, the law of the continuous growth of labour productivity and the law of the balanced (proportional) development of the economy make the measurement of outlay an extremal problem. The most general form of this problem, the maximisation of the rate of growth of labour productivity, is the same as that characteristic of communism. Therefore systematic deviations of prices from values are explained by the subordination of the law of value under socialism to the same extremal problems which will exist in general in a communist society as well.[1] (Of course the stage of solution of these problems will be different.)

The law of the planned proportional development of the economy (when fully developed) takes away from the law of value its function as a regulator of production, creating the conditions for the planned determination of the standards of effectiveness required in the measurement of differential outlay. Therefore our scheme for the construction of optimal balances of means of production under communism is also relevant under socialism, as a goal which must be aimed for in the elaboration of methods of planning and measuring outlay. However, saving the law of value, the expression of outlay in terms of labour time in this scheme must be replaced by the corresponding value quantities. Thus, the outlay of living labour (c_i) must be expressed as the sum of the wages which have to be paid for the production of the ith final product in all the enterprises manufacturing it.

The standards of effectiveness will have various specific meanings, depending on the means of production to which they apply.

1. For reproducible objects of labour (existing at the start of the planning period) these standards express their prices, which were formed on the principle of feedback outlay (the generalised principle of costs of reproduction).

2. For previously produced instruments of labour—buildings, machinery—the standards must be in the form of rent for their use, calculated according to their effectiveness, i.e. with respect to physical wear and tear and obsolescence.

3. For natural resources, they represent the differential rent.

4. For investment, they represent the standard effectiveness (for credit financing, the payment for credit).

The value expression of differential outlay can be called the social cost. This is a transformed form of value, just as differential outlay is a transformed form of cost of production.

In order that the social cost (i.e. for the economy as a whole) of the total final output shall be equal to its value, wages must be less than the value of the manufactured product by $a\%$ where

$$a = \left(1 - \frac{\sum_{i=1}^{n} c_i}{\sum_{i=1}^{n} S_i} \right) \times 100$$

[1] The deviations of prices and cost estimates from values in our economy are often attributed to State policy. This is true, but is not the whole truth. For the policy of a socialist state is not arbitrary: it is based on a knowledge of the economic laws of socialism. Systematic deviations of prices and cost estimates from values can be explained only by the subordination of the law of value to other economic laws.

Obviously, in essence this process is exactly the same as the reduction of differential outlay so that it equals the cost of production of the whole final output (see pp. 128-9).[1]

The model we have prepared for constructing an optimal plan was then adapted to the condition of a socialist economy and shows how the law of value may be utilised in drawing up a plan. The model incorporates the use of planning as a policy instrument. The economic objectives (the composition of final output and the level of savings) are taken as given. The 'value' form of the model, social cost, is a suitable unit for economic measurement but does not allocate resources. Here it is substantially different from the price of production, in which the assumption of a normal rate of profit involves the allocation of all production by demand.

The directive nature of planning is the cause of the differences in the structure of prices of the means of production and of the means of consumption.

The prices of those means of production which can no longer be produced must reflect the feedback outlays which their use involves.

The prices of new means of production manufactured during the planning period must, as a rule, be formed from the average social cost,[2] but when there is a lack of balance (or incomplete changes are made in the planned balance) between productions, deviations from this rule are advisable.

Prices of the means of consumption are variously related to prime cost, the variations reflecting the collective control of accumulation and consumption. Here the sum of the prices of means of consumption can be equal to the sum of their social costs only if the whole social product is covered by the total sum of feedback outlays.[3]

If the product for the society is not covered by this sum, then the sum of the prices of the means of consumption must be greater than the sum of their social costs. This is advisable from the point of view of economic accounting too, so that unprofitable production units do not result from the deviations of the prices of the means of consumption from their social costs. Turnover tax must compensate for the resulting differences in profitability.

Thus, social cost is a special, socialist form of value, deprived of the function of a regulator of production. But it is for this very reason that it allows the more complete use of the measuring function of the law of value in the formulation and fulfilment of the plan; for the oscillations of prices associated

[1] However, it must not be considered as obligatory to equate the sum of social costs to the sum of values; the sum of social costs of the means of consumption must clearly be less than the sum of their prices (equal to the sum of values). But this does not have any essential significance. What is essential is that the minimum social cost of each product included in the variants of production shall be the same as the minimum value of the whole final output of the economy.

[2] The average social cost expresses the legitimate level of outlays: chance deviations from it cancel out.

[3] We are ignoring the role of the increase in workers' savings, taxes and other workers' payments.

with their function as regulators of production which occur under capitalism, are an obstacle to the correct measurement of outlay.

Just as standards of effectiveness can be used for the indirect centralisation of management in a communist economy, so their value expression provides the basis for the most proper organisation of economic accounting. When each enterprise is guided by the minimum social cost, it will apply the principle of the maximum total economy of labour.

Just as under communism, the total claims of the consumers of the means of production will balance with the production or supply of these means. For the standards of effectiveness (prices, rents, differential rents, standards of effectiveness of investment) are fixed by the balance method and so the effective requirement in each means of production does not exceed its supply.

This leads to a conclusion which is important both in the theory and the practice of the utilisation of the law of value under socialism. The equality of the demand for the means of production and their supply is a necessary element of the law of value under socialism. Without it the law of value cannot completely fulfil its function of measuring the outlay of labour, and cannot be completely subordinate to the specific economic laws of socialism. In particular, the equality of demand for the means of production and their supply is a value form of the general principle of the establishment of standard feedback outlay, a principle which will be most effective only under communism.

The social costs of the same product produced under different conditions of the application of labour tend to be equal, because the inclusion in them of standard net income, differentiated with respect to the quality of the means of production, places the different enterprises in economically identical conditions of the application of labour.

This property of social cost is very important not only for economic accounting, but also for distribution according to labour. The law of distribution according to labour requires that the value indicators of the successful operation of a particular stage of production (of the enterprise, shop, and so on) shall not depend on those conditions of the application of labour over which it has no control. Otherwise these indicators cannot be used for this purpose.

The need for reducing value indicators to identical conditions of the application of labour is confirmed by socialist practice, when, in determining the performance indicators, the attempt is made to isolate them from the effects of factors which do not depend on the enterprise. True, the methods used are as yet imperfect; it is well known that performance indicators are largely dependent on factors over which the enterprise has no control. However, they can only be 'freed' from this dependence by the measurement of social cost.

The normalisation of net income according to the conditions of application of labour, and not according to the level already attained, is a development of the newest progressive tendency in the economy of the USSR—the normalisation of production tasks in accordance with the conditions of application of labour (according to the means of production). This has already been carried out in the rural economy: the normalisation of the deliveries of agricultural products according to the level of production has been replaced by the 'per hectare' principle of deliveries. The subsequent development of the normalisation of tasks according to the conditions of labour must eventually lead to the normalisation of net income according to groups of homogeneous and equally effective means of labour, i.e. by fixing standards of rent for means of labour allotted to the enterprises, of differential rents, and so on.

The normalisation of net income according to groups of means of labour allows the much fuller realisation of the principles of democratic centralism than is possible today. On the one hand, the general management of the economic decisions of enterprises can be more centralised (by means of establishing many value standards at present lacking and attaining a greater correspondence between economic accounting and economic indicators); and on the other, for this reason, greater independence can be given to enterprises in their choice of means to fulfil the plan.

Of course it is a very complicated problem to work out the system of value standards of effectiveness of the means of production. Our scheme for doing this throws more light on the laws of measurement of outlay in a socialist economy than on the method for measuring it, which has still to be developed. The technique for finding a set of value standards ('multipliers' in the scheme) is in itself an enormous computing problem, impossible to do without electronic computers. But perhaps even more complicated is the organisation of the selection of material to feed into the computers. Essentially it is a problem of considerably increasing all round the level of planning, project-making and economic operation.

However it is a gratifying problem: the expenditure of labour on it is one of the most effective outlays, for it is a matter of the fullest utilisation of the most important advantages of socialism, and the importance of these advantages for the development of the productive forces has already been amply demonstrated by history.

Thus the search for a way to the most complete and exact realisation of the socialist form of value is at the same time the process of perfecting the organisation of planning the economy.

11. The Measurement of Differential Expenditure in a Capitalist Economy

The reader will certainly have noticed that the standards of effectiveness r_h and r_k are mathematically similar to the average rate of profit and land rent, and that differential outlay is similar to the price of production. This similarity is not merely accidental. It is explained by the fact that there is feedback between the outlays on different products in a capitalist economy which are spontaneously taken into account.

Each capitalist attempts to minimise his costs: the overall minimum for the entire economy is of no concern to him. But the individual minima of capitalists' costs of production are incompatible (due to the shortage of the best natural resources and of accumulation), and this finds its expression in the impossibility of satisfying the demand for the best means of production by offering them at prices equal to costs of production. When competition exists, the shortage of the best means of production raises their prices to a level at which the individual minima of costs of production become compatible (for otherwise, the competition of demand would raise them still higher).[1]

Competition equalises the rates of profit and transforms value into prices of production. In this way the standard feedback outlay associated with the investment of capital is formed.

Competition makes the various individual prices of production equal to a common price of production. During the process capitalist 'standards of effectiveness' relative to the best natural resources or the most productive capital investment for their use are constructed.

Thus the capitalist calculation of feedback outlay is made as a result of the joint action of the desire for profits and of competition. Thus the important social function of the measurement of differential outlay is carried out in an anarchic and extremely rough way. But the savings in the value of the total social product which results from it benefit the capitalists.

'... Every particular sphere of capital, and every individual capitalist, have the same interest in the productivity of the social labour employed by the sum total of capital. For two things depend on this productivity: first, the mass of use-values in which the average profit is expressed; and this is doubly important, since this average profit serves as a fund for the accumulation of new capital and as a fund for revenue to be spent for consumption. Second, the value of the total capital invested (constant and variable), which, the amount of surplus-value, or profit, for the whole capitalist class being given, determines the rate of profit, or the profit on a certain quantity of capital.'[2]

It follows that the calculation of feedback outlay is doubly profitable to the capitalist. By lowering the total value of commodities, he raises both the rate of profit and the mass of use-values in which the profit is expressed.

Thus, the similarity of the general rate of profit and ground rent to the standards of effectiveness is explained by the fact that they all serve to measure feedback outlay.

[1] In our economy the incompatibility of individual minima of costs cannot lead to such consequences, since the prices of the means of production are fixed by the state and not by the market. Therefore the incompatibility of individual minima of costs is immediately felt (although not through prices) in the form of a shortage of the relatively best means of production. This shortage in its turn prompts the calculation of feedback outlay, and, for example, the fixing of higher prices for the scarce materials.

[2] K. MARX, *Capital*, Vol. III, p. 194.

However, if this exhausts the role of the standards of effectiveness, then profit and ground rent fulfil this function only 'pluralistically'. Profit and ground rent are not only forms of the measurement of outlay, but also regulators of production and forms of distribution. Private ownership of the means of production enables the owner to appropriate for himself the total effect from the use of the relatively best means of production and even more than this (if we remember absolute ground rent).

The general rate of profit is a regulator of capitalist production. Standards of effectiveness are only a means of measuring outlay, and they influence the relation between production units only indirectly, as factors determining the magnitude of a certain part of the outlay on the individual products.

Finally, the capitalist calculation of feedback outlay cannot reduce the value of the final output to a minimum.

For in order to minimise outlay, it is first necessary to find it. But in a capitalist economy, outlay is made before its minimum can be found. The market verifies that the expenditure already made is correct, instead of verifying proposed expenditure. The correctness of the standards of feedback outlay is tested by comparing variants which have already been put into practice, and not merely planned.

An unsuccessful combination of plan variants could be quickly replaced by another combination without loss, but when the variants are already implemented, the combination cannot be changed very quickly. When the means of labour have a long life, the time required to correct existing errors can be measured in years, and during this time the initial conditions change. This means that the standards of effectiveness must be adapted to new conditions instead of former ones, and new errors arise in the choice of production variants. While they are being corrected, the initial conditions change once more, and so on. The result is that there are always variants which have been put into effect, but which to a certain degree do not correspond to the minimum costs for the whole economy.

Thus, the capitalist's way of reckoning feedback outlay is internally contradictory: mathematically, he attempts to find the least total outlay, but economically his method precludes the possibility of doing so.

The deviations of prices of production from values outwardly give the impression that they are distorting the measurement of the outlay of labour. Essentially, however, these deviations make prices approach the very outlay of social labour, the cost of each separate product, if we measure the outlay on each product dynamically, with its interdependences, i.e. the differential outlays.

'We call it price of production . . . , because in the long run it is a prerequisite of supply, of the re-production of commodities in every individual sphere.'[1] But the social prerequisite of the production of each separate commodity is the differential outlay. It is this which expresses the increase

[1] K. MARX, *Capital*, Vol. III, p. 194.

in the real cost of production of the final social product which is associated with the production of the given commodity.

It follows that the price of production is based not only on capitalist competition; it has yet another, more solid basis. This was first pointed out by Marx.

The generally-accepted notion of the price of production is that it is only a converted form of commodity value in which the commodity enters in the competition prices. But Marx gave it still another feature, reflecting another side of this category.

According to Marx, the basis of the price of production is that 'the aggregate capital [fixed and circulating] serves materially as the creator of products, the means of labour as well as the materials of production, and the labour'. We read further: 'The total capital materially enters into the actual labour-process, even though only a portion of it enters the process of self-expansion. This is, perhaps, the very reason why it contributes only in part to the formation of the cost-price, but totally to the formation of surplus-value. However that may be, the outcome is that surplus-value springs simultaneously from all portions of the investment capital.'[1]

This reveals the deep foundation of the price of production, a basis which exists not only in a capitalist economy, but also in a socialist economy and in a communist one as well. For then both instruments of labour and production materials and labour will enter materially in the actual labour-process.

True, this feature of the price of production is not complete.[2] But it does not follow that it can be ignored. On the contrary, only by starting from both features of the price of production which Marx gives can we correctly understand its essence and function in a capitalist economy.

A connexion can be found between the two features. Let us attempt to do this.

The price of production is a result of competition. But competition is engendered by the objective conditions of the social economy and therefore leads to socially important results.

The first social condition is that 'the aggregate capital serves materially as the creator of products, the means of labour as well as the materials of production, and the labour'. This fact is clear to each capitalist and is directly accounted for in competition: 'The capitalist . . . *expects* an equal profit upon all the parts of the capital which he advances.'[3]

[1] K. MARX, *Capital*, Vol. III, p. 36.

[2] In the above quotation, this feature is expressed in the form of a hypothesis, but it was not just mentioned casually, and Marx was to return to it more than once. Thus he writes elsewhere that the capitalist 'cannot exploit this labour unless he makes a simultaneous advance of the conditions for performing this labour, namely means of labour and subjects of labour, machinery and raw materials'. And further: 'Although it is only the variable portion of capital which creates surplus-value, it does so only if the other portions, the conditions of production, are likewise advanced.' (*Capital*, Vol. III, pp. 41, 42.)

[3] MALTHUS, *Principles of Political Economy*, p. 268, 2nd ed., London, 1836 (quoted by MARX, *Capital*, Vol. III, p. 36).

This ties up with another condition: the restriction on accumulation in the whole economy extends to all invested capital, and not only to its variable part, so that all parts of capital equally involve feedback outlay.

This is the fact which capitalists do not see, but which is bound up with the other one. By accounting for the first fact, competition necessarily takes the second into account also.

In fact, from the point of view of the capitalist, every rouble of invested capital must yield the same profit. From the point of view of society, every rouble of investment, taken separately, equally involves feedback outlay to the extent of the minimum effectiveness of the accepted variants of investment.

When the capitalist takes it into account that all capital is materially necessary for production, he is realising the existence of feedback outlay for all invested capital, and not only for its variable part.

Finally, competition between capitalists leads to the formation of a common normal rate of profit, the magnitude of which roughly reflects (i.e. tends to reflect) the feedback outlay caused by the investment of one rouble of capital. In fact, capitalist competition reduces the prices of production to a minimum.[1] As a result, the general rate of profit must be the least permissible, and not the average rate.[2]

This proposition is contrary to the generally accepted interpretation of the price of production, but this is explained by the incompleteness of the characteristics of the basis of the price of production contained in the generally accepted expositions.

In Marx we find the following remark: 'The individual rates of profit in various spheres of production are themselves more or less uncertain; but in so far as they appear, it is not their uniformity but their differences which are perceptible. The general rate of profit, however, appears only as the lowest limit of profit, not as an empirical, directly visible form of the actual rate of profit.'[3]

This proposition is a necessary part of the study of the price of production.

True, Marx discusses the formation of the general rate of profit starting from the assumption that this is equal to $\frac{m}{k}$, i.e. to the average rate (m is the total sum of surplus value, k is the total social capital). However, the basic result of his discussion (the deviation of prices of production from values, the relation between these deviations and the organic composition of capital)

[1] See K. MARX, *Capital*, Vol. III, p. 82. *Collected Works* (Russian ed.).

[2] We have already proved that the choice of variants using the formula $C+Kr$ = min always leads to r being the lowest limit of effectiveness of the accepted variants. If we make the notation: C—capitalists' costs of production, K—capital, r—the general rate of profit, then $C+Kr$ will represent the price of production, and the proof will show that the general rate of profit is always its lower limit (see pp. 97-98).

[3] K. MARX, *Capital*, Vol. III, p. 360. *Collected Works* (Russian ed.).

also holds good when the general rate of profit is at a minimum, and not the average.[1] It is only the equality of the general normal rate of profit to the average $\left(=\frac{m}{k}\right)$ which must be discarded. But this equality assumes that all surplus value (including additional profit from the use of better natural resources) is divided only between the capitalists extracting it. While if the general rate of profit is its lower limit, then part of the surplus value will remain for the ground rent.

This means that the determination of the general rate of profit as a minimum is inwardly bound up with the whole system of Volume III of *Capital*. We cannot therefore consider it to be only a casual remark of Marx's. On the contrary, the equality of the general rate of profit to the average must be considered as a first approximation in the discussion of the formation of prices of production, for the simplest hypothetical case.

As a result, exchange according to prices of production corresponds to a higher stage of development of the economy and can more fully realise the principle of the economy of labour than the exchange of commodities according to their values. The price of production reinforces the measuring function of the law of value, its subordination to the law of the economy of labour, and also its social character. The price of production is a form of value, the social function of which is no longer in the power of capitalism and has outgrown the limits of the law of value. A capitalist approach to the price of production is contrary to its potential social function. The latter presupposes planning and capitalism precludes it.

The price of production is the first, and still very incomplete, expression of differential outlay. The development of its potential function for finding the least total outlay is possible only outside the limits of a capitalist system. Only in a collective economy can all economies of labour which the measurement of differential outlay makes possible be fully exploited.

In a capitalist economy, however, the development of the use of differential outlay is retrogressive: the growth of capitalist monopolies distorts the effect of competition, which is the force transforming value into the price of production and imposing economy of outlay.

Our study of the principles of measurement of outlay under communism and socialism has helped us to understand those 'imitations in a higher animal' in prices of production which it was difficult to explain without knowing the laws of measurement of outlay in a higher social system. We have also explained those elements of Marx's teaching concerning the price of production, which previously seemed to be unconnected with the rest.

Finally, we have shown that deviations of prices of production from values

[1] As we have seen, the deviation of the reduced differential outlay from costs of production depends on the relation between the costs of production and investment. These deviations are analogous to the deviations of the price of production from value. Here the standard effectiveness of investment is not the average, but the minimum (see pp. 128-9).

improve the measurement of outlay of labour on each product rather than make it worse. In this way, the gulf between the theory of value and the history of the measurement of outlay, that 'strange law' of which we spoke at the beginning of this article, has been bridged.

CHAPTER VI

THE PROBLEM OF THE MAXIMUM GROWTH OF LABOUR PRODUCTIVITY

1. The Role of a Qualitative Economic Analysis in the Solution of the Problem

It is not only the interests of the near future which guide a socialist economy, but also those of more distant years, even of future generations. This is one of the advantages of a socialist system, and one of the prerequisites for its vitality.

This far-sighted concern about the future manifests itself both in the careful use of natural resources, and in high rates of accumulation, and must be a guiding principle in the determination of the effectiveness of planning and project variants.

Applied to the principle of the economy of labour, this means that the most effective variant is that which corresponds to the long-term minimum outlay of labour, i.e. to the maximum continuous growth of labour productivity, rather than that which promises a short-term economy of outlay.

How can this variant be found?

We must be guided first of all by a qualitative analysis of the effect of different paths of economic development on labour productivity.

A model for such a long-term analysis was the Leninist idea of socialist revolution as a necessary prerequisite for the preservation of the independence of our country. The First World War demonstrated that the elimination of economic backwardness was a vital necessity; in the framework of capitalism, weighed down by the powerful remnants of serfdom, the backwardness of Russia not only did not decrease, but was ever growing. Only a new, more advanced method of production, with its characteristic higher rate of growth of labour productivity, in other words, socialism, could eliminate the age-old backwardness of Russia.

Such a far-sighted aim became the central idea of the first five-year plan, the idea of having a permanent systematic increase in the relative size of the socialist economic sector.[1] By ensuring this, the first five-year plan built the foundation for higher rates of growth of labour productivity in the following plans.

The objectives of eliminating the considerable differences between physical and mental labour and between town and country were closely bound up

[1] See 'The CPSU in Resolutions . . .', Part II, p. 451 (7th ed.).

with the problem of the long-term minimum of outlays. Indeed, by raising the cultural and technical level of manual workers to that of engineers and technologists, by providing the rural economy with the most advanced techniques, not only was labour productivity raised to a level which would otherwise have been unattainable, but at the same time the conditions were created for the widest spreading of technical creativity (among the people) and, consequently, for higher rates of growth of labour productivity in the future.

This means that when we are comparing different project variants, it is not enough to take into account only the economy of labour promised by each of them now; the important points are the extent to which each of them contributes to the transformation of the nature of labour, the growth of the cultural level of the workers, the fulfilment of the aims of a gradual transition to communism, at the same time creating possibilities for still greater economy of labour then.

Thus, the problem of the long-term minimum of outlay is solved primarily on the basis of a qualitative analysis of the law of development of a socialist economy.

However, this problem has its quantitative side as well.

When their overall economic effects are the same, various plan- (project-) variants will differ in their outlays only. But outlays can and must be measured. This means that, in these cases, the comparative effectiveness of the variants can be determined by calculation.

The question is how to find that variant among those with identical economic effects which corresponds to the long-term minimum outlay for the whole economy or to the maximum rate of growth of labour productivity.

In Chapters IV and V we avoided this aspect of the problem, directing our attention to the question of finding the minimum outlay associated with different conditions of the application of labour, given restrictions on the best (most effective) conditions of its use (best natural resources, best machinery, etc.).

Thus, in those chapters we concentrated on everything to do with the conditional nature of minimum outlay, assuming the volume of accumulation in the whole economy (and, therefore, the total volume of investment) to be fixed.

2. The Extremal Problem of the Planning of Accumulation in the Economy

If investment in the planning period is taken as given, then the determination of the standard effectiveness of investment differs in no way from the determination of the standard rent for the use of individual instruments of labour and of the standard differential rent for the use of natural resources. All these standards reflect the economy of labour which results from the use of labour under these conditions. They are interconnected, and must be determined jointly.

In this sense the measurement of the effectiveness of capital investment raises no special problem which can be set apart from the general problem of the measurement of outlays and results for every choice of investment variant. In each case, the selection of the variant is determined by the minimum social cost of output. And if today the problem of the effectiveness of investment arises in each individual case where there is investment (particularly when new techniques are being introduced) this is only because the methods of measuring outlay do not correspond to the principles of its measurement.

However, this does not remove the problem of effectiveness of investment, for it remains as part of the problem of accumulation. In planning the volume of accumulation for the whole economy, it is necessary to know the effect obtained from its use. In our scheme for determining the least total outlay, we took the volume of accumulation as given, and so simplified the problem. In reality, investment is one of the unknowns in economic planning. It is important that the rational determination of the volume of accumulation shall also obey extremal principles, for it obeys the law of the growth of labour productivity. But the criterion will not be the minimum outlay for the output given by the plan, but the maximum rate of continuous growth of labour productivity.

Even at the XVth Congress of the Party the principle of the optimal relationship between accumulation and consumption which would secure a faster rate of development over a long period was put forward.

'It is necessary to bear in mind, when considering the relation between production and consumption, that we must not start from the once-for-all maximum figure of something or other, . . . for this is an insoluble problem, or from the one-sided interests of accumulation in the given period of time . . . , or from the one-sided interests of the consumer. Bearing in mind their relative contradictions, interdependence and connexion, we must start from the optimal combination of both these aspects from the point of view of their long-term development which, in general, will be compatible.'[1]

This is one of the most important propositions of socialist political economy. Unfortunately, its content is far from adequately understood in our economic literature. The most important and difficult aspect is the explanation of the conditions in which the interests of accumulation and consumption will, in general, coincide. This coincidence of interests is possible only in terms of long-term development, as they are opposed to one another during each separate short period of time. Once we have elucidated the conditions for this, we shall have formulated the conditions for the optimal combination of accumulation and consumption.

There was a very important remark in this connexion at the XVth Congress of the Party on the question of the rate of development:

'When considering the rate of development it is equally necessary to bear

[1] 'CPSU in Resolutions . . .', Part II, p. 333 (7th ed.).

in mind the extreme complexity of the problem. Here we must start not from the maximum rate of accumulation over the next year or years, but from the relation between the elements of the economy which would in the long-term secure a faster rate of development.'[1]

This means that the optimal relation between accumulation and consumption is that which secures the fastest rate of development over a long time. But the rate of development depends on the rate of growth of labour productivity, on the rate at which the expenditure of labour per unit of output is reduced. Hence, the optimal relation between accumulation and consumption is that which secures the maximum continuous growth of labour productivity.

Thus, the volume of accumulation can and must be determined together with the solution of the problem of finding the maximum continuous growth of labour productivity.

The most effective accumulation is the one that ensures the fastest long-term rate of development. Any further increase in accumulation will withdraw from the economy more than it gives back. Indeed, accumulation invested in productive capital gives economy of labour, but at the same time it requires additional labour, and as production continuously expands, the accumulation requires continuously increasing additional labour. If there is too much accumulation, it can happen that over a long time part of it gives less economy of labour than its requirements of additional labour during the same period.

Now we can explain how, from the long-term point of view, the interests of accumulation and consumption coincide.

If we take a sufficiently short interval of time during which the accumulation cannot yet produce results, then accumulation and consumption appear to be opposed: the greater the accumulation during this interval, the smaller will the consumption be. But if we take a longer time interval, then accumulation and consumption will be in harmony.

Before the optimal relation between them is attained, they will grow together.

Indeed, if the accumulation is small, the technical level of labour and, therefore labour productivity, grows slowly. Consequently the national income also increases slowly, and this restricts the possibilities for consumption and accumulation.

Now if we imagine that the share of accumulation in the national income is increased, then after a certain length of time consumption will increase with the accumulation, for the latter will add more to the national economy than it takes from it in the form of additional labour. This is the explanation of the simultaneous growth of accumulation and consumption in the USSR.

The absolute dimensions of the two reach their maximum when accumulation reaches its optimal size. The national income, taken over a long period

[1] op. cit., p. 334.

of time, then reaches a maximum. If the accumulation grows beyond its optimum, consumption is cut as compared to its possible maximum, and in its turn this restricts the growth of labour productivity, the growth of national income and therefore the extent of accumulation. Thus, if the share of accumulation exceeds its optimum, the absolute magnitudes of accumulation and consumption taken over a long period of time continue to be directly related, but are reduced instead of increased.

3. The Long-term Average Standard of Effectiveness of Investment and the Maximum Possible Rate of Growth of the Economy

Over a long period of time the factors which determine the standard effectiveness of investment are fully revealed, since this standard is directly dependent on the volume of accumulation and the distribution of possible investment according to its effectiveness. This follows from Chapter Four, where the problem of finding the maximum total effect of investment in a socialist economy was posed. But this is insufficient. The question which arises is how this volume of accumulation is to be determined. It can be answered only by a consideration of the long-term problems and conditions of development of the economy.

We have seen that accumulation must assist the long-term maximum rate of development of the economy. This means that by gravitating towards its optimal share in the economy, it controls the long-term level of the standard effectiveness of investment. Therefore, given the optimal overall economic plans, the average standard effectiveness of investment taken over a long period is associated with the maximum possible rate of growth of labour productivity.

Here the whole system of value standards for the calculation of outlays must in the last analysis be determined by the maximum rate of continuous growth of labour productivity: for all value standards (prices of the means of production, differential rent, rent for the use of productive funds, standards of effectiveness of investment) are inter-related.

The relation between the standard effectiveness of investment and the rate of growth exists only for the economy as a whole. The ratios of the rate of growth and the effectiveness of investment in various sectors can differ. For let us assume the contrary, and see where this leads us to.

Let us suppose that the standards of effectiveness are different in each sector and are directly proportional to the rate of growth of the corresponding sector: the higher the rate of growth, the higher the permissible minimum effectiveness of investment will be. Then the higher the rate of development of each sector, the lower the level of the rate of technical development will be.

A high standard effectiveness in the leading sectors will preclude any variant of production with considerable investment outlay. On the other hand, those sectors with lower rates of growth will make greater use of the 'capital-intensive' means of production and technological processes. This clearly contradicts the laws of socialist economic development. For if it were true, then our leading sector, the engineering industry, would have to be content with cheap machinery and buildings.

Thus, the long-term level of the standard effectiveness of investment depends on the rate of growth of the economy as a whole, and not on that of the individual sectors.

4. The Problem of Making Allowance for Future Changes in the Standard Effectiveness of Investment when Selecting Project Variants

The standard effectiveness of investment must change from time to time in accordance with changes in the conditions which determine it. It is probable that this will happen before the most durable means of labour are worn out. Consequently, the means of labour which were constructed for a previous standard no longer correspond to the new one. This causes losses which could have been averted or reduced by selecting several investment variants which have short lives but did not correspond to the maximum total effect of investment for the previous standard. To make up for this, they enable the economy to adapt itself more rapidly to the changed conditions expressed by the new standard.

On the other hand, variants of long-term investment must be assessed not only from the point of view of the present standard, but also from that of future ones.

For example, if the standard was calculated over five or six years, it would be incorrect to use it alone as a basis for setting up enterprises with a working life of fifty years and more. However, it is impossible to carry out all construction on the basis of future standards, since the balance of accumulation and investments will not be the same.

Hence, an approach to future standards in the choice of variants with the longest period of obsolescence causes an opposite deviation (from the actual standard) in the selection of short-lived variants. The purpose of the deviations must be the long-term minimum outlay of labour, i.e. the maximum continuous growth of labour productivity.

Let us give a very simple example to show the losses which arise from the long-term investments that have already been made but do not correspond to the new conditions.

Consider a combination of variants of two production units A and B. The indicators of these variants are shown in Table 39.

Suppose that the actual standard effectiveness of investment is equal to 11% per year, and let us assume that after five years this is lowered to 8% per year. With the standard at 11%, the following combination of variants is the best:

$$I_A + II_B$$

TABLE 39

A					B				
Variant	Investment (in million roubles)	Prime Cost of Annual Output (in million roubles)	Effectiveness of Additional Investment (as % of Investment)	Period of Obsolescence of Fixed Capital (in years)	Variant	Investment (in million roubles)	Prime Cost of Annual Output (in million roubles)	Effectiveness of Additional Investment (as % of Investment)	Period of Obsolescence of Fixed Capital (in years)
I_A	100	115	—	20	I_B	100	117	—	5
II_A	200	105	10	20	II_B	200	105	12	20

If the units *A* and *B* are constructed according to variants I_A and II_B this combination can only be replaced by one which conforms to the new conditions fifteen years after the new standard has been fixed, since the life of the fixed capital of variant I_A is twenty years. Thus, during the course of fifteen years the fixed capital of *A* will not correspond to the new conditions of the economy. But if instead of the combination I_A+II_B we had taken II_A+I_B with the same total investment, then after five years, variant I_B could be replaced by variant II_B.

True, during these five years the combination II_A+I_B, compared with the combination I_A+II_B, would require an additional prime cost of

$$(105+117)-(115+105) = 2 \text{ million roubles per year.}$$

On the other hand, during the remaining fifteen years, the combination II_A+II_B would yield an economy in prime cost amounting to

$$(115+105)-(105+105) = 10 \text{ million roubles per year,}$$

compared with the combination I_A+II_B.

However, it must be remembered that the combination II_A+II_B requires 100 million roubles more investment than the combination I_A+II_B, which could save prime cost, according to the new standard (8%), to the extent of eight million roubles per year. This means that the net economy in prime cost which II_A+II_B gives in comparison with I_A+II_B is $10-8 = 2$ million roubles per year.

Thus, if the combination of variants II_A+I_B is followed by the combination II_A+II_B, then over the course of twenty years we gain an economy in prime cost equal to $2\times15-2\times5 = 20$ million roubles, compared with the outlay for the combination I_A+II_B.

It is clear therefore that in finding the long-term maximum effect of investment of the whole economy the principle of having only one standard effectiveness of investment is applicable only if this standard is not changed during the longest life of all the fixed capital. If this condition is not fulfilled, then future standards of effectiveness of investment must be taken into account together with the present ones.

However, it is clear that this cannot be done by establishing different standards for long-term and short-term investments. This is shown by our example. The standards of effectiveness of investment indicate that the best combination is that of the variants $II_A + I_B$ if

(1) the additional investment for variant II_A is more effective than the standard effectiveness for long-term investment, but

(2) the additional investment for variant II_B proves to be less effective than this standard.

We can see from Table 39 that the effectiveness of the additional investment for II_A is equal to 10% per year, and the effectiveness of the additional investment for II_B to 12% per year. This means that, if standards of effectiveness are used in selecting the combination of variants $II_A + I_B$, that for long-term investment must be less than 10%, but greater than 12%; which is absurd.

True, we can find a way out of this difficulty by fixing such a low standard for short-term investment that the variant I_B becomes more effective than II_B even when the effectiveness of long-term investment is estimated on the basis of a standard less than 10%. Thus, if we take the long-term standard equal to 9% and the short-term one less than 6%, the best combination will be of the variants $II_A + I_B$. For then the most effective variant for *A* will obviously be II_A. It will be necessary to use two standards for *B*: one for the variant I_B, say 5%, and the other for the variant II_B, say 9%. Subtracting the sum of the prime cost from the product of the investment and its standard effectiveness, we obtain:

$$\text{for variant } I_B\text{: } 117 + 100 \times 0{\cdot}05 = 122 \text{ million roubles,}$$
$$\text{for variant } II_B\text{: } 105 + 200 \times 0{\cdot}09 = 123 \text{ million roubles.}$$

The smaller of the two is that for variant I_B. Thus, by taking the standard equal to 9% per year (long-term) and 5% per year (short-term) we can solve our problem. The only trouble is that this solution will apply to the two production units in our example alone, and not for the economy as a whole, since, by hypothesis, the present standard effectiveness of investment is equal to 11%. Thus, if instead we fix a lower standard (9% or 5%) for all production units, then the balances of investments and accumulation will differ: the need for investment will be greater than the accumulation.

Thus, if we take future standards of effectiveness of investment into account, we restrict the role of the unique current standard, for variants will in some cases have to be chosen in spite of this standard. However, this restriction on the unique current standard must be imposed not by replacing it by several different standards, but by introducing corrections to the balances of investments and accumulation based on it.

The procedure for doing this is as follows.

1. We construct the optimal balance of accumulation and investments according to the rules given in Chapters IV and V, determining the standard effectiveness of investment. We call this the 'present' standard, as opposed to the 'future' ones.

2. We work out the perspectives of changes in this standard, and summarise them in the future standard.

3. We divide the project variants not included in the balance of investments and accumulation into two groups:

(*a*) variants with short capital turnover periods and an effectiveness greater than the present standard (I_B in our example).

(*b*) variants with long capital turnover periods and an effectiveness lying between the present and future standards (II_A in our example).

4. We make the following corrections to the balance of investments and accumulation as in point 1.

(*a*) We substitute some of the accepted variants with long lives by variants of the first group in the same line of production (so that the final output is unaltered); as a result the total sum of investments in the balance is reduced (in our example, we replace variant II_B by variant I_B).

(*b*) We substitute the other accepted variants (with long lives) by variants of the second group in the same line of production (so that the final output is unaltered); this must increase the investment in the balance (in our example we replace variant I_A by variant II_A).

5. These corrections to the balance of investments and accumulation must satisfy the following conditions:

(*a*) the total sum of investments after all the rearrangements of variants have been made must be the same as before, i.e. equal to the planned accumulation;

(*b*) the losses caused by the rearrangement during the effective time of the present standard must be less than the increase in effect of investments over the remaining life of the fixed capital of variants in the second group.

Let us put the second condition in mathematical terms.

We use the following notation: the effectiveness of a variant which is replaced by a variant of the first group is r_0; the effectiveness of a variant in the second group is r_2; the present standard effectiveness is r_p; the future standard effectiveness is r_f; the life of a variant of the first group is T_1; the life of a variant of the second group is T_2; the remaining effective period of the present standard is t.

A rearrangement of the investments which replaces a variant with an effectiveness equal to r_0 (this variant is replaced by a variant of the first group with smaller investment) by a variant of the second group causes losses equal to $K(r_0-r_2)$ roubles per year, where K is the sum of investments which are being rearranged. Over the whole lifetime of the variants of the second group these losses are

$$KT_2\,(r_0-r_2) \text{ roubles} \qquad \ldots \quad [6.1]$$

However, this substitution has its advantageous side: the variants of the first group after T_1 years are replaced by variants with an effectiveness equal to r_0 (i.e. by those variants which earlier gave up their place in the balance of investments to variants of the first group). This increases the investment by the sum K. The effectiveness of the investment K is greater than the new future standard effectiveness

$$r_0 > r_f$$

Hence, the substitution gives an increase in the annual effect of the investment K equal to $K(r_0 - r_f)$. After the time between the (T_1+1)th year and the T_2th year, inclusive, this increase is

$$K(T_2 - T_1)(r_0 - r_f) \qquad \ldots [6.2]$$

Comparing this with the losses [6.1] we find the condition so that the substitution of the variants in the investment balance shall increase the total effect of investments after the time T_2:

$$K(T_2 - T_1)(r_0 - r_f) > KT_2(r_0 - r_2) \qquad \ldots [6.3]$$

This gives the following equivalent inequalities:

$$(T_2 - T_1)(r_0 - r_f) > T_2(r_0 - r_2); \qquad \ldots [6.4]$$

$$T_2(r_2 - r_f) > T_1(r_0 - r_2) \qquad \ldots [6.5]$$

$$\frac{r_2 - r_f}{r_0 - r_f} > \frac{T_1}{T_2} \qquad \ldots [6.6]$$

The inequality [6.5] reproduces the procedure given above for calculating the gains and losses caused by the substitution of variants in our arithmetic example. [6.6] is the simplest expression of the conditions of the effectiveness of the substitution of variants.

However, none of these inequalities is quite accurate. They are all based on the assumption that the loss of one rouble in the near future is equal to the loss of one rouble in the more distant future. Yet this is not so. Indeed, let us replace the immediate loss in our example by an equal amount at a much later date. Then it seems possible, without limiting consumption and without increasing outlay, to increase the immediate investments to the same extent. After the time for which the loss was postponed, this sum has enabled us to obtain a certain economy in prime cost of output, an economy which we would not have obtained if the immediate loss had not been postponed.

On the other hand, the increase in the effect of investments obtained in the substitution of the variants can also be invested in production. While the losses are aggravated by the lost effect of their possible investment, the growth of effect is increased due to the possible effect from its investment in production. The inequality [*6.6*] can then be more accurately replaced by the much more complicated inequality[1]:

$$\frac{r_2-r_f}{r_0-r_2} > \frac{(1+r_f)^{T_2-T_1}\left\{\frac{r_f}{r_p}[(1+r_p)^t-1]+(1+r_p)^{t-1}(1+r_f)[(1+r_f)^{T_1-t}-1]\right\}}{(1+r_f)^{T_2-T_1}-1} \quad \ldots [6.7]$$

This inequality makes the lower limit of r_2 approach nearer to r_0 than inequality [*6.6*] did.

For example, if $r_0 = 0{\cdot}1$ $(=r_p)$, $r_f = 0{\cdot}05$, $t = T_1 = 10$ years, $T_2 = 30$ years, then it follows from [*6.6*] that $r_2 > 0{\cdot}067$ and from [*6.7*] we have $r_2 > 0{\cdot}078$.

Of course, in project-making practice it is realised that for long-term investments it is necessary to consider the conditions in the more distant future along with those in the near future. Consequently, the effectiveness of long-term and short-term investments is determined according to the different standards of pay-off period of investments.

Thus, it is not only due to the lack of obligatory normatives that the standards of effectiveness of investment used in practice are of such variety. This variety has a rational kernel. The standards used conform in general to their turnover periods. Clearly this is based on the idea that as our accumulation grows, the standard of efficiency is lowered, since potentially effective investments will be more completely and widely used.

However, the actual differences between the pay-off periods of long-term and short-term investments are clearly too large. Inequalities [*6.6*] and [*6.7*] justify comparatively modest differences only.

For example, if $r_2 = 0{\cdot}04$, $r_0 = 0{\cdot}3$, and $\frac{T_1}{T_2} = 0{\cdot}1$ then r_f must not be greater than 0·01. Such a low standard of effectiveness is hardly compatible with intensive technical progress and high rates of growth of labour productivity. Therefore there is no justification for a considerable difference between the effectiveness of long-term and short-term investments (for example 0·04 – 0·3) if the quantitative aspect only is considered. If the long-term investments give qualitatively different effects, it is another matter. When the effects of plan-variants are qualitatively different, the comparison of outlay does not answer the question of their effectiveness. However, the above rule refers to all types of outlays, and not only to investment. It is the general rule for comparing the effectiveness of plan-variants.

In this chapter we have discussed only one aspect of the problem of the long-term minimum of outlays, namely the role of changes in the standard effectiveness of investment.

As we have seen, these changes must be taken into account in the planning of investment.

[1] We omit its proof.

However, it is not only the standard which changes, but also the productivity of labour, the relative prices of the means of production, the composition of natural resources used, and so on.

In determining the long-term minimum of outlays it is necessary to take these into account as well.

CHAPTER VII

THE PROBLEM OF MEASURING THE RESULTS OF LABOUR IN A SOCIALIST ECONOMY

1. Two Objectives of the Measurement of the Effectiveness of Labour

The determination of the minimum outlay on a given final output is a necessary, but not sufficient, condition for the construction of the optimal plan. It is still necessary for the volume and composition of the final output to correspond to the requirements of the whole economy. As we have shown, in order to construct the production plan it is necessary to compare ('weigh up') the 'useful effects' of different objects of consumption with one another and with the necessary outlay of labour.

The measurement of the effectiveness of a definite outlay of living labour is necessary for the organisation of production and for distribution according to labour. The correct management of production in an enterprise, shop or working-place cannot be achieved merely with a knowledge of what the outlay of living labour at each of these stages gives to society. How could the enterprise, the shop or the workers continue to struggle for increased labour productivity if they did not know the results of their labour? If the indicators of the results of labour happen to be incorrect, then the attempt to raise them might actually lead to a decrease in labour productivity. The more exactly the results of living labour are measured, the more effective the struggle to raise them will be, and the more strictly the law of the continuous growth of labour productivity will be obeyed.

The correct measurement of the results and effectiveness of living labour is of great importance in a socialist economy; for of all social systems, only socialism works on the principle of distribution according to labour, and it is only under socialism that the principle of the individual material interest of the worker in the results of his labour holds good. But a necessary prerequisite for the operation of this principle is the correct measurement of what each producer gives to society. The more exactly the results of living labour are determined, the more effective will be the law of distribution according to labour, and the closer the connexion between individual and social interests.

The strict observance of the principle of distribution according to labour is in its turn an important condition for the continuous growth of labour productivity and the prosperity of the workers. But this is not all. The exact measurement of the results of living labour is of great importance also to the planned management of the economy as a whole: the effectiveness of economic accounting depends on it. If the indicators of the results of labour (of enterprise, shop or individual workers) incorrectly reflect what this labour gives to society, economic accounting will make it more difficult to apply the law of planned development: it will encourage less productive expenditure and obstruct the fulfilment of the more productive plan targets.

We can accordingly formulate the two objectives of the measurement of the effectiveness of labour:

1. the measurement of the effectiveness of labour in the production of definite products.
2. the measurement of the effectiveness of a definite expenditure of labour (of collectives, of individual workers).

In practice, both the objectives must be fulfilled: the first is the basic one on which the solution of the second depends.

2. The Problem of the Comparison of Heterogeneous Use-values

Although different use-values are qualitatively incommensurable, in practice they are compared with one another. The indicators of 'physical volume of output', 'commodity turnover', 'national income' and so on are calculated as masses of use-values. The results of work are measured in money terms. Lastly, outlays are compared with results in order to determine the success (profitability) of production.

It is true that in practice these calculations are treated with a certain caution, and even suspicion, but they are not actually rejected, because, clearly, they are indispensable. But then, what economic sense is there in comparing heterogeneous use-values? Moreover, is it at all right to pose the problem of comparing mutually incommensurable phenomena? It is obvious that this problem cannot be solved by any direct method, but one is still able sometimes to measure a quantity which is associated with all the incommensurable quantities, i.e. to make an indirect comparison (as when measuring temperature by the change in volume of mercury).

It is possible to do this while comparing use-values; for all production is associated with the one general quantity—outlay of labour—so that the different use-values can be indirectly compared. Assuming that either the outlay per unit of each product or the outlay on the total produced mass of use-values is unchanged, we relate changes in outlay to changes in use-values only; either the changes in their size (if the outlay per unit of each product is unchanged) or the changes in relative value ('weights') of the different use-values (if the outlay on the whole final output is unchanged).

The comparison of the total volume of outlay on the assumption of unchanged outlay per unit of each product (commodity) is the basis for the construction of indices of physical volume of output, commodity-turnover, national income, and so on.

The comparison of the outlays on each product, when the total sum of outlays on all products is unchanged, is the basis for the comparison of outlays and results with regard to the extent to which they meet requirements.

The essence of this last comparison lies in the fact that the outlays appear, on the one hand, as the sum of outlays on consumer goods and, on the other, as the sum of consumer incomes. If commodities are sold at prices which are in accordance with the balance of supply and demand, then the ratio of prices to outlay for the various commodities will show to what extent the production of each commodity corresponds to needs. For these prices reflect the resultant 'weighing up of useful effects' of the various products by the mass of consumers. Therefore the results of production calculated from these prices can be used to compare outlays and results taking into account how far the results correspond to needs. If the price of each product is equal to the differential outlays on it, this means that the production corresponds (proportionally) to needs (as far as they are expressed in demand).

However, demand reflects needs which have already been affected by the distribution of incomes. The more unequal this distribution is, the less will demand reflect the requirements of the population and the more it will express the income-distribution.

Under capitalism the great inequality in income distribution is accompanied by as great an inequality in the share of consumption among the different classes. Thus, outlays on the manufacture of various luxuries are socially necessary, while outlays on the production of articles of prime importance for raising the consumption of the majority of the population to the 'subsistence minimum' turn out to be socially unnecessary. By satisfying their needs with the labour of others and not their own, those with large incomes are not aware of any limits on their consumption set by the results of their own work.

Under socialism, distribution according to labour relates the consumption of each member of society to his individual part in the social production process. Therefore total demand is incomparably more closely connected with needs than under capitalism, although the requirements of different groups of workers have a different share in the total demand of the population.

It is conceivable that demand will accurately reflect needs only when monetary incomes are distributed according to need, i.e. under communism when, strictly speaking, demand has ceased to exist. This unexpected conclusion forces us to wonder whether it is true that the calculation of needs in terms of demand is associated only with the law of value. Does not demand represent an imperfect form of the system of calculating needs which can be realised most fully only under communism?

In order to discover the 'intimations of a higher animal' in the law of the equality of demand and supply, let us try to state the principles of the most effective distribution according to needs under communism, i.e. distribution in which the use of consumption funds gives the greatest degree of total satisfaction of need.

Distribution according to needs presupposes a very high level of labour productivity, where labour becomes the first vital need (owing to changes in the nature of physical labour, better conditions, a shorter working day and so on). But distribution according to needs must not be thought of as the absence of any restrictions on consumption. Just because there is an abundance of products, this does not mean that they are free gifts, 'manna from Heaven'. Under all conditions products are the result of labour, and though this can be exceptionally large, it cannot be unlimited.

Of course, some requirements are as limited as the results of highly-productive labour are, or even more so, such as the need for food. Naturally when products are abundant such needs can be satisfied without any restriction and the necessary volume of production for these can be calculated on scientifically based standards. However, there is a number of requirements whose limits cannot be defined beforehand, and we cannot construct an objective standard for them in order to establish their volumes of production that will satisfy these needs most fully (such as the requirement for refrigerators of different designs).

If some product can be distributed without limit (such as water, when pipes have been laid), then the other part of the consumption fund must be distributed in the form of definite quotas corresponding to the objective individual needs. The unit of measurement of these quotas must be the same as that in which the outlays are measured, for otherwise the results and outlays would be incommensurable and it would be impossible to determine needs correctly. In order to distribute the consumption fund 'cheques', expressed in the units of measurement of outlays, can be issued.

A determination of needs which takes account of the outlays required to satisfy them can be put in a form similar to the consumer demand for those products which must be paid for by 'cheques', according to the outlay on each. When the total sum of orders, the 'demand' for each product, is equal to the total production of it, this will indicate that the production corresponds to needs.

The rule that results must be measured in the same units as outlays is a general one, common to both communism and socialism, the only difference being that under communism the unit of measurement will be working time instead of money.

Another common notion is that under socialism the prices of consumer goods ensure the balance of supply and demand. An excess of demand over the supply of consumer goods lowers the standard of living of the people which could be possible with the given consumption fund: to the labour outlay on production is added a further outlay not accounted for in the costs of production—the real outlay of time and effort in the search for scarce commodities and in standing in queues. In addition, unproductive, even criminal, acts (speculation in scarce goods, bribery of the sellers of these goods and so on) become a source of unjustified enrichment, diverting labour from production. Thus, the balance of 'demand and supply' in consumer goods under socialism obeys both the law of distribution according to labour and the law of economy of labour.[1]

However, in socialist conditions needs appear not only in the form of consumer demand. A socialist economy cannot draw up the production plan of the final output on the basis of consumer demand alone. First, consumer demand does not completely solve the question of accumulation, the expansion of production, which by its very nature requires a centralised solution. The question of the rate of accumulation cannot depend on the volume of individual savings of the workers (as applied to accumulation, consumer demand is expressed in consumers' savings), since this would mean restricting the share of accumulation in the national economy within much narrower limits than under capitalism.

Second, consumer demand cannot be considered as the best criterion for determining the composition of production of consumer goods. We have seen that demand can correctly reflect consumer needs only when there is distribution of income according to need. But there is more to it than this. The transition to communism presupposes the education of needs, their rationalisation. Even highly cultured people are often wrong about what food is most useful to them, what clothing suits them best; for such questions can be correctly answered only after special studies. At the same time, no man can be an expert in everything connected with the rationalisation of consumption. Therefore in a socialist economy consumer demand cannot categorically dictate production.

One of the important ways of rationalising consumption, cultivating new needs, and fighting against survivals from the past is that of price regulation. This is why the prices of 'cultural' goods (such as cameras, gramophone records, television sets, not to mention books and papers) are relatively lower in the USSR than in capitalist countries. This is not just accidental. It is typical of the cultivation of new needs among the population. Distribution according to labour, together with the rationalisation of consumption, makes it possible for a socialist society to make more effective use of consumption funds than a capitalist economy.

In other words, given the production of consumer goods, a socialist economy attains a much higher *per capita* standard of living, i.e. general level of satisfaction of needs, than a capitalist one.

It follows that although the prices of consumer goods under socialism take demand into account, production is not determined by demand. In

[1] However, when normal economic proportions are abruptly disturbed, as in time of war, the same laws can lead to a deviation from the balance of supply and demand. However, a system of rationing then becomes necessary.

other words, the prerequisite for well-balanced production is not the equality between the demand prices and the outlays possible under the given production conditions, but the equality between these outlays and that required from a social point of view. Only this equality determines the socially necessary outlays.

In a socialist economy the necessary outlays are not a simple summary of the individual orders of the population as expressed in demand, but are the organised collective order, the sum of the reciprocal weighing-up of the 'useful effect' of the given product in comparison with other products and with outlays.

Therefore although the prices of consumer goods must correspond to demand, production must be geared to the socially necessary outlays and not to prices; the latter two may or may not coincide. It follows that the measurement of results in terms of the selling prices of consumer goods (which express demand) cannot be used as a basis for comparing outlays with results; for this are needed the socially necessary outlays. In so far as results are realised according to the demand prices, the determination of results according to the socially necessary standards can be made only by means of introducing corrections in the actually realised results.

This is the economic function of turnover tax. Turnover tax compensates for the deviation of demand price from socially necessary outlays. Results measured without turnover tax must reflect the socially necessary outlays on them. If the sum of social costs of production of the means of consumption was equal to the sum of their prices (= the sum of their values), then the turnover tax could only level out all the results in accordance with the socially necessary outlays by taking negative values, i.e. by becoming a form of subsidy, in some cases. However, if the sum of social costs of production of the means of consumption is less than the sum of their prices, then the turnover tax can carry out its regulating function fully without taking negative values.

3. The Measurement of Results and Effectiveness of Living Labour

The measurement of the results of living labour is based, firstly on the measurement of output, and secondly on the measurement of material costs. This is because living labour does not only give output: it also takes it (means of production). Hence the product of living labour can be expressed as the difference between what the labour gives to the economy and what it takes from it, or as an increment in the mass of use-values produced by it. This difference cannot be measured in natural units, due to the heterogeneity of the use-values of the output and the means of production expended on it. But it can be measured indirectly in value units or in terms of labour outlays (under communism). In the measurement of labour productivity it is necessary that this indirect measurement of output shall reflect the 'physical volume' of the resulting increment in use-values, i.e. shall be based on comparable prices. While if we measure the result of living labour taking into account the extent to which it corresponds to needs (in real prices), then the ratio of the result to the outlay of labour represents the effectiveness.

The actual measure of the results of living labour is well-known. It is net output, or the newly created value: the difference between the value of output and the value of the means of production expended on it.

The ratio of net output to actual outlay of labour indicates to what extent living labour satisfies the standard outlays of living and past labour. It is easiest to explain this essence of the measurement of the productivity of living labour if we leave the monetary measurement of outlays, so that the ratio of net output (expressed in standard working time) to actual working time will be a general indicator of the satisfaction of all the standards of both manufacture and expenditure of past labour. For example, if this ratio is equal to 2, this means that the given labour contributes twice as much to the national income as is required by the plan standards; or in other words, this labour expends half as much present and past labour on the creation of the output as is required by the standards of manufacture and material expenditure.

In the value measurement of net output, the productivity of living labour is not dimensionless, but is expressed in the dimensions of a relative quantity, such as roubles per man-hour. However, its meaning is similar to that of the indicator of satisfaction of standards expressed in man-hours. Indeed, if three roubles of net output corresponds on the average to one man-hour of labour, and in the given instance six roubles of net output is produced, this means that this labour in general expended half as much present and past labour on the creation of the output it produced as is required by the standards of manufacture and material costs.[1]

However, net output is calculated by the Central Statistical Office of the USSR only to determine the national income, i.e. the result of labour for the economy as a whole, and not for the individual sectors. It is not even calculated by the enterprises. This results in the obvious inconsistency that the most important economic indicator is not used for the separate sectors of the economy.

[1] The meaning of the measurement of productivity of living labour as an indicator of the fulfilment of standards becomes still clearer if we express the labour outlays in the same units as net output. Of course it would be incorrect to replace the labour outlays by actual wages, for wages depend on other factors than just the quantity and quality of the expended labour (such as the sector, region, results of labour and so on). Of particular importance here is the dependence of the actual wage on the results of labour. Because of this dependence the outlay on wages becomes to a certain extent an indicator of results, and not of costs. When labour productivity changes, the monetary expression of labour outlays must depend only on the quantity and quality of labour, and for this purpose a single system of stable inter-temporal rates is needed, similar to a system of fixed (comparable) prices, but very much simpler (such a system would be useful not only for the measurement of labour productivity, but also for the analysis of wages).

Then the indicator of labour productivity would be a dimensionless quantity, expressing the general level of fulfilment by living labour of the standards of expenditure of living and past labour.

What prevents the measurement of the results of labour of the separate enterprises in terms of net output?

The usual answer given is that wholesale industrial prices and obligatory procurement prices (in agriculture) of producer goods are disproportionate to the corresponding values.[1] However, this explanation is hardly convincing. First, in practice net output is compared with the wages paid for its production. Indeed profit represents the implicit difference between realised net output and the wages paid for its production. This means that the disproportionality of prices and values does not prevent the calculation of net income, which is an indicator of great practical importance.

Second, and above all, the problem of measuring the results of living labour in an enterprise is not solved by prices being equal to values. Net output depends on the conditions of application of labour: the technical equipment, the quality of the natural resources it uses, its site and other conditions. These usually differ in the same industry, and this is the reason for two important shortcomings in net output.

1. The incompatibility of the individual maxima of net output of enterprises, sectors, regions, i.e. of the separate parts of the national economy.
2. Its unsuitability for distribution according to labour.

Let us consider each of these in more detail.

The fact that the best conditions of application of labour do not meet the requirement in them not only causes feedback between the outlays on different products, but also feedback between the results of labour in the different stages of production. The use of the best means of production increases the net output of one enterprise at the cost of a reduction in the possible net output of other enterprises. Hence, if all parts of the economy attempt to produce the maximum net output, their attempts will be incompatible, since they could only be successful if all enterprises were supplied with the best natural and technical conditions for the application of labour; which is impossible.

Thus feedback between outlays entails not only incompatability of the individual minimum costs of production, but also incompatability of the individual maximum results of living labour.

Because of the incompatability of the individual maxima of net output, the dynamics of net output in different parts of the national economy does not reflect the movement of the national income which each part causes. Thus, if the net output of an enterprise increases by 1 million roubles, this does not mean that the national income thereby increases by the same sum. If the enterprise has increased its net output at the cost of using scarce raw materials which were previously required by other enterprises, then the

[1] Cf., for example, D. V. Savinskii, *A Course of Industrial Statistics*, p. 110, Gosstatizdat, Moscow, 1954.

national income might even decrease. This will happen if the net output of the other enterprises is reduced by more than 1 million roubles as a result of having to use the poorer raw materials.

The divergence between the movement of net output of an enterprise and the movement of the national income is explained by the fact that the net output of one enterprise can grow at the cost of a reduction in the net output of others. Thus the urge of the individual enterprises towards maximum net outputs can prove to be not only incompatible with one another but also with the maximum growth of the national income, with the law of the continuous growth of labour productivity.

The other shortcoming of net output is its unsuitability for distribution according to labour. The payment for labour according to net output would destroy the principle of distribution according to quantity and quality of labour. Workers in those enterprises which were best equipped, used the best natural resources, and so on, would receive a higher wage for the same labour as workers in enterprises which were less favourably placed.

If the inequality of conditions of application of labour is attended by shortcomings in net output, then to eliminate these, net output must be reduced to equal conditions of application of labour, so that:

1. each increase in the reduced net output will correspond to an increase in national income;

2. labour which is identical in quality and quantity will give the identical reduced output in any socially necessary conditions of production.

The principal and most difficult problem of the measurement of the effectiveness of living labour is to fulfil these requirements. Theoretically the problem has still to be formulated, but in practice there is an awareness of it, and efforts have been made to solve it.[1]

In practice, attempts are made to isolate profitability from the influence of changes and differences in the conditions of application of labour. Thus in determining the size of profits in excess of the plan, or the economies effected through a reduction in prime cost, changes caused by factors which are independent of the productive activity of the enterprise must be allowed for. These include changes in the prices of raw materials, semi-manufactures, fuel and other materials; changes in railway and other tariffs; the replacement in the planned priority of basic types of raw material and fuel; changes in wage-rates and extra charges on wages; changes in the amortisation standards; changes in selling prices of output, etc.

[1] The need to reduce net output to equal conditions of application of labour is a special case of the general principle of making all standards in a socialist economy equally difficult, or uniform. This principle is the basis for distribution according to labour, and for the standardisation of labour outlays. The measurement of the results of living labour must also be based on it, for otherwise payment according to results would in many cases transgress the law of distribution according to labour. This is because the ratio of net output to labour outlays is no more than the indicator of the fulfilment of all the standards of expenditure of both living and past labour, by living labour.

The problem of removing the effect on the results of labour of differences in the conditions under which it is applied in different enterprises is more complicated. Turnover tax, intra-sectoral accounting prices, the regulation of prices of substitutable producer goods in accordance with their respective savings and differential rent are used for this purpose.

Turnover tax is used mainly to level out differences in profitability of the production of various commodities which occur as a result of pricing policy.

Given a single wholesale price, accounting prices inside a sector (between markets and groups of enterprises) iron out the effect of differences in natural sources of raw materials in the accounting profitability of its production. Here the single wholesale price is formed on the basis of the average prime cost of output in the sector. This is the predominant system in the extractive industry.

The correspondence of wholesale prices of the means of production to the value of their saving is realised by fixing higher prices for the more economic output and lower prices for the less economic output used for the same purpose. These price differences compensate to a certain extent for differences in the economic use of the means of production. They include, for example, the higher prices for scarce materials and fuel (non-ferrous metals, solid fuel).

Payments similar to differential rent remove the effect of differences in natural resources and transport from the prime cost of output. In 1949 for instance the timber industry introduced a small charge for every tree cut down, allowing somewhat for differences in natural and transport facilities between the government purveyors. The single wholesale price is based on the prime cost of the enterprises working in less favourable conditions, and the additional profit of the favoured enterprises goes to the State.

So we can see that several methods are used in practice to abstract profitability from external influences. However, all of them only approximate to their aim, and so, when planning the profit for each enterprise, we must allow for those differences in the conditions of application of labour which remain effective. This means that this process of equalising these conditions in the various enterprises is carried out not so much by means of reducing the result indicators to equal conditions, as by planning the objectives of the enterprises in accordance with their production potentialities. So far, however, this method is imperfect, many subjective elements often entering into it. As a result, it sometimes happens that it is the enterprise which has had less success, rather than that which has achieved a more important increase in results, which receives most incentives.

However, if the planning were to be based on the attained level, other negative consequences would occur. For example, the profits in excess of the plan only refer to results achieved by the group of enterprises during the course of the given year. The results of labour which become evident later are included in the accounts of later years. Thus, bonuses for extra profit give an incentive only to those achievements which produce results immediately. But technical progress and the organisation of production do not usually yield an immediate result, frequently requiring a long time to show any effect. For this reason, planning based on the attained level holds back technical development and the organisation of production.

With the aim of eliminating these shortcomings, the latest practice is to put forward the principle of the standardisation of objectives according to the conditions of application of labour. This is already carried out in the agricultural sphere, where the standardisation of supplies of agricultural produce according to the attained level has been replaced by the 'per hectare' principle.

This principle is also used in industry. In particular, it is suggested that the planning profitability according to the level previously attained should be replaced by long-term standards of profitability, based on the typical characteristics of the enterprises in each industrial sector.[1]

Subsequent development of this principle must lead to the standardisation of net income for groups of homogeneous and equally effective means of labour. Standard profitability for the enterprises as a whole does not include all the indicators which the enterprise needs to make best use of the means supplied to it, and therefore allows only a comparatively modest development of its initiative in selecting the means to implement the plan directives.

In addition to these standards, data is required for determining the most advisable way of using each means of production. Enterprises cannot themselves make a study of all the social conditions of production and demand for each instrument of labour. Therefore they must either obtain direct instructions, controlling their use of the means of labour, or they must have planning standards of the effectiveness of this use. Planning norms of net income, fixed for each means of labour, can be used to reduce net output (and net income) to equal conditions of application of labour. In fact, by including the standard of net income from each means of labour in the prime cost of output (in the form of rent, differential rent and so on) we are placing the different enterprises in economically identical conditions.

It seems to us that this is the fundamental method of reduction to equal conditions of labour, fulfilling two requirements: the changes in net output of the enterprise correspond to changes in the national income, and the indicators of the results of living labour correspond to its quantity and quality. Indeed, if the charges for the means of production place all enterprises in identical conditions, there is no possibility of an increase in the net output of one enterprise at the expense of an even greater reduction in the net output of others.

It is not difficult to show that the standardisation of net income according to the conditions of application of labour is no more than fixing the very standards of effectiveness of the use of the means of production which are

[1] Cf. E. Liberman, The planning of Industrial Production, *Kommunist*, 1956, No. 6.

required in the calculation of social costs. These standards remove the incompatability of the particular minima of individual values, which is associated with that of the particular maxima of the results of living labour—of net output, net income (for the particular minima of social costs are compatible).

Thus the construction of a system of standards of effectiveness solves the twofold problem:

1. of the overall minimum of outlays (= the minimum value of the final output) using the particular minima of social costs;
2. of the overall maximum of results (the national income, the net income of society) using the particular maxima of results reduced to equal conditions (reduced net output, reduced net income of an enterprise).

The indicator of reduced productivity of labour calculated on this basis will represent the degree to which the reduced standards of manufacture and quality of output, standards of material expenses, effectiveness of use of fixed and circulating capital and natural resources are fulfilled. As a result, it is inevitably the most important and principal indicator in economic accounting.

When this indicator is introduced, there will probably no longer be any divergence between the economic-accounting gain and the social interest. Economic-accounting success will be a true index of success from the point of view of the whole economy.

This will pave the way for a perfect system of distribution according to labour, for the closest identification of individual interests with social interests, for the fullest concern of each worker in the growth of the national income. The payment of labour according to the reduced net output obeys the law according to which 'each separate producer receives from society exactly as much as he gives to it'.[1]

The indicator of profitability will remain, but it will acquire a different meaning which will be more in accordance with the conditions of socialism than it is today. The comparison of the reduced net output and wages must be made so that distribution according to labour can be more accurate, and so that the fulfilment of the standards of consumption can be checked. This comparison can be made by finding the difference between the reduced net output and wages, or the ratio of the two, or, finally, the ratio of their difference to the wage. These three forms of comparison give the indicators of reduced net output, reduced gross incomes and reduced profitability respectively.

Obviously, this profitability—the profitability of labour—will have quite a different meaning from the standard profit. Profitability of labour is an indicator of distribution according to labour; the standard profit is an indicator of distribution of surplus value according to capital.

[1] MARX and ENGELS, *Selected Works*, Vol. II, p. 14, 1948 (Russian edition).

Let us attempt to make these forms of measurement of the effectiveness of living labour on the basis of net output somewhat more concrete. Naturally this can only be done hypothetically, by starting from the observed trends in the development of economic accounting.

Since all enterprises must operate profitably, the prime cost of output under the worst production conditions necessary to fulfil the plan must not be greater than the wholesale price. Over time, therefore, intrasector accounting prices will disappear. We shall be able to reduce net output to equal conditions of application of labour by means of charging for the use of the relatively good means of production.

The standardisation of net income according to the kinds of means of production has many advantages in comparison with the establishment of standard profit for the enterprise as a whole. It fosters a material interest in the most effective use of each means of production. It gives overall economic standards for the least permissible effect from the use of each instrument of labour. Thus the conditions are created for the greater democratisation of planning and for the growth of the creative initiative of the mass of the people in the completion of the economic plan.

When a perfect standardisation of profit according to the means of production is achieved, labour which is identical in both quality and quantity will produce an identical reduced net output for any socially necessary conditions of its application, i.e. it will produce the same newly created net output, after the standard reductions have been made from it for the better means of production. The total of such reduced output, when the means of production are charged for, will then be the full net output for the calculation of the national income.

At the present time the conditions for the measurement of labour productivity on the basis of net output do not yet exist. In order to create these conditions gradually, it must be remembered that the accuracy of all measurements (both technical and economic) must be economically justified; it must be sufficient, yet not superfluous. Since superfluous accuracy is wasteful, the calculation of the results of labour in terms of net output is economically justified only where many elements of material expenses depend on the workers, and where the cost of calculating net output does not exceed the economy achieved.

The results of labour of small aggregates (production units or brigades) and separate workers must include only those elements of net output which depend on the workers. There are more of such elements in the results of joint labour than in the results of individual labour. Hence it is hardly necessary to measure net output for each worker. At the same time, the calculation of the results of joint labour requires the fullest knowledge of the elements of net output. In any case, a correct understanding of the results of labour as reduced net output gives us the key for 'weighing up' and comparing the individual indicators of the results of living labour.

CONCLUSION

The problem which arises in the measurement of outlays and their results under socialism is that in practice this measurement does not agree with the measurement of outlays on each product by the labour spent on its production, i.e. by its value. The prices of the means of production systematically deviate from their values, and the calculation of outlays must include, in addition to prime cost, capital investment, the outlay of scarce means of production and other quantities incommensurable with prime cost.

The divergence between the practice and the theory of the measurement of outlays is mainly a result of the failings of theory, which is at the moment quite firmly convinced that the principle of the measurement of labour outlays on each product is always the same under all conditions; it believes that outlays are measured by the labour of production (or reproduction) of the given product.

This idea does not stem from Marxist-Leninist theory, and in particular it does not follow from Marx's teachings concerning prices of production. It is not historically justified, nor does it comply with dialectical materialism. It arose only because the development of the measurement of outlays was inadequately studied, and the experience of socialist construction was not known and generalised.

In reality, however, neither the methods nor even the principle of measurement of outlays are invariable. They change as the economy develops and new forms of measurement must be created in the process.

Marx's proposition that the price of production is dependent both on the value of a given commodity and also on the total value of all commodities, together with the conception of the average rate of profit, also gives the formula for the general standard of profit as the minimum limit of actual profit. The marginal nature of the profit standard leads to the hypothesis that the price of production fulfils certain extremal functions; its dependence on the value of all commodities prompts us to ask whether it is not the increment in value of all commodities which is caused by the production of the given one. And if so, is not this the way to change the principle of measuring outlays?

In simple commodity production the grounds for converting value into a more complicated form did not exist. Due to the poor development of the division of labour economic interdependence was very limited, and feedback between outlays for different purposes was either absent, or not in practice subject to calculation. Therefore the minimum outlay could be found simply by comparing the individual values of a commodity under different production conditions.

With the rise of capitalism, economic interdependence became much more complex. The use of capital in any sector engendered feedback between the individual values of the various commodities. The minima of the individual values of the different products and the minima of the outlays of different enterprises became incompatible.

Competition between capitalists led to the equalisation of profit standards, and turned values into the prices of production, thereby making a crude allowance for feedback outlays entailed in the investment of capital. Competition also made the various individual prices of production equal to the common price of production, creating differential rent in the process, and making some allowance for the feedback outlays involved in the use of natural resources.

In its own way, the price of production is a value expression of differential outlays, but it is a very imperfect reflection of it. For the correct measurement of differential outlays requires planning and the use of standards of effectiveness for economic measurement. But capitalism precludes planning, and forms of distribution are used instead of standards of effectiveness of the means of production.

With the rise of socialism, the law of value frees itself from its function as a regulator of production, and the standards of effectiveness of investment and natural resources are no longer forms of distribution. Planning makes use of the law of value for the measurement of outlays and results, and the correct measurement of differential outlays in value form becomes possible. A new converted form of value, prime cost, is created. This socialist form of value is at the moment in the making, and does not yet include all the elements of differential outlays. Feedback outlays are represented only very incompletely in it, and so in practice other indicators must be used besides prime cost, such as capital investment, indicators of the use of productive capital, outlay of scarce means of production, construction periods.

The progressive trends of practice lead to the transformation of prime cost from the outlays of an enterprise (which is different from social outlays) into a form of value, which reflects the increase in social outlays caused by the production of each separate product.[1] The standards for the calculation of outlays (prices of the means of production, standards of the effectiveness of investment and the utilisation of fixed capital and of natural resources) must then become the most important tool for drawing up and fulfilling the overall economic plan.

The transformation of prime cost as the costs of an enterprise into a form of value will lead to a number of positive results. In particular, it will remove the present considerable divergence between economic-accounting gains and overall economic effectiveness.

Under communism, the measurement of outlays on each product will be

[1] We have called the full cost of production a transformed form of value, the social cost.

carried out most perfectly, in the form of differential outlays expressed in units of working time, with the closest links between all the accounting standards and the plan.

Thus the measurement of outlays has developed as follows:

(*a*) from elementary forms to more complex, dialectical forms which study the movement and interdependence of outlays;

(*b*) from the disorderly and very imperfect use of dialectics to its use in planning;

(*c*) from the indirect (value) to the direct measurement of outlays of labour, or, in general, from quite primitive methods of measurement suitable for the solution of the simplest extremal problems posed by the law of economy of labour to the measurement of outlays as a means of solving the most complex general problem of finding the maximum rate of growth of the productivity of social labour.

The general trend of development in the measurement of outlays is determined by general economic laws: the law of the correspondence of the relations of production to the level of productive forces; the law of the economy of labour, and so on. These laws are a reflection of economic progress, the transition from the lowest to the highest stages of development, and on them depends progress in the measurement of outlays. The general extremal problem of the economy, the maximisation of the rate of growth of labour productivity defines the historical measure of the level of an economic system. (The system which ensures the highest rates of growth of labour productivity is the highest and must prevail.) It follows that the degree of perfection in the measurement of outlays is determined by the degree to which it corresponds to the problem of the maximisation of the rate of growth of labour productivity. The more exactly the measurement of outlays helps to solve this problem, the more nearly perfect it is.

The general extremal problem of economics finds its expression in the various stages of development in the special extremal problems determined by the effect of specific economic laws. The measurement of outlays too depends primarily on the nature of the economic system. Thus its development has four stages:

1. value—for simple commodity production;
2. the price of production—under capitalism;
3. full social cost—under socialism;
4. differential outlays—under communism.

However, in addition to these different characteristics, there exist some which are common to all, or several, stages. Thus, for all stages it is true that outlays consist of labour only. The three last stages have the common feature that differential outlays in some form or other are measured. It is this which explains the formal similarity between the measurement of outlays under socialism, and even under communism, and the price of production.

This similarity might appear to indicate the transfer of capitalist categories into the conditions of communism. However, the mathematical similarity in this case is only a consequence of such common conditions as:

(*a*) the material conditions for the formation of the price of production (about which Marx wrote);

(*b*) the subordination of the measurement of outlays to extremal problems;

(*c*) the conditional nature of the attained extremum;

(*d*) the necessity of using auxiliary multipliers in the solution of the extremal problem.

These conditions do not refer to the relations of production: in their different forms they exist under both capitalism and communism. And it is just these conditions which give the general features of the measurement of outlays under different economic systems. The spontaneous unconscious use of auxiliary multipliers in economics arose long before they were discovered as a method for finding the conditional extremum. They were borrowed by mathematics from practice, just as the 'concepts of number and of figure were borrowed from the real world' (Engels), and in the same way they are unrelated to the relations of production.

Of course this outline of the development of the measurement of outlays is only a 'first approximation'. If, however, even its essential meaning is true, then the conclusion that it is impossible to form prices and measure the outlays on separate products according to their value is indisputable. To attempt to do this is like attempting to construct socialism using the techniques of the feudal epoch. Another conclusion is that the formula of the price of production is inapplicable in a socialist economy, in which is inherent a special transformed form of value which cannot be derived from this formula, because all the standards for calculating social costs are determined from and for the optimal planning of the whole economy.

In conclusion, we may say that our main aim has been to explain the basic trends and principles of the measurement of outlays (the measurement of the results of labour was studied only in order to clarify the questions connected with the measurement of outlays). The specific methods for this measurement have still to be developed, although it is certain that the problem will be completely solved within the next few years. The interests of the socialist economy urgently require theory to light up the road for practice.

Some Observations on Input-Output Analysis

Oskar Lange

1. The Scope of Input-Output Analysis

The analysis of inter-industry relations, usually referred to as input-output analysis, serves the purpose of establishing the quantitative relations between various branches of production which must be maintained in order to assure a smooth flow of production in the national economy. It studies the conditions of mutual consistency of the outputs of the various branches of the national economy which result from the fact that the output of one branch is the source of input in other branches.

The idea that certain proportions must be maintained between the outputs of various branches of the national economy is at the basis of the equilibrium analysis of classical political economy and neo-classical economics. The proportions referred to are, however, conceived by classical and neo-classical economic theory basically in 'horizontal' terms, i.e. as proportions between final products designed to satisfy the wants of consumers. Under conditions of competitive capitalism, of free mobility of capital, the tendency of the rate of profit towards a 'normal' level in each branch of the national economy leads towards an equilibrium of output of the various branches. In equilibrium, output is adjusted to the demand for the various products. In a planned economy, it is believed, proper planning should assure the establishment of equilibrium proportions.

While this idea of 'horizontal' equilibrium proportions undoubtedly points to an important aspect of the relations between the output of the various branches of the national economy, it overlooks the need of maintaining another kind of proportions, determined not by conditions of consumers' demand, but by the conditions of technological relations associated with the fact that the output of certain products serves—entirely or in part—as input in the process of producing other products. We may call this a problem of 'vertical' proportions.

This problem of 'vertical' proportions is the subject matter of input-output analysis. The problem was first posed by Quesnay in his famous 'Tableau Économique'. Its insight was lost by classical and neo-classical economic theory. A systematic treatment as well as the fundamental solution of the problem was given by Marx in his schemes of reproduction of capital contained in Volume II of *Das Kapital.* Outside of Marxist political economy the problem was scarcely seen, neo-classical economics confining itself to the study of equilibrium conditions of the 'horizontal' type.

However, in business cycle theory of bourgeois economists the problem of 'vertical relations' between investment goods and consumers' goods was bound to reappear, for it is this type of relation which is at the bottom of the phenomenon of crises and depressions. Consequently it plays an important role in Keynesian theory. The 'vertical' character of the relations involved is the cause of 'disproportionalities' in this field not being automatically solved by the process of competition through capital moving from less profitable to more profitable branches of the economy. It also explains why smooth economic development is not automatically assured under conditions of capitalism, even independently of the handicaps resulting from the specific features of monopoly capitalism.

The importance of a study of the 'vertical' relations between various branches of the economy, i.e. of input-output analysis, is not limited to conditions of a capitalist economy. As was already pointed out by Marx, since input-output relations are based on technological conditions of production, proper proportions in this field must be maintained in any economic system. A study of such relations is therefore necessary for purposes of socialist economic planning as well as for the understanding of the working-mechanism of capitalist economy. Under conditions of socialism input-output analysis is a necessary tool for ascertaining the internal consistency of national economic plans.

In the socialist countries input-output analysis takes the form of various 'statistical balances' which serve as tools of national economic planning. These balances are conceived as concretisations of the general idea underlying the reproduction schemes of Marx. In the USA Professor Leontief has developed a type of input-output analysis which, too, can be conceived as a concretisation of Marx's idea of input-output relations taking place in the process of reproduction of the national product. Professor Leontief's analysis explicitly takes into account the technological relations between output and input. Though applied first to the economy of the USA, this analysis like all input-output analyses is also applicable to a socialist economy. Indeed it seems to me, that this analysis achieves its full justification only if applied as a tool of economic planning. Its technique, though first applied to a capitalist economy, points beyond the historical limitations of capitalism and can come fully into its own only under conditions of planned economy.

2. The Marxian Schemes

Marx's analysis of reproduction is based on two premises. First, the value of the total national product during a period of time (e.g. a year) is considered as being composed of three parts—the value of the means of production used up during this period (to be denoted by c—in Marx's terminology the constant capital used up), the value of the labour power directly engaged in production (to be denoted by v—in Marx's terminology the variable capital, i.e. the revolving wage fund), the surplus generated (to be denoted by s). Thus:

$$\text{Total social product} = c+v+s$$

Here, c is the replacement of the means of production used up, $v+s$ is the total value added (or national income).

Secondly, the national economy is divided into two departments: one producing means of production, the other producing consumers' goods. Using the subscripts 1 and 2 to indicate the two departments, respectively, we shall write:

$$\begin{aligned} \text{total output of means of production} &= c_1+v_1+s_1 \\ \text{total output of consumers' goods} &= c_2+v_2+s_2 \\ \text{total social product} &= c+v+s \end{aligned}$$

where $c = c_1+c_2$, $v = v_1+v_2$, $s = s_1+s_2$.

In a stationary economy (Marx's simple reproduction):

$$\begin{aligned} \text{total demand for means of production} &= c_1+c_2 \\ \text{total demand for consumers' goods} &= v_1+v_2+s_1+s_2 \end{aligned}$$

The total demand for means of production is equal to the joint replacement requirement of both departments, the total demand for consumers' goods is equal to the joint wage fund and surplus of both departments.

Putting equal demand and output of means of production, we obtain

$$c_1+c_2 = c_1+v_1+s_1 \qquad \ldots \quad [2.1]$$

which simplifies to

$$c_2 = v_1+s_1 \qquad \ldots \quad [2.2]$$

The same result is obtained from putting equal total demand and output of consumers' goods.

That is

$$v_1+v_2+s_1+s_2 = c_2+v_2+s_2 \qquad \ldots \quad [2.3]$$

This is so, because the total social product $c+v+s$ is being given. Equation [2.3] can be deduced from equation [2.1].

Equation [2.2] indicates an input-output relation between the two departments of the national economy. Indeed, let us write,

$$\begin{array}{ccc} c_1 & + & \boxed{v_1+s_1} \\ \hline \boxed{c_2} & + & v_2+s_2 \end{array} \qquad \ldots \quad [2.4]$$

Department 1 produces means of production. Part of its output equal in value to c_1 is retained within the department for replacement of the means of production used up. The remainder (in the rectangle) equal in value to v_1+s_1 is transferred to department 2 in exchange for consumers' goods. Department 2 produces consumers' goods. Part of its output equal in value to v_2+s_2 is retained within the department for consumption. The remainder (in the rectangle) equal in value to c_2 is transferred to department 1 in exchange for the means of production needed for replacement of those which were used up. In order that production goes on smoothly, the output of the two departments must be co-ordinated in such a way that a balanced exchange takes place between the two departments, i.e. $c_2 = v_1+s_1$. The above table [*2.4*] thus indicates the input-output relations between the two departments: equation [*2.2*] gives the condition of proper balance between the two departments.

In an expanding economy (Marx's expanded reproduction) not all the surplus is consumed; part of it is accumulated to increase the amount of means of production and to employ more labour power. We shall express this by writing,

$$s = \bar{s}+s_c+s_v$$

where $\bar{s}$ is the part of the surplus consumed, s_c the part of the surplus used to increase the amount of means of production, s_v the part of the surplus used to employ more labour power.

Dividing the economy into two departments, as before, we have,

total output of means of production $= c_1+v_1+\bar{s}_1+s_{1c}+s_{1v}$
total output of consumers' goods $= c_2+v_2+\bar{s}_2+s_{2c}+s_{2v}$
total social product $= c+v+\bar{s}+s_c+s_v$

Furthermore:

total demand for means of production $= c_1+c_2+s_{1c}+s_{2c}$
total demand for consumers' goods $= v_1+v_2+s_{1v}+s_{2v}+\bar{s}_1+\bar{s}_2$

The total demand for means of production is equal to the joint replacement and expansion requirement of both departments. The total demand of consumer's goods is equal to the joint wage fund, the joint expansion of the wage fund and the joint surplus consumed in both departments.

Equality of demand and output of means of production implies

$$c_1+s_{1c}+c_2+s_{2c} = c_1+v_1+\bar{s}_1+s_{1c}+s_{1v} \quad \ldots \quad [2.5]$$

which leads to

$$c_2+s_{2c} = v_1+\bar{s}_1+s_{1v} \quad \ldots \quad [2.6]$$

The same result can be obtained from the condition of equality of demand and output of consumer's goods.

Equation [*2.6*] indicates the input-output relation between the two departments in an expanding economy. It can be presented by means of the following table:

$$\begin{array}{l} c_1+s_{1c} + \boxed{v_1+\bar{s}_1+s_{1v}} \\ \hline \boxed{c_2+s_{2c}} + v_2+\bar{s}_2+s_{2v} \end{array} \quad \ldots \quad [2.7]$$

In department 1 part of the product equal in value to c_1+s_{1c} is retained within the department for replacement of the means of production used up and for expansion of the amount of means of production in the department. The remainder (contained in the rectangle) is transferred to department 2 in exchange for consumers' goods. In department 2 part of the product equal in value to $v_2+\bar{s}_2+s_{2v}$ is retained for consumption. The remainder (contained in the rectangle) is transferred to department 1 in exchange for means of production for replacement of the means of production used up and for expansion of the amount of means of production in the department. The proper balance between the two departments is thus expressed by equation [*2.6*].

3. Input-Output Relations in a Multi-sector Model

Professor Leontief's input-output tables are designed to study the relations between a larger number of sectors of the national economy. Let the economy be divided into n production sectors denoted by the indices $1, 2, \ldots, n$. Denote by X_i the total or gross output of the ith sector, by x_{ij} the quantity of the product of the ith sector transferred to the jth sector where it is used as input. Further denote by x_i the net output of the ith sector, viz. that part of the gross output X_i which is not allocated to another sector to be used there as input.[1] The net output x_i can be consumed, exported, or accumulated for the purpose of investment.

We have thus,

$$X_i = \sum_{j=1}^{n} x_{ij}+x_i \quad (i = 1, 2, \ldots, n) \quad \ldots \quad [3.1]$$

It is convenient to represent the input-output relations between the sectors of the economy in the form of a table as follows:

$$\begin{array}{c|cccc|c} X_1 & x_{11} & x_{12} & \ldots\ldots\ldots & x_{1n} & x_1 \\ X_2 & x_{21} & x_{22} & \ldots\ldots\ldots & x_{2n} & x_2 \\ \cdot & \cdot & \cdot & \ldots\ldots\ldots & \cdot & \cdot \\ X_n & x_{n1} & x_{n2} & \ldots\ldots\ldots & x_{nn} & x_n \end{array} \quad \ldots \quad [3.2]$$

The items in the square matrix in the centre of the table represent the input-output relations, or the 'interflows' between the various branches of

[1] This part of the output in the given branch is a material component of the net output of the whole national economy, but its value is not equal to the newly created value in the given branch. (Ed.)

the national economy (also called 'intersector deliveries'). The column on the right hand side represents the net outputs and the column on the left hand side the gross outputs of the various products. The rows are subject to the balance relation indicated by equation [*3.1*].

Since the process of production requires not only the use of means of production but also the application of direct labour, we may supplement the above input-output table by introducing the amounts of labour force employed in production. Let us denote the total labour force available in the national economy by X_0 the labour force employed in producing the output of the ith sector of the economy by x_{0j} and, finally, by x_0 the labour force not employed productively. The latter may be either unemployed (labour reserve) or employed in non-productive occupations, i.e. in occupations which do not produce material goods (e.g., personal services). With regard to the allocation of the total labour force the following equation holds:

$$X_0 = x_0 + \sum_{j=1}^{n} x_{0j} \qquad \ldots \quad [3.3]$$

Introducing the allocation of the labour force into the input-output table, we obtain the following table:

$$\begin{array}{c|cccc|c}
X_0 & x_{01} & x_{02} & \ldots\ldots\ldots & x_{0n} & x_0 \\
\hline
X_1 & x_{11} & x_{12} & \ldots\ldots\ldots & x_{1n} & x_1 \\
X_2 & x_{21} & x_{22} & \ldots\ldots\ldots & x_{2n} & x_2 \\
\cdot & \cdot & \cdot & \ldots\ldots\ldots & \cdot & \cdot \\
X_n & x_{n1} & x_{n2} & \ldots\ldots\ldots & x_{nn} & x_n \\
\hline
 & Y_1 & Y_2 & \ldots\ldots\ldots & Y_n &
\end{array} \qquad \ldots \quad [3.4]$$

The items in the square matrix in the centre of the table are 'interflows' for 'inter-sector deliveries'. The upper row in the centre represents the allocation of the labour force to the various branches of the economy. Similarly as before, the column at the right represents the remainder of the labour force not allocated productively (x_0), and the net outputs of the various products (x_i; $i = 1, \ldots, n$). The column on the left hand side represents the total labour force X_0 and the gross outputs X_i ($i = 1, 2, \ldots, n$) of the various branches.

Entries in the table may be expressed either in physical units or in value units. In the latter case, the table is sometimes called a 'transaction table' rather than our input-output table. Whatever the units, the rows of the table can always be summed, for each row is expressed in the same units (e.g. man-hours, tons, gallons, yards, pieces). Thus the equations [*3.1*] and [*3.2*] hold under all circumstances. We may call them the 'allocation equations'.

The columns, however, can be summed only if the entries of the table are expressed in value units (e.g. rupees), i.e. if the table is a transaction table, otherwise the items of a column would be non-homogeneous. We shall write these sums in the following form:

$$Y_j = x_{0j} + \sum_{i=1}^{n} x_{ij} \qquad (j = 1, 2, \ldots, n) \qquad \ldots [3.5]$$

Obviously, Y_j is the cost of the output of the jth branch, x_{0j} being the cost of the labour force employed and Σx_{ij} the cost of the means of production used up in producing the output. We may call the equations [3.5] the 'cost equations'. The costs of producing the output of the various branches of the economy are indicated in the row at the bottom of table [3.4].

The excess of the value of the output of a branch of the national economy over the cost of producing the output is the surplus produced in this branch. Denoting the surplus produced in the jth branch by s_j, we have,[1]

$$s_j = X_j - Y_j \qquad \ldots [3.6]$$

and in view of [3.5], $X_j = x_{0j} + \sum_{i=1}^{n} x_{ij} + s_j \quad (j = 1, \ldots, n) \qquad \ldots [3.7]$

This is the relation which in a multi-sector model corresponds to the Marxian decomposition of the value of the output of a branch of the national economy into $c_j + v_j + s_j$ $(j = 1, 2)$. Here Σx_{ij} stands for c_j and x_{0j} stands for v_j in the Marxian notation. The value added in the sector is $x_{0j} + s_j$.

Introducing the surplus produced in the various branches of the economy into the transaction table and taking account of the relation [3.7] we obtain the following transaction table:

X_0	$x_{01}\ x_{02} \ldots\ldots\ldots x_{0n}$	x_0
X_1	$x_{11}\ x_{12} \ldots\ldots\ldots x_{1n}$	x_1
.	. . . .	.
X_n	$x_{n1}\ x_{n2} \ldots\ldots\ldots x_{nn}$	x_n
	$s_1\ s_2 \ldots\ldots\ldots s_n$	
	$X_1\ X_2 \ldots\ldots\ldots X_n$	

... [3.8]

From table [3.8] it is apparent that the gross output of a branch, say X_i, can be obtained either by summation of the entries of a row or by summation of the entries of a column. Consequently, we have

$$\sum_{j=1}^{n} x_{ij} + x_i = x_{0i} + \sum_{j=1}^{n} x_{ji} + s_i \qquad (i = 1, \ldots, n) \qquad \ldots [3.9]$$

This results directly from the equations [3.1] and [3.7]. On both sides of equation [3.9] x_{ii} is appearing under the summation sign: it is the part of

[1] The author is here taking rouble evaluations equal to the corresponding values. (Ed.)

the output retained in the sector for replacement. Eliminating x_{ii} from the equation, we obtain

$$\sum_{j \neq i} x_{ij} + x_i = x_{0i} + \sum_{j \neq i} x_{ji} + s_i \quad (i = 1, \ldots, n) \qquad \ldots [3.10]$$

This equation states that (measured in value units) the outflow from the sector to other sectors—plus the net output[1] is equal to the inflow from other sectors plus the value added in the sector.

Equation [*3.10*] is the analogue, in a multisector model, of the Marxian equations [*2.2*] and [*2.6*] of the previous section which hold in a two-sector model. The mentioned Marxian equations are obtained—just like equation [*3.10*]—by putting equal the value of the output of the sector and the total allocation of the sector's output and by eliminating on both sides the part of the output retained in the sector.

In order to see the exact analogy of equation [*3.10*] and the equations of the Marxian two-sector model, let us transform equation [*3.10*] in the following way. Suppose that the net output x_i is partly reinvested in the sector and partly consumed or allocated to other sectors; the corresponding parts will be indicated by x_i' and x_i'' respectively. Thus we have

$$x_i = x_i' + x_i'' \quad (i = 1, \ldots, n) \qquad \ldots [3.11]$$

Further, suppose that the surplus produced in the sector is used partly for consumption, partly for employment of additional labour force in the sector, and partly for addition to the means of production used in the sector. Denote these quantities by $\bar{s}_i$, s_{i0} and x_i' respectively. Thus

$$s_i = \bar{s}_i + s_{i0} + x_i' \qquad \ldots [3.12]$$

Substituting [*3.11*] and [*3.12*] into equation [*3.10*] and eliminating x_i' on both sides, the equation reduces to

$$\sum_{j \neq i} x_{ij} + x_i'' = \sum_{j \neq i} x_{ji} + x_{0i} + s_{i0} + \bar{s}_i \quad (i = 1, \ldots, n) \ldots [3.13]$$

In this form not only the quantities x_{ii} retained in the sector for replacement but also the quantity retained in the sector for expansion is eliminated. Equation [*3.13*] states that the net outflow to other sectors and to consumption is equal to the inflow from other sectors and to the part of the value added not retained in the sector. This is the exact counterpart—in a multisector model—to the Marxian equation [*2.6*] in the previous section.

If the number of sectors is reduced to two, equation [*3.10*] becomes identical with equation [*2.6*] of the preceding section. In this case [*3.13*] reduces to

$$x_{12} + x_1'' = x_{21} + x_{01} + s_{10} + \bar{s}_1 \qquad \ldots [3.14]$$

[1] In the sense of the definition given on p. 195. (Ed.)

The corresponding transaction table takes the form:

X_0	x_{01}	x_{02}	$x''_{01}+x'_{02}+x''_0$
X_1	x_{11}	x_{12}	$x'_1 + \quad x''_1$
X_2	x_{21}	x_{22}	$x'_2 + \quad x''_2$
	$\bar{s}_1$	$\bar{s}_2$	
	s_{10}	s_{20}	
	x'_1	x'_2	

... [3.15]

Sector 1 produces means of production, sector 2 produces consumers' goods. As consumer's goods are not a means of production, $x_{21} = 0$ (as also x_{22}), and as means of production are not consumed, x''_1 are the means of production allocated to sector 2 for expansion. Using the notation of the preceding section, we shall write:

$$x_{01} = v_1; \quad x_{02} = v_2$$
$$x_{11} = c_1; \quad x_{12} = c_2; \quad x_{21} = 0$$
$$x''_2 = s_{2c}; \quad s_{10} = s_{1v}$$

Thus equation [3.14] takes the form

$$c_2+s_{2c} = v_1+s_{1v}+\bar{s}_1$$

which is identical with equation [2.6] of the preceding section. In a stationary economy, $s_{2c} = s_{1v} = 0$, and the equation reduces to $c_2 = v_1+s_1$, i.e. to equation [2.2] of the preceding section.

It should also be noticed that of the equations [3.10] or [3.13] (which are equivalent to [3.10], only $n-1$ are independent. From the transaction table [3.8] it is apparent that

$$\sum_i \left(\sum_j x_{ij} + x_i \right) = \sum_i \left(x_{0i} + \sum_j x_{ji} + s_i \right) = \sum_i X_i \quad \ldots \quad [3.16]$$

This implies directly that one of the equations [3.10] can be deduced from the remaining $n-1$. This corresponds to the property of the Marxian two sector model where only one relation like equation [2.6] or [2.2] of the preceding section holds between the two sectors.

Eliminating the double sums on both sides of the identity [3.16], we obtain

$$\sum_i x_i = \sum_i x_{0i} + \sum_i s_i \quad \ldots \quad [3.17]$$

which indicates that the net product of the national economy, or national income is equal to the total value added during the period under consideration.

Input-output analysis, then, is a method of applying Marx's production formulas in concrete terms. Marx put forward the general idea that a balanced exchange of products among the various subdivisions of the national economy was essential if the processes of production and reproduction were to continue smoothly; in input-output analysis this idea is applied to the relationships arising among a large number of sectors of the national economy. As can be seen from equations [*3.10*] and [*3.16*], the concrete expression of the idea consists in presenting the means of production used up in the process of production (represented by Marx as the gross c) as the sum of the means of production produced by individual sectors of the national economy, $\sum_i \sum_j x_{ij}$. The middle term of equation [*3.16*] can just as well be written in Marx's symbols, as $v+c+s$. The general idea behind Marx's theory of reproduction thus finds concrete expression in input-output analysis, which makes it possible to construct more detailed economic 'balances'.

4. Technological Relations and Value Relations

In order to study the effect of the technological conditions of production upon input-output relations we have to distinguish sharply between input-output tables expressed in physical units and transaction tables which are expressed in value units. For this purpose we shall use a separate notation.

The physical output of the ith sector will be denoted by Q_i, the physical net output by q_i and the physical interflow from the ith to the jth sector by q_{ij} $(i, j = 1, \ldots, n)$. The total labour force (measured, for instance, in properly weighted man-hours) will be denoted by Q_0, the physical labour power employed in the ith sector by q_{0i} and the remainder not employed productively by q_0. The physical input-output table can thus be written in the form

$$\begin{array}{c|cccc|c} Q_0 & q_{01} & q_{02} & \cdots & q_{0n} & q_0 \\ Q_1 & q_{11} & q_{12} & \cdots & q_{1n} & q_1 \\ Q_2 & q_{21} & q_{22} & \cdots & q_{2n} & q_2 \\ \cdot\cdot & \cdot & \cdot & \cdots & \cdot & \cdot\cdot \\ Q_n & q_{n1} & q_{n2} & \cdots & q_{nn} & q_n \end{array} \qquad \ldots \quad [4.1]$$

The rows of the table are subject to the allocation balance

$$Q_i = \sum_j q_{ij} + q_i \qquad (i = 0, 1, 2, \ldots, n) \qquad \ldots \quad [4.2]$$

The technological conditions of production can be described by the technical coefficients, called also coefficients of production:

$$a_{ij} = \frac{q_{ij}}{Q_i} \qquad (i = 0, 1, \ldots, n;\ j = 1, \ldots, n) \qquad \ldots \quad [4.3]$$

The coefficient a_{0j} indicates the labour power employed in producing a unit of output of the jth sector, the remaining coefficients a_{ij} indicate the amount of output of the ith sector needed to produce a unit of output of the jth sector.

In the socialist countries the values of these coefficients are generally available in form of the 'technical norms' used in planning and administration of production. These norms indicate the amounts of labour power, raw materials etc., which are allowed to be used per unit of output. In the absence of such 'technical norms' in the industries the technical coefficients can be obtained approximately from statistical input-output tables, according to formula [*4.3*]. This method was employed by Professor Leontief.

Introducing the technical coefficients [4.3], the allocation equations [*4.2*] become

$$Q_i = \sum_j a_{ij} Q_j + q_i \qquad (i = 0, 1, \ldots, n)$$

It is convenient to separate the first equation relating to labour power from the remaining ones. We have then

$$Q_0 = \sum_j a_{0j} Q_j + q_0 \qquad \ldots \quad [4.4]$$

and the remaining equation can be written in the form

$$(1-a_{ii}) Q_i - \sum_{j \neq i} a_{ij} Q_j = q_i \quad (i = 1, \ldots, n) \quad \ldots \quad [4.5]$$

Thus the equations [*4.5*] can be solved separately from equation [*4.1*]. The matrix of the coefficients of these equations

$$\begin{pmatrix} 1-a_{11}, & -a_{12} & \cdots & -a_{1n} \\ \cdots & \cdots & \cdots & \cdots \\ -a_{n1}, & -a_{n2} & \cdots & 1-a_{nn} \end{pmatrix} \qquad \ldots \quad [4.6]$$

is called the 'technical matrix'. It describes the technological conditions of production.[1]

In the system [*4.5*] there are n equations and $2n$ variables, i.e. the gross outputs $Q_1, \ldots, Q_n$ and the net outputs, $q_1, \ldots, q_n$. If the technical matrix is non-singular as we shall assume to be the case, there are thus n degrees of freedom. We can fix in the national economic plan the net outputs $q_1, \ldots, q_n$ and the gross outputs $Q_1, \ldots, Q_n$ are then uniquely determined by the equations [*4.5*]. Or, instead, we can fix in the plan the gross outputs and the net outputs available which will result uniquely from the equations. Or, finally, we can fix in the plan a number of gross outputs and of net outputs, together n in number—and the remaining n gross and net outputs are determined by the equations.

[1] It should be noticed that this technical matrix differs from the matrix used by Professor Leontief in so far that in Professor Leontief's matrix the coefficients a_{ii} in the diagonal are absent; his diagonal consists only of unities. This is due to the fact that he does not take into account the fact that part of the output is retained in the sector as means of production, e.g. part of the output of agriculture is retained as seed and as fodder for breeding of animals, part of the coal is retained in the coal mines as fuel etc. If the number of sectors in the model is small, the sectors being accordingly large, this omission may be serious.

If the technical matrix happens to be singular, the number of degrees of freedom is increased according to the order of nullity of the matrix. Thus if the rank of the matrix is m ($m<n$), the order of nullity is $n-m$ and the number of degrees of freedom is $n+n-m$. Thus we must fix in the plan $2n-m$ variables, the remaining m variables being then obtained from the equations [*4.5*].

Having the gross outputs $Q_1, \ldots, Q_n$ either from the equations [*4.5*] or directly from the plan, we can substitute them into equation [*4.4*]. This gives us the total labour force employed $\sum_{j=1}^{n} a_{0j}Q_j$, and taking the total labour force Q_0 as a datum, we can calculate q_0, i.e. the labour force remaining outside productive employment.

To show the relation between the transaction table and the physical input-output table [*4.1*], we must explicitly take account of prices. Denote by p_0 the remuneration of a unit of labour force, and by $p_1, p_2, \ldots, p_n$ the prices of the products of the various sectors. Further p_0' denotes the earning of the labour force not employed in production. We have then

$$\begin{aligned} X_i &= p_i Q_i, \; x_i = p_i q_i \\ x_0 &= p_0' q_0, \\ x_{ij} &= p_i q_{ij} \end{aligned} \qquad \ldots [4.7]$$

We shall also denote by Π_i the surplus per unit of gross physical output of the sector, i.e.

$$s_i = \Pi_i Q_i \qquad (i = 1, \ldots, n) \qquad \ldots [4.8]$$

Introducing these relations into the transaction table [3.15] of the preceding section we obtain the following form of the transaction table:

$$\begin{array}{r|l|l} p_0 \Sigma q_{0j} + p_0' q_0 & p_0 q_{01}, \; p_0 q_{02} \; \cdots\cdots \; p_0 q_{0n} & p_0' q_0 \\ \hline p_1 Q_1 & p_1 q_{11}, \; p_1 q_{12} \; \cdots\cdots \; p_1 q_{1n} & p_1 q_1 \\ p_2 Q_2 & p_2 q_{21}, \; p_2 q_{22} \; \cdots\cdots \; p_2 q_{2n} & p_2 q_2 \\ \cdot\; \cdot & \cdots\cdots\cdots\cdots & \cdot\; \cdot \\ p_n Q_n & p_n q_{n1}, \; p_n q_{n2} \; \cdots\cdots \; p_n q_{nn} & p_n q_n \\ \hline & \Pi_1 Q_1, \; \Pi_2 Q_2 \; \cdots\cdots \; \Pi_n Q_n & \\ & p_1 Q_1, \; p_2 Q_2 \; \cdots\cdots \; p_n Q_n & \end{array} \qquad \ldots [4.9]$$

Summing the columns we obtain the equations

$$p_0 q_{0i} + \sum_j p_j q_{ji} + \Pi_i Q_i = p_i Q_i$$

which are identical with equations [*3.7*] in the preceding section. Taking account of the technical coefficients (a_{ij}), these equations can be written:

$$a_{0i} p_0 + \sum_j a_{ji} p_j + \Pi_i = p_i$$

or, more conveniently,

$$(1-a_{ii})\,p_i-\sum_{j\neq i}a_{ji}p_i-a_{0i}p_0 = \Pi_i \qquad \ldots \quad [4.10]$$

The matrix of the coefficients is

$$\begin{pmatrix} 1-a_{11}, & -a_{21} & \ldots & -a_{n1}, & -a_{01} \\ \ldots & \ldots & \ldots & \ldots & \ldots \\ -a_{1n}, & -a_{2n} & \ldots & 1-a_{nn}, & -a_{0n} \end{pmatrix} \qquad \ldots \quad [4.11]$$

There are n equations and $2n+1$ variables, i.e. n prices $p_1, \ldots, p_n$ the wage rate p_0 and n per-unit surpluses, $\Pi_1, \ldots, \Pi_n$. If the matrix is of rank n, there are thus $n+1$ degrees of freedom. We can fix, for instance, the wage rate p_0 and the per-unit surpluses $\Pi_1, \ldots, \Pi_n$, the n prices are then uniquely determined. Or, instead, we can fix the n prices mentioned and the wage rate; the per-unit surpluses are then uniquely determined, or any other combination of $n+1$ variables can be fixed, the n remaining ones resulting from the equations.

If the rank of the matrix is less than n, the number of degrees of freedom increases correspondingly. The important point to be noticed is that these relations between prices of products, wage rate and per-unit surpluses are entirely determined by the technological conditions of production as represented by the technical matrix of the coefficients of equations [*4.10*]. The $n\times n$ submatrix containing the first n columns is simply the transpose of the technical matrix [*4.6*].

Now we can show the relation between the physical input-output relations and the input-output relations in value terms as expressed in a transaction table. The rows of the transaction table [*4.9*] are subject to the allocation balance.

$$p_iQ_i = \sum_j p_iq_{ij}+p_iq_i$$

or, introducing the technical coefficients according to [*4.3*]

$$p_iQ_i = \sum_j p_ia_{ij}Q_j+p_iq_i$$

This can also be written in the form

$$p_iQ_i = \sum_j a'_{ij}\,p_jQ_j+p_iq_i \qquad \ldots \quad [4.12]$$

where $$a'_{ij} = (p_i/p_j)\,a_{ij} \qquad (i, j = 1, 2, \ldots, n) \qquad \ldots \quad [4.13]$$

In view of [*4.7*], the equation [*4.12*] can be written in the form

$$X_i = \sum_j a_{ij}X_j+x_i$$

or $$(1-a'_{ii})\,X_i+\sum_{j\neq i}a'_{ij}X_j = x_i \qquad (i = 1, 2, \ldots, n) \qquad \ldots \quad [4.14]$$

These equations establish the relations between the value of the net outputs $x_1, \ldots, x_n$, and the value of the gross outputs of the various sectors.

The matrix of the coefficients of these equations is

$$\begin{pmatrix} 1-a'_{11}, & -a'_{12} & \ldots & -a'_{1n} \\ \ldots & \ldots & \ldots & \ldots \\ -a'_{n1}, & -a'_{n2} & \ldots & 1-a'_{nn} \end{pmatrix} \qquad \ldots [4.15]$$

i.e. analogous to the matrix [*4.6*], only that the coefficients a'_{ij} appear instead of the coefficients a_{ij}.

The coefficients a'_{ij} can be written in the form

$$a_{ij} = \frac{x_{ij}}{X_j} \qquad \ldots [4.16]$$

They indicate the value of the input of the product of the ith sector ($i = 1, \ldots, n$) required to produce a unit of value of output of the jth sector. We shall call these coefficients the 'input coefficients'.

In addition, input coefficients of the type

$$a_{0j} = \frac{x_{0j}}{X_j} \qquad \ldots [4.17]$$

can be introduced which indicate the value of direct labour power needed to produce a unit of value of product of the jth sector. With the aid of these coefficients the value of the total labour force employed in production can be calculated, i.e.

$$X_0 - x_0 = \sum_j a_{0j} X_j \qquad \ldots [4.18]$$

The input coefficients derive their significance from their simple behaviour with regard to aggregation of two or several sectors into one single sector. For instance, let us aggregate the jth sector and the kth sector and denote the new sector thus obtained as the lth sector.

The value of the gross output of the new sector is then

$$X_l = X_j + X_k \qquad \ldots [4.19]$$

and the value of the part of the product of the ith sector allocated as input to the new sector is

$$x_{il} = x_{ij} + x_{ik} \qquad \ldots [4.20]$$

The new input coefficient is, consequently,

$$a'_{il} = \frac{x_{il}}{X_l} = \frac{x_{ij} + x_{ik}}{X_j + X_k}$$

In view of the definition [*4.16*], this is equal to

$$a'_{il} = \frac{a'_{ij}X_j + a'_{ik}X_k}{X_j + X_k} \qquad \ldots \quad [4.21]$$

i.e. the new input coefficient is the weighted mean of the input coefficients before aggregation.

The input coefficients can be given a simple interpretation on the basis of the Marxian theory of value. If the prices of the products express the amount of socially necessary labour required to produce a physical unit of output, the input coefficients indicate the quantity of social labour engaged in one sector necessary to produce in another sector a unit of value (i.e. an amount representing a unit of social labour). This quantity is entirely determined by the technological conditions of production. The transaction table indicates the allocation of the social labour among the various sectors of the national economy and shows the interflow of social labour between the various sectors of the economy. Aggregation of sectors can be performed by mere summation and the input coefficients are transformed under aggregation by simple averaging.

The Marxian theory, however, points out that in a capitalist economy prices do not exactly reflect the amount of social labour necessary to produce a unit of output. Systematic deviations arise between the 'prices of production', i.e. equilibrium prices under competitive capitalism, and the values of products measured in labour. These deviations are the result of the technologically determined differences in ratios of capital goods and direct labour employed on one hand, and the equalisation of the rates of profit by competition on the other hand. Monopoly produces further systematic deviations. Consequently, transaction tables of a capitalist economy give only an approximate picture of allocation of social labour. In a socialist economy transaction tables give a picture of the allocation of social labour to the extent that prices express the amount of social labour required in production. Therefore, in a socialist economy, a proper system of prices reflecting the amounts of social labour required in production is a necessary instrument of effective accounting of the allocation of society's labour force among the various branches of national economy.

5. Consumption and Investment

The net output of any sector of the national economy may be consumed, exported or accumulated for future use. Accumulated output may be designed for future consumption or allocated to increase the quantity of means of production, i.e. invested in the process of production. In the first case we shall consider it as another form of consumption; the last mentioned use will be called productive investment. The part of the net output exported can be considered as destined for consumption or productive investment in proportion as the goods imported in return consist of consumers' goods or means of production. Thus the total net output of a sector may be divided up into a part consumed and a part utilised for productive investment.

Consider the net physical output q_i of the ith sector and denote the part consumed by $q_i^{(1)}$ and the part invested productively by $q_i^{(2)}$. Then

$$q_i = q_i^{(1)} + q_i^{(2)} \qquad \ldots [5.1]$$

Further

$$k_i = \frac{q_i^{(1)}}{Q_i}; \quad \alpha_i = \frac{q_i^{(2)}}{Q_i} \qquad \ldots [5.2]$$

Thus k_i is the proportion of the gross output Q_i of the sector i consumed, and α_i is the proportion of the gross output Q_i used for productive investment. We shall call them the 'rate of consumption' and 'rate of investment', respectively.

Obviously,

$$q_i = (k_i + \alpha_i)\, Q_i \qquad \ldots [5.3]$$

The allocation equations [4.5] of the preceding section can then be written as homogeneous equations of the form

$$(1 - a_{ii} - k_i - \alpha_i)\, Q_i - \sum_{j \neq i} a_{ij}\, Q_j = 0 \quad (i = 1, \ldots, n) \qquad \ldots [5.4]$$

In order that these have a non-trivial solution it is necessary that

$$\begin{vmatrix} 1 - a_{11} - k_1 - \alpha_1, & -a_{12} & \cdots & a_{1n} \\ \cdots & \cdots & \cdots & \cdots \\ -a_{n1}, & -a_{n2} & \cdots & 1 - a_{nn} - k_n - \alpha_n \end{vmatrix} = 0 \qquad \ldots [5.5]$$

i.e. the rates of consumption and rates of investment of the various sectors cannot be fixed independently of each other. Their mutual relations depend on the rank of the matrix of [5.5].

This may be conveniently illustrated by the example of a two sector model. Taking the sectors 1 and 2, the determinantal equation [5.4] becomes

$$(1 - a_{11} - k_1 - \alpha_1)(1 - a_{22} - k_2 - \alpha_2) = a_{12} a_{21} \qquad \ldots [5.6]$$

or,

$$\frac{1 - a_{11} - k_1 - \alpha_1}{a_{12}} = \frac{a_{21}}{1 - a_{22} - k_2 - \alpha_2} \qquad \ldots [5.7]$$

This means that the fractions of the gross output of each sector going to the other sector for current use in production, i.e. $1 - a_{ii} - k_i - \alpha_i$ is proportional to the technical coefficients relating the two sectors to each other. It is seen from [5.6] that if the rates of consumption are kept constant, the rate of investment of one sector can be increased only at the expense of reducing the rate of investment of the other sector. A similar relation holds for the rates of consumption of the two sectors, if the rates of investment are kept constant.

Now suppose that sector 1 produces means of production and sector 2 produces consumers' goods. Means of production are needed to produce consumers' goods but themselves are not consumed; consequently, $a_{12}>0$ and $k_1=0$. Consumers' goods are only usable for consumption; they are neither needed currently to produce means of production nor are they investable in production. Consequently, $a_{21}=0$ and $\alpha_2=0$. Thus the equation [5.6] turns into

$$(1-a_{11}-\alpha_1)(1-a_{22}-k_2) = 0$$

As consumers' goods are not invested, their total net output is consumed, i.e. $1-a_{22}-k_2 = 0$. Consequently, $1-a_{11}-\alpha_1$ is arbitrary and the rate of investment α_1, can be arbitrarily fixed.

In a communist economy distribution of the national product is divorced from the input of labour and follows the principle, 'to each according to his need'. Under such circumstances, the rates of consumption can be set by policy provided their mutual relations resulting from [5.5] are observed. These relations are entirely expressed in physical terms and no value relations are involved; they depend entirely on the technical coefficients.

In a socialist economy distribution of the national product is based on the remuneration for labour performed. Under capitalism it depends also on property in means of production which permits certain classes to appropriate the surplus generated in production. Therefore, in a socialist economy the rates of consumption are related to the remuneration of the labour force both in productive and non-productive employment. In a capitalist economy they depend also on the use property owners make of the surplus they appropriate.

In order to determine the rates of consumption, it is best to start from a transaction table. We have seen in section 3, equation [3.17], that the net product of the national economy is equal to the total value added in production, i.e.

$$\sum_i x_i = \sum_i x_{0i}+\sum_i s_i$$

Introducing the rates of consumption and of investment, we can write this in the form

$$\sum_i k_i X_i = \sum_i x_{0i}+\sum_i s_i-\sum_i \alpha_i X_i \qquad \ldots \quad [5.8]$$

The left-hand side of this equation represents the part of the total value of the net product of the economy (national income) devoted to consumption.

Let W_i be the fraction of the part of the national income devoted to consumption spent for the product of the ith sector ($i = 1, \ldots, n$). We consider these fractions to be 'behavioural data' and shall call them 'consumption parameters'. Then

$$k_i X_i = W_i \Big(\sum_j x_{0j}+\sum_j s_j-\sum_j \alpha_j X_j\Big), \quad (i=1, \ldots, n; \Sigma W_i=1) \qquad \ldots \quad [5.9]$$

(The subscripts in the summation signs on the right-hand side are denoted by j in order to avoid confusion with the subscript i on the left-hand side.)

Introducing input coefficients and writing

$$s_j = \Pi'_j X_j \qquad (j = 1, \ldots, n) \qquad \ldots [5.10]$$

we can write

$$k_i X_i = W_i \Big(\sum_j a'_{0j} X_j + \sum_j \Pi'_j X_j - \sum_j \alpha_j X_j \Big) \quad (i=1, \ldots, n) \ldots [5.11]$$

Substituting this in the allocation equations [4.14] of the preceding section which indicate the allocation balances in the rows of the transaction table, we obtain

$$[1 - a'_{ii} - \alpha_i - W_i(a'_{0i} + \Pi'_i - \alpha_i)] X_i - \sum_{j \neq i} [a'_{ij} + W_i(a'_{ij} + \Pi'_j - \alpha_j)] X_j = 0$$

$$(i = 1, \ldots, n) \qquad \ldots [5.12]$$

In order that these equations have a non-trivial solution we must have the determinant

$$\begin{vmatrix} 1 - a'_{11} - \alpha_1 - W_1 (a'_{01} + \Pi'_1 - \alpha_1), \ldots, \\ -a'_{1n} - W_1 (a'_{0n} + \Pi'_n - \alpha_n) \\ \cdots\cdots\cdots\cdots \\ -a'_{n1} - W_n (a'_{01} + \Pi'_1 - \alpha_1), \ldots, \\ 1 - a'_{nn} - \alpha_n - W_n (a'_{0n} + \Pi'_n - \alpha_n) \end{vmatrix} = 0 \qquad \ldots [5.13]$$

This condition establishes the relations which must be maintained between the rates of investment $\alpha_1, \ldots, \alpha_n$ when the rates of consumption are determined by the 'demand equations' [5.11].

The expressions

$$a'_{0j} + \Pi'_j - \alpha_j \qquad (j = 1, \ldots, n) \qquad \ldots [5.14]$$

which occur in the determinant [5.5] indicate the part of the value added per unit of output value of the sector which is devoted to consumption. By multiplying these expressions by W_i we get the fraction of it which goes into consumption of the product of the ith sector.

For illustration let us consider a two sector model. The determinantal equation can then be written in the form

$$\frac{1 - a'_{11} - \alpha_1 - W_1(a'_{01} + \Pi'_1 - \alpha_1)}{a'_{12} + W_1(a'_{02} + \Pi'_2 - \alpha_2)} = \frac{a'_{21} + W_2(a'_{01} + \Pi'_1 - \alpha_1)}{1 - a'_{22} - \alpha_{22} - W_2(a'_{02} + \Pi'_2 - \alpha_2)} \ldots [5.15]$$

This equation indicates that the fraction of the value of gross output of each sector remaining after deduction of the part retained in the sector for replacement (a'_{ii}), and for consumption $W_i (a'_{0i} + \Pi'_i - \alpha_i)$ and of the part devoted to investment (α_i) is proportional to the total demand (per unit of value of its output) of the other sector for the product of the first. The latter is equal to the sum of the input coefficient—a'_{ij} and the output of the other sector required for consumption, i.e. $W_i\,(a'_0+\Pi'_i-\alpha_j)$.

Transforming the input coefficients into technical coefficients according to formula [*4.13*] of the preceding section and observing that

$$\Pi'_j = \frac{\Pi_j}{p_j} \qquad (j = 1, \ldots, n) \qquad \ldots \quad [5.16]$$

we can write the determinantal equation [*5.13*] in the abbreviated form

$$\left| \delta_{ij}\,(1-\alpha_1) - \frac{p_i}{p_j}a_{ij} - W_i\left(\frac{p_0}{p_j}a_{0j} + \frac{\Pi_j}{p_j} - \alpha_j\right)\right| = 0 \quad \ldots \quad [5.17]$$

where $\delta_{ij}=1$ for $i=j$ and $\delta_{ij}=0$ for $i\neq j$. This equation contains the wage rate p_0, the product prices $p_1, \ldots, p_n$ and the per-unit surpluses $\Pi_1, \ldots \Pi_n$. These quantities cannot be eliminated from the equation.

Thus when the rates of consumption are determined by 'demand equations' like [*5.11*] linking them to the national income, the relation between the rates of investment in the various sectors of the national economy cannot be expressed in purely physical and technological terms. They have to be expressed in value terms and are found according to [*5.13*] to depend on the input coefficients, the rates of surplus $\Pi'_1 \ldots, \Pi'_n$ and the consumption parameters $W_1 \ldots, W_n$ of the various sectors.

As in the light of the Marxian theory of value the input coefficients can be interpreted as indicating technological conditions of production, the relations between the rates of investment are found to depend, in addition to the technological conditions of production, on behavioural parameters relating consumption of the various products to national income and on the per-unit surpluses in the various sectors. The latter can be considered as 'sociological parameters'. In a capitalist economy they are equal to the proportion of the value of each sector's output appropriated by the owners of means of production. In a socialist economy the surpluses are set by considerations of social policy, providing the resources for productive investment and for society's collective consumption. It would therefore be better to call this surplus the value 'of the product-for-society'.

6. Investment and Economic Growth

The part of the net outputs of the various sectors invested in production is added to the means of production available in the next period. This makes possible in the next period an increase in the output of the various sectors of the national economy. The investment done in one period adds to the amount of means of production in operation in the next period. In consequence, a larger output is obtained in the next period. The outputs of successive periods (years, for instance) are linked up in a chain through the investments undertaken in each period. Thus, productive investment generates a process of growth of output.

Let $Q_i(t)$ be the gross physical output of the ith sector of the economy during the time period indicated by t, e.g. the year 1955, and let α_i be the rate of investment of the ith sector as defined by [*5.2*] in the preceding section. The quantity of the output of the sector invested is thus $\alpha_i Q_i(t)$. By this amount increases the stock of product of the ith sector available in the economy as means of production.

This increment is partly retained in the sector and partly allocated to other sectors. Denote the increment allocated to the jth sector by $\Delta q_{ij}(t)$, $(i, j = 1, \ldots, n)$. The index t indicates the period during which the allocation takes place.

We have

$$\alpha_i Q_i(t) = \sum_j \Delta q_{ij}(t) \qquad \ldots [6.1]$$

However, not all the increment allocated is used up by the various sectors during a single unit period of time. For instance, if it consists of machines or other durable equipment it will last for several units of time (years) and only a fraction of it is used up during a unit period of time. Let the durability of the part of the output of the ith sector allocated to the jth sector as additional means of production be T_{ij} units of time. T_{ij} is taken as a parameter given by the technological conditions of production and may be called the 'turnover period' of the particular type of productive equipment. The reciprocal of the turnover period, i.e. $1/T_{ij}$ is the rate of used up per unit of time; it is also called 'rate of replacement' or 'rate of amortisation'.

In order to produce a unit of physical output of the product of the jth sector during a unit period of time the quantity a_{ij} of the product of the ith sector must be used up during that period of time; a_{ij} is the technical coefficient. Thus to increase in the next period the output of the jth sector by an additional unit, the quantity of output of the ith sector $a_{ij}T_{ij}$ must be allocated to the jth sector. Then exactly a_{ij} of output of the ith sector will be used up in the next unit period in the sector and this will produce one unit of output.

The quantities

$$b_{ij} = a_{ij}T_{ij} \qquad (i, j = 1, \ldots, n) \qquad \ldots [6.2]$$

may be called the 'investment coefficients'. The investment coefficients indicate the quantity of output of one sector which must be invested in the other sector in order to increase by one unit the other sector's output in the next unit period.

The investment coefficients as well as their reciprocals reflect technological conditions of production; given the technical coefficients, the investment coefficients are proportional to the turnover periods of the various types of means of production.

Write $Q_j(t)$ for the physical gross output of the jth sector in the unit period under consideration and $Q_j(t+1)$ for the physical gross output of this sector in the next unit period. An increment of output of the jth sector equal to $Q_j(t+1)-Q_j(t)$ requires the investment in the sector of the following quantity of the output of ith sector:

$$\Delta q_{ij} = b_{ij}[Q_j(t+1)-Q_j(t)] \quad (i, j = 1, \ldots, n) \qquad \ldots [6.3]$$

In view of [*6.1*], we have

$$\alpha_i Q_i(t) = \sum b_{ij}[Q_j(t+1)-Q_j(t)] \quad (i = 1, \ldots, n) \qquad \ldots [6.4]$$

These equations express the relations between the allocation of the part of the net product of each sector devoted to investment in the various sectors of the economy and the increments of output obtained in the various sectors in the next unit period.

If the amounts of product of the various sectors invested during the unit period t, i.e. $\alpha_i Q_i(t)$ are given ($i = 1, \ldots, n$), the increments of output in the next unit period can be calculated from the equations [*6.4*]

$$B \equiv \begin{pmatrix} b_{11}, b_{12} \ldots\ldots b_{1n} \\ b_{21}, b_{22} \ldots\ldots b_{2n} \\ \ldots\ldots\ldots\ldots \\ b_{n1}, b_{n2} \ldots\ldots b_{nn} \end{pmatrix} \qquad \ldots [6.5]$$

the matrix of the investment coefficients. The increments of output in the various sectors are then

$$Q_j(t+1)-Q_j(t) = \frac{1}{|B|}\sum_i |B_{ij}|\, \alpha_i Q_i(t) \qquad \ldots [6.6]$$

where $|B|$ is the determinant of the matrix B and $|B_{ij}|$ is the co-factor of the element b_{ij}.

It is convenient to write

$$B_{ji} = \frac{B_{ij}}{|B|} \qquad \ldots [6.7]$$

and express [*6.6*] in the form

$$Q_j(t+1)-Q_j(t) = \sum_i B_{ji}\alpha_i Q_i(t) \quad (j = 1, \ldots, n) \qquad \ldots [6.8]$$

The coefficients B_{ij} indicate the increment of output obtained in the jth sector from an additional unit of the ith sector's product invested in the jth sector. They may be called 'intersector output-investment ratios'. The matrix of the coefficients B_{ij}, is the inverse of the matrix B.

The increments of output in the various sectors depend on the investment coefficients and on the amounts of product of the various sectors invested. The investment coefficients, in turn, depend on the technical coefficients and turnover periods. By virtue of [*6.2*] the matrix of investment coefficients can be presented as follows:

$$B = \begin{pmatrix} a_{11}T_{11}, & a_{12}T_{12} & \dots\dots & a_{1n}T_{1n} \\ \dots & \dots & \dots & \dots \\ a_{n1}T_{n1}, & a_{n2}T_{n2} & \dots\dots & a_{nn}T_{nn} \end{pmatrix} \quad \dots [6.9]$$

In this way the investments made in one unit period lead to an increase of output in the next period. If the rates of investment remain constant, the investments in the successive unit periods are

$$\alpha_i Q_i\,(t+1),\ \alpha_i Q_i\,(t+2), \dots, \quad (i = 1, \dots, n)$$

The investments of the first unit period t are the initial 'shock' which sets in motion the process of economic growth. The investments in the successive unit periods carry the process forward from one stage to another.

The course of the process of economic growth can be deduced from the equation [*6.4*] or, for that matter, also from the equivalent equation [*6.8*]. These are linear difference equations with constant coefficients. The characteristic equation of the system [*6.4*] is

$$0 = \begin{vmatrix} \alpha_1 + b_{11}\,(1-\lambda), & b_{12}\,(1-\lambda) & \dots\dots & b_{1n}\,(1-\lambda) \\ \dots & \dots & \dots & \dots \\ b_{n1}\,(1-\lambda), & b_{n2}\,(1-\lambda) & \dots & \alpha_{nn} + b_{nn}\,(1-\lambda) \end{vmatrix} \quad \dots [6.10]$$

The solution of the difference equations indicating the gross output in the unit period t_s can be written in the form

$$Q_j(t_s) = \sum C_k h_{jk}\,\lambda_k^{ts} \qquad (j = 1, \dots, n) \qquad \dots [6.11]$$

where the λ_k are the roots of the characteristic equation, the C_k are constants determined by the outputs $Q_j(t_s)$ in the initial unit period t_s and the h_{jk} are constants determined by the matrix of the coefficients of equation [*6.4*], i.e. by the matrix

$$\begin{pmatrix} \alpha_1 + b_{11}, & b_{12} & \dots\dots & b_{1n} \\ \dots & \dots & \dots & \dots \\ b_{n1}, & b_{n2} & \dots\dots & \alpha_n + b_{nn} \end{pmatrix} \quad \dots [6.12]$$

Thus the constants C_k reflect the initial situation of the national economy while the constants h_{jk} depend on the technological structure of the economy as expressed by the technical coefficients and the turnover periods as well as on the rates of investment.[1]

This analysis can be generalised by considering the rates of investment as variable in time, i.e. considering functions $\alpha(t)$ instead of constants

[1] In the above, the roots λ_k are assumed to be all distinct. In case of a multiple root the corresponding h_{jk} on the right hand side of [*6.11*] is not a constant but a polynomial of degree one less than the multiplicity of the root. The coefficients of this polynomial are determined by the technological structure of the economy expressed by the matrix and the rates of investment. The coefficients C_k remain determined by the initial situation.

α_i $(i = 1, \ldots, n)$. In a similar way, changes in technical coefficients and turnover periods can be investigated. Instead of the constant investment coefficients, we should have to consider functions of time $b_{ij}(t)$, where $i, j = 1, \ldots, n$. The difference equations [*6.5*] become then,

$$\alpha_i(t)\, Q_i(t) = \sum_j b_{ij}(t)\, [Q_j(t+1) - Q_j(t)] \qquad \ldots \; [6.13]$$

Since the coefficients in these equations are not constant, the equations require more complicated methods of treatment.

The increments in output from one unit period to the next one can, however, be easily computed. They are, in analogy with [*6.8*],

$$Q_j(t+1) - Q_j(t) = \sum_i B_{ij}\alpha_i(t)\, Q_i(t), \qquad \ldots \; [6.14]$$

the matrix of the coefficients B_{ij} being now the inverse of the matrix

$$B(t) = \begin{pmatrix} b_{11}(t),\ b_{12}(t) & \ldots & b_{1n}(t) \\ \ldots & \ldots & \ldots \\ b_{n1}(t),\ b_{n2}(t) & \ldots & b_{nn}(t) \end{pmatrix} \qquad \ldots \; [6.15]$$

The relations between investment and the process of growth of output are here presented entirely in physical terms. They are found to depend solely on the technological structure of the economy and on the rates of investment chosen. The process of economic growth, however, can also be presented in value terms.

In such a case, the technological investment coefficients b_{ij} are replaced by a set of coefficients,

$$b'_{ij} = \frac{\Delta X_{ij}}{X_j(t+1) - X_j(t)} \qquad (i, j = 1, \ldots, n) \qquad \ldots \; [6.16]$$

indicating the value of the output of the *i*th sector which must be invested in the *j*th sector in order to obtain in the latter a unit increment of output value. These coefficients may be called 'investment-outlay coefficients' or simply, 'outlay coefficients'.[1]

In view of the relations [*4.7*] in section 4, the outlay coefficients are related to the investment coefficients as follows:

$$b'_{ij} = \frac{p_i}{p_j} b_{ij} \qquad \ldots \; [6.17]$$

[1] Usually the term 'capital-coefficients' is used to denote the outlay coefficients. However, the term 'capital' is not appropriate in a socialist economy because it covers up the fundamental difference between capital as value of means of production used by their owners to appropriate the surplus produced in the national economy and means of production as an instrument in the physical process of production. We, therefore, prefer to use the term 'outlay coefficients', meaning by 'outlay' the money value of the physical investments.

Taking into account [6.2], they can also be written in the form:

$$b'_i = a'_{ij}\, T_{ij} = \frac{p_i}{p_j} a_{ij}\, T_{ij} \qquad \ldots \quad [6.18]$$

Using the relations [4.7] of section 4 the difference equations [6.4] expressing the relations between investments in the various sectors of the economy and the increments of output obtained can be written in the value form:

$$\alpha_i X_i(t) = \sum_j b'_{ij} \left[X_j(t+1) - X_j(t)\right] \qquad \ldots \quad [6.19]$$

and the solutions of these equations are obtained by means of their characteristic equation which is

$$0 = \begin{vmatrix} \alpha_1 + b'_{11}(1-\lambda), & \ldots & b'_{1n}(1-\lambda) \\ \ldots & \ldots & \ldots \\ b_{n1}(1-\lambda), & \ldots & \alpha_n + b'_{nn}(1-\lambda) \end{vmatrix} \qquad \ldots \quad [6.20]$$

The process of growth of the value of the output of the various sectors of the economy is thus determined—given the values of the initial outputs $X_1(t_0), \ldots, X_n(t_0)$ by the outlay coefficients b_{ij} and the rates of investment α_{ij}.

The outlay coefficients behave under aggregation of two or several sectors into one sector in a similar way like the input coefficients. The outlay coefficients of the new sector resulting from aggregation are the weighted means of the outlay coefficients of the sectors aggregated.

Indeed, denote by the subscript l the sector resulting from aggregation of the jth sector and the kth sector. The outlay coefficients of the new sector are then

$$b_{il} = \frac{\Delta x_{il}}{X_l(t+1) - X_l(t)}$$

Since

$$\begin{cases} \Delta x_{il} = \Delta x_{ij} + \Delta x_{ik} \\ X_l(t) = X_j(t) + X_k(t) \\ X_l(t+1) = X_j(t+1) + X_k(t+1) \end{cases} \qquad \ldots \quad [6.21]$$

we obtain, taking into account the definition [6.16],

$$b'_{il} = \frac{b'_{ij}\left[X_j(t+1) - X_j(t)\right] + b'_{ik}\left[X_k(t+1) - X_k(t)\right]}{\left[X_j(t+1) - X_j(t)\right] + \left[X_k(t+1) - X_k(t)\right]} \qquad \ldots \quad [6.22]$$

The merit of presentation of the process of growth of output resulting from investment in value terms consists in the possibility it gives to aggregate sectors. But it must be pointed out that the outlay coefficients do not reflect only the technological structure of the economy. As seen from [6.17], they depend also on the relative prices of the products. The result of their averaging under aggregation also depends on the relative prices of the products of the sectors aggregated.

However, on the basis of the Marxian theory of value, the outlay coefficients may, under appropriate circumstances, be interpreted as indicating the quantity of social labour employed in the sector of the economy which must be 'stored up' in order to increase the output of another by an amount representing one unit of social labour. Under such interpretation, which requires that prices reflect the amounts of social labour necessary to produce a physical unit of product, the outlay coefficients too represent the technological structure of the economy.

The way in which the growth of output set in motion by investment depends entirely on the technological structure of the economy is further elucidated by the fact that the investment coefficients are, according to [*6.2*], products of the technical coefficients and the turnover periods, or that the outlay coefficients, according to [*6.8*] are the products of the input coefficients and the turnover periods.[1] Thus the technological conditions determining the growth of output resulting from investment consist entirely of two factors, one the technical coefficients indicating current input-output relations during a unit period, the other the turnover periods which simply indicate the durability of the various means of production and, consequently, the rate of use-up of the means of production in a single unit period of time.

This disposes definitely of any mystical notions about the 'productivity' of a mythical entity 'capital' conceived as a separate factor of production distinguished from the physical means of production. Such metaphysical entity is proved to be non-existent.

In a capitalist economy 'capital' consists of private property rights to means of production which permit the owners of the means of production to appropriate the surplus produced in the national economy. 'Capital' is the power to appropriate surplus. This power, under capitalism, is measured by the money value of the means of production and hired labour-power a person (or corporation) can command. In a socialist economy such property rights are absent. There exist simply physical means of production and certain technological conditions expressed by the technical coefficients and turnover periods. From these technological conditions there result certain consequences concerning the quantity of social labour which must be 'stored up' in order to achieve a planned increase in output. Thus there is no need in a socialist economy for any concept of 'capital'. Such concept would only obscure the technological character of the conditions of the process of economic growth.

[1] The fact that the investment coefficients are not independent of the technical coefficients but are derived from them by multiplication by the turnover periods seems to have been pointed out first by DAVID HAWKINS, 'Some conditions of macroeconomic stability', *Econometrica*, 1948, p. 313. Usually they are wrongly taken as independent data, as for instance by Professor LEONTIEF in *Studies in the Structure of the American Economy*, p. 56, Oxford University Press, New York, 1953.

7. Effects of Investment on National Income and Employment

The equations [*6.19*] of the preceding section can be transformed in a shape analogous to equation [*6.8*], i.e. in a shape which presents the increment of the value of output of a sector of the national economy as a linear combination of the investments undertaken in the various sectors. For greater generality it is convenient to consider the rates of investment, α_i, as variable in time, i.e. $\alpha_i(t)$. We obtain then,

$$X_j(t+1) - X_j(t) = \sum_i B'_{ij}\, \alpha_i(t)\, X_i(t) \quad (j = 1, \ldots, n) \qquad \ldots [7.1]$$

The coefficients B'_{ij} are the elements of a matrix $(B_{ij})^{-1}$ which is the inverse of the matrix of the outlay coefficients

$$B' = \begin{pmatrix} b'_{11}, b'_{12} \ldots\ldots\ldots b'_{1n} \\ \ldots\ldots\ldots\ldots\ldots \\ b'_{n1}, b'_{n2} \ldots\ldots\ldots b'_{nn} \end{pmatrix} \qquad \ldots [7.2]$$

This means that,

$$B'_{ij} = \frac{B'_{ij}}{|B'|} \qquad (i, j = 1, \ldots, n) \qquad \ldots [7.3]$$

where $|B'|$ is the determinant of B' and B'_{ij} is the co-factor of the element b'_{ij}.

The coefficients B'_{ij} may be called 'intersector output-outlay ratios'. They indicate the increment of the output (measured in value) of the jth sector resulting from a unit increase of investment outlay in the ith sector.

Summing the equation [*7.1*] over all sectors of the national economy, we obtain

$$\sum_j [X_j(t+1) - X_j(t)] = \sum_j \sum_i B'_{ij}\, \alpha_i(t)\, X_i(t)$$

or, writing

$$\beta_i = \sum_j B'_{ij} \qquad (i = 1, \ldots, n) \qquad \ldots [7.4]$$

$$\sum_j (X_j(t+1) - X_j(t)) = \sum_i \beta_i\, \alpha_i(t)\, X_i(t) \qquad \ldots [7.5]$$

The left-hand side of equation [*7.5*] is the increment, from one unit period to the next, of gross national product. The coefficient β_i on the right-hand side indicates the effect of a unit increase in investment outlay in the various sectors of the economy on national gross product. They can be called simply 'output-outlay ratios' of the various centres.

A further simplification of equation [*7.5*] can be achieved by expressing the investment outlays in the various sectors as a fraction of the total investment outlay in the national economy. Denote by $\alpha(t)$ the overall rate of investment in the national economy during the unit period t. The total investment outlay during the unit period is

$$\alpha(t) \sum_i X_i(t)$$

Denoting further by $\mu_i(t)$ the proportion of the total investment outlay which is undertaken in the ith sector of the economy, we have

$$\alpha_i(t)\, X_i(t) = \mu_i(t)\, \alpha(t) \sum_i X_i(t);$$
$$\Big(\sum_i \mu_i(t) = 1\Big) \qquad \ldots \quad [7.6]$$

Substituting the relation [7.6] into equation [7.5] and observing that

$$\sum_i X_i(t) = \sum_j X_j(t),$$

we arrive at

$$\sum_j (X_j(t+1) - X_j(t)) = \alpha(t) \sum_j X_j(t) \sum_j \beta_i\, \mu_i(t),$$

which also can be written as

$$\frac{\sum_j (X_j(t+1) - X_j(t))}{\sum_j X_j(t)} = \alpha(t) \sum_j \beta_i \mu_i(t) \qquad \ldots \quad [7.7]$$

The left-hand side of [7.7] is the rate of increase of gross national product and will be denoted by $r(t)$. In order to simplify the right-hand side we shall put

$$\beta(t) = \sum_i \beta_i\, \mu_i(t) \qquad \ldots \quad [7.8]$$

Since $\sum_i \mu_i(t) = 1$, β can be interpreted as the average output-outlay ratio of the national economy. Equation [7.7] can thus be expressed in the simple form

$$r(t) = \alpha(t)\, \beta(t) \qquad \ldots \quad [7.9]$$

Thus the rate of increase of gross national product is the product of the overall rate of investment and of the average output-outlay ratio.

Now we can calculate the effect of a given investment programme upon gross national income after a number of unit periods of time. Let $\sum_j x_j(t_0)$ be the gross national product in the initial unit period t_0, and let the investment programme be given by the overall rates of investment $\alpha(t_0), \ldots, \alpha(t_n)$ and the fractions $\mu_i(t_0), \ldots, \mu_i(t_n)$ of the total investment outlay allocated to the various sectors of the economy, $(i = 1, \ldots, n)$. We obtain, then, the average output-outlay ratios, $\beta(t_0), \ldots, \beta(t_n)$. The gross national product in unit period $t_s (t_s > t_0)$ is,

$$\sum_j X_j(t_s) = \prod_{t=t_0}^{t_s} [1 + \alpha(t)\, \beta(t)] \sum_j X_j(t_0) \qquad \ldots \quad [7.10]$$

If the overall rate of investment $\alpha(t)$ and the allocation fractions $\mu_i(t)$ are the same during each unit period, say α and μ_i, this reduces to

$$\sum_j X_j(t_s) = (1+\alpha\beta)^{t_s-t_0} \sum_j X_j(t_0) \qquad \ldots \quad [7.11]$$

National income is the value of the total net output of the national economy. The value of the net output of the ith sector in unit period, t is according to the allocation equation [*4.12*] or [*4.14*]

$$x_i(t) = X_i(t) - \sum_j a'_{ij} X_j(t), \qquad \ldots \quad [7.12]$$

where the a'_{ij} are input coefficients.

National income in period t is

$$\sum_i x_i(t) = \sum_i X_i(t) - \sum_i \sum_j a'_{ij} X_j(t)$$

The double sum on the right-hand side is that part of the total social product used in the period of time taken as unity to replace the means of production used up (amortisation). Let us denote the replacement (amortisation) rate in the period t by

$$\sigma(t) = \frac{\sum_i \sum_j a'_{ij} X_j(t)}{\sum_i X_i(t)}$$

We can then write

$$\sum_i x_i(t) = \sum_i X_i(t)\,[1-\sigma(t)]$$

Let $r(t)$ denote the rate of growth of the national income. We then have

$$1+r(t) = \frac{\sum_i x_i(t+1)}{\sum_i x_i(t)} = \frac{\sum_i X_i(t+1)\,[1-\sigma(t+1)]}{\sum_i X_i(t)\,[1-\sigma(t)]}$$

where

$$1+r(t) = [1+R(t)]\,\frac{1-\sigma(t+1)}{1-\sigma(t)} \qquad \ldots \quad [7.13]$$

expresses the ratio between the rate in increase of the national income $\frac{r(t)}{R(t)}$ and the rate of growth of the total social product.

In this ratio $1+r(t)$ is the growth factor of the national income, $1+R(t)$ is the growth factor of the total social product, $1+\sigma(t)$ and $1+\sigma(t+1)$ are the fractions of the gross national product, during periods t and $(t+1)$ respectively, which are not used for replacement; they can be called the net production ratios. Equation [*7.13*] thus establishes that the growth factor of the national income is equal to that of the total social product multiplied by an expression showing the variation in the net production ratios.

The ratio of national income during a period t_s to national income during an initial period $t_0 (t_s > t_0)$ is expressed by a formula similar to [*7.10*] and [*7.12*]:

$$\sum_i x_i(t_s) = \prod_{t=to}^{t_s} [1 + r(t)] \sum_i x_i(t) \qquad \ldots \quad [7.14]$$

In cases where r = const.,

$$\sum_i x_i(t_s) = (1+r)^{t_s - to} \sum_i x_i(t_0)$$

In view of [*7.9*] and [*7.13*] we can write [*7.14*] in the more accurate form

$$\sum_i x_i(t_s) = \prod_{t=to}^{t_s} \left\{ [1 + \alpha(t)\, \beta(t)] \frac{1 - \sigma(t+1)}{1 - \sigma(t)} \right\} \sum_i x_i(t) \quad \ldots \quad [7.15]$$

The total employment generated by the gross national product is calculated as follows. Denote, as in section 4, by a'_{0j} the input coefficient indicating the value of direct labour force needed to produce a unit of value of product in the jth sector. We shall call them for convenience 'employment coefficients'. The total employment (in value units) corresponding to gross national product in unit period t is, according to the balance equation [*4.1*]

$$\sum_j a'_{0j}\, X_j(t)$$

Consequently, the increment of total employment from one unit period to the next is $\sum_j a'_{ij} [X_j(t+1) - X_j(t)]$.

Taking into account equation [*7.1*], we find

$$\sum_j a'_{0j} [X_j(t+1) - X_j(t)] = \sum_j a'_{0j} \sum_i B'_{ij}\, \alpha_i(t)\, X_i(t),$$

or, in view of [*7.6*],

$$\sum_j a'_{0j} [X_j(t+1) - X_j(t)] = \sum_j a'_{0j} \sum_i B'_{ij}\, \mu_i(t)\, \alpha(t) \sum_i X_i(t) \quad \ldots \quad [7.16]$$

This expression can be simplified as follows. Write

$$\gamma_i = \sum_j a'_{0j}\, B'_{ji} \qquad (i = 1, \ldots, n), \qquad \ldots \quad [7.17]$$

γ_i is the additional amount of employment (in value units) created in the national economy by a unit increase in investment outlay in the ith sector of the economy. We may call it the 'employment outlay ratio' of the ith sector. Then we obtain

$$\frac{\sum_j a'_{0j} [X_j(t+1) - X_j(t)]}{\sum_j X_j(t)} = \alpha(t) \sum_i \gamma_i\, \mu_i(t)$$

or, by introducing the average employment-outlay ratio of the national economy

$$\gamma(t) = \sum_i \gamma_i \, \mu_i(t), \qquad \ldots [7.18]$$

$$\frac{\sum_j a'_{0j} \, [X_j(t+1) - X_j(t)]}{\sum_j X_j(t)} = \alpha(t) \, \gamma(t) \qquad \ldots [7.19]$$

The left-hand side of [*7.19*] indicates the increment of total employment from one unit period to the next in relation to the value of the gross national product in the initial unit period. Let us write

$$a'_0(t) = \frac{\sum_j a'_{0j} \, X_j(t)}{\sum_j X_j(t)}, \qquad \ldots [7.20]$$

i.e. the average employment coefficient of the national economy. Substituting this into [*7.19*] we obtain the rate of increase of total employment from one unit period to the next;

$$\frac{\sum_j a'_{0j} \, X_j(t+1) - X_j(t)}{\sum_j a'_{0j} \, X_j(t)} = \frac{\alpha(t) \, \gamma(t)}{a'_0(t)}$$

or, denoting the left-hand side by $\rho(t)$,

$$\rho(t) = \frac{\alpha(t) \, \gamma(t)}{a'_0(t)} \qquad \ldots [7.21]$$

Thus we find that the rate of increase of total employment is the product of the rate of investment and the average employment-outlay ratio divided by the average employment coefficient of the national economy.

The total employment in unit period t is related to the total employment in the initial unit period $t_0 (t_s > t_0)$ by the formula

$$\sum_j a'_{0j} \, X_j(t_s) = \prod_{t=t_0}^{t_s} \left[1 + \frac{\alpha(t) \, \gamma(t)}{a'_0(t)} \right] \sum_j a'_{0j} \, X_j(t_0) \qquad \ldots [7.22]$$

Comparing [*7.21*] with [*7.9*], we can establish a relation between the rate of increase of employment and the rate of increase of national income (or, which is the same, of gross national product). Denote by $\nu(t)$ the ratio of these two rates, i.e.

$$\nu(t) = \frac{\rho(t)}{r(t)}; \qquad \ldots [7.23]$$

we now have

$$\nu(t) = \frac{1}{a'(t)} \times \frac{\gamma(t)}{\beta(t)}; \qquad \ldots [7.24]$$

i.e. this ratio is proportional to the ratio of the average employment-outlay ratio and the average output-outlay ratio.

Total employment grows faster, equally fast, or more slowly, than national income according as to whether

$$\frac{\gamma(t)}{a'_0(t)} \gtreqless \beta(t) \qquad \ldots \; [7.25]$$

However, $\gamma(t)$ and $\beta(t)$ are averages depending on the allocation of the total investment outlay among the various sectors of the national economy. Remembering [7.8] and [7.18] we have

$$v(t) = \frac{\sum_i \gamma_i \, \mu_i(t)}{a'_0(t) \sum \beta_i \, \mu_i(t)} \qquad \ldots \; [7.26]$$

Since the coefficients γ_i and β_i are determined by technological conditions and $a'_0(t)$ is determined by the employment coefficients a'_{0j} and by the way the national product is composed of outputs of the various sectors, $v(t)$ can be influenced only by a proper choice of the allocation of investment fractions $\mu_i(t)$.

In order to obtain the greatest rate of increase of national income (or of gross national output) the allocation fractions $\mu_i(t)$ have to be chosen so as to maximise the average overall output-outlay ratio $\beta(t)$. In order to achieve this, investment outlays must be allocated to the sectors with the highest overall outlay ratios, β_i.

In order to obtain the greatest possible rate of increase of total employment the allocation fraction $\mu_i(t)$ have to be chosen so as to maximise the average employment outlay ratio $\gamma(t)$. This requires that the investment outlays be allocated to the sectors with the highest overall employment outlay ratio γ_i.

These considerations refer to the rate of increase of national income or of total employment in a given unit period t. If the goal of the policy is to obtain the greatest possible increase of total employment after a longer period of time, an additional factor has to be brought into consideration. From [7.21] we see that the rate of increase in total employment is proportional to $\alpha(t)$, i.e. the rate of investment in the unit period. The rate of investment, however, may depend on the national income, because an increase in national income makes it possible to have a greater rate of investment.

Consequently, it may be possible to obtain in the long run a greater increase in total employment by allocating investment outlays not in a way that directly raises the rate of growth of total employment but in a way which produces the greatest rate of increase of national income. The slower rate of increase of employment in the initial period is then more than compensated by a more rapid rate of increase of employment in the later period due to an increased rate of investment.

For instance, let

$$\alpha(t) = cI(t), \qquad \ldots \quad [7.27]$$

where $I(t) = \Sigma\, x_j(t)$ is the national income in unit period t and c is a factor of proportionality $(0 < c < 1)$. Then,

$$\rho(t) = \frac{cI(t)\,\gamma(t)}{a_0'(t)} \qquad \ldots \quad [7.28]$$

Taking into account relation [7.14], we find that in any given unit period t_k the rate of increase of total employment is

$$\rho(t_k) = c\,\frac{\gamma(t_k)}{a_0'(t_k)}\quad I(t_0) \prod_{t=t_0}^{t_k} (1+r(t)) \qquad \ldots \quad [7.29]$$

where $I(t_0)$ is the national income in the initial unit period, t_0.

Thus the rate of increase of total employment in any given unit period is proportional to the increase of national income which took place between the initial unit period and the unit period under consideration.

In expression [7.29] $\gamma(t_k)$ depends on the values of the investment allocation fractions $\mu_i(t_k)$ $(i = 1, \ldots, n)$ in unit period t_k whereas $r(t)$ depends on the values of the allocation of investment fractions $\mu_i(t)$ in all the unit periods from t_0 to t_k. This can be seen immediately from the formulae [7.8], [7.15] and [7.18]. A change of the values of the allocation (of investment) fractions in each period from t_0 to t_k thus produces a change in the rate of increase of total employment in unit period t_k equal to

$$d\rho(t_k) = \frac{c}{a_0'(t_k)}\, I(t_0) \left[\prod_{t=t_0}^{t_k} (1+r(t))\, d\,\gamma(t_k) + \gamma(t_k)\, d \prod_{t=t_0}^{t_k} (1+r(t)) \right] \ldots \quad [7.30]$$

The change is positive, zero, or negative, according to the sign of the expression in braces on the right-hand side, i.e. according as to whether

$$\frac{d \prod_{t=t_0}^{t_k} (1+r(t))}{\prod_{t=t_0}^{t_k} (1+r(t))} \gtreqless \frac{d\gamma(t_k)}{\gamma(t_k)} \qquad \ldots \quad [7.31]$$

The left-hand side of [7.31] can be written in the form

$$d \log \prod_{t=t_0}^{t_k} (1+r(t)) = \sum_{t=t_0}^{t_k} \frac{dr(t)}{1+r(t)}$$

Hence, the expression [7.31] becomes

$$\sum_{t=t_0}^{t_k} \frac{dr(t)}{1+r(t)} \gtreqless -\frac{d\gamma(t_k)}{\gamma(t_k)} \qquad \ldots \quad [7.32]$$

Let us start with values of the allocation of investment fractions which in each unit period from t_0 to t_k maximise the average employment-outlay ratio $\gamma(t)$. Then let us change these fractions so as to maximise $r(t)$. In each unit period $dr(t) > 0$ and $d\gamma(t_k) < 0$, except in the trivial case when $\gamma(t) = \beta(t)$ in each unit period, in which case $dr(t) = 0 = d\gamma(t)$. Thus the left-hand side of [7.32] increases monotonously with the value of t_k. By choosing t_k large enough it is possible to make the left-hand side in [7.32] greater than the right-hand side, i.e. to achieve a greater rate of increase of total employment than would be the case if the investment allocation fractions were chosen so as to maximise in each unit period the immediate effect on total employment.

Total employment in the unit period $t_s(t_s \geqq t_k \geqq t_0)$ is according to [7.22]

$$\sum_j a'_{0j} X_j(t_s) = \prod_{t_k=t_0}^{t_s} [1+\rho(t_k)] \sum_j a'_{0j} X_j(t_0) \qquad \ldots \text{[7.33]}$$

Taking logarithms, we find

$$d \log \sum_j a'_{0j} X_j(t_s) = \sum_{t_k=t_0}^{t_s} \frac{d\rho(t_k)}{1+\rho(t_k)} + \text{constant} \qquad \ldots \text{[7.34]}$$

As we have seen, a change of the allocation of investment fractions designed to maximise $r(t)$ in each unit period leads to $d\rho(t_k) > 0$ from a certain unit period onwards. Beginning with that unit period the right-hand side of [7.34] increases monotonously, with the value of t_s. By choosing t_s large enough it is possible to make [7.34] positive, i.e. to make total employment larger than would be the case if the rate of increase of national income were not maximised in each unit period.

Denote by t_c the critical value of t_s at which the expression starts becoming positive. Over planning periods which are shorter than $t_c - t_0$ the greatest possible total employment is obtained by allocating investment outlays among the various sectors of the national economy so as to maximise in each unit period $\gamma(t)$ by directing them always to the sectors with greatest employment-outlay ratios. Over planning periods exceeding $t_c - t_0$ the greatest possible total employment is obtained by maximising in each unit period $r(t)$, i.e. by allocating investment outlays always to the sectors with the greatest output-outlay ratios.

More complicated conditions for allocation of investment outlays among the various sectors of the national economy are obtained when the principal goal of the policy, i.e. greatest possible increase of national income or of total employment during a period of time, is subject to additional conditions like, for instance, a certain predetermined rate of growth of consumption. Such problems can be solved on the basis of the relations established in this chapter by means of the techniques of linear programming.

Mathematical Methods of Production Planning and Organisation[1]

L. V. Kantorovich

INTRODUCTION[2]

The tremendous tasks outlined in the third five-year plan demand the highest output obtainable by the best possible use of available industrial reserves—materials, labour force and equipment.

There are two ways to increase the productive efficiency of a workshop, of a factory, or of a whole branch of industry. One way is to make use of technical improvements, e.g. new features on individual machine tools, improved technological processes, new and better raw materials. The other way, much less used hitherto, is to improve the organisation and planning of production. This includes such questions as the distribution of jobs between different plants and equipment inside an enterprise, the correct allocation of orders to different enterprises, the correct distribution of various types of raw materials, fuel etc. This was very clearly stated in the decisions of the eighteenth Party Congress. There it is pointed out that 'the most important condition for the fulfilment of tasks posed by the programme of increased production during the third five-year period is . . . broad intensification of efforts to introduce the latest techniques and scientific organisation of production'.[3] This stresses both the factors mentioned above: along with the introduction of latest techniques the role of scientific organisation of production is underlined.

In connexion with a problem presented to the Institute of Mathematics and Mechanics of the Leningrad State University by the Laboratory of the Plywood Trust, we found that a whole group of problems relating to the scientific organisation of production of the most varied types lead to the same

[1] This contribution is a reproduction, with minor changes, of a book by L. V. Kantorovich published 1939 by the Leningrad University. (Editor's note)

[2] This introduction is based on a considerably enlarged stenographic record of a paper presented on 13 May 1939, at the Leningrad State University, in the presence of representatives of industrial research institutes. It also uses information on which was based a lecture dealing with building problems, given on 28 May 1939, at the Leningrad Institute of Industrial Building.

[3] *C.P. of the USSR, resolutions and decisions of congresses, conferences and plenary sessions of the Central Committee*, Vol. II, Part 7, p. 896.

group of (extremal) mathematical problems. The questions relate to optimum distribution of work for machine tools and apparatus, maximum reduction of waste, best utilisation of raw materials and of locally available materials, fuel, transport etc. These problems are not directly suitable for mathematical analysis; or rather they appear superficially suitable and even prove to be simple, but the method of solution is quite impracticable, since it involves the solution of tens of thousands or even millions of systems of equations.

We have succeeded in finding a relatively simple general method of solving this group of problems, which is applicable to all types of problems mentioned above, and which is sufficiently straightforward and effective for its application to practical conditions.

It should be stressed that most of these problems, dealing with organisation and planning of production, are bound up with the Soviet economic system, and do not occur in the economics of the capitalist society. There the choice of production is determined not by the plan, but by the interests of individual capitalists. The owner of an enterprise chooses for production those goods which at the moment happen to have the highest price, are easy to sell, and thus are likely to produce the highest profit. He chooses the materials which he can buy cheaply, not those which are plentiful in his country. The question of the fullest utilisation of equipment does not arise, since in any case the majority of enterprises work only at half capacity.

The situation in the USSR is different. The main task of each enterprise is to fulfil and to exceed its plan, which forms part of the overall plan for the country. Thereby it is not enough to fulfil the plan as a whole—in respect of total value or weight of production; it is necessary to fulfil it in detail, i.e. for various types of products, for completeness of manufactured articles, for the output of composite products and so forth.

For us these considerations—to fulfil the plan as a whole and as regards the product-mix—are most important, since they are additional factors to be taken into account when solving the problems of achieving the highest possible output. Very important also is the use of materials, which should be chosen, not in some sort of *a priori* fashion, but because they are actually available on the spot, in particular local materials, which should be used depending on the quantities produced in the area concerned. It should be pointed out that our methods permit the solution of problems arising from such realistic conditions and circumstances.

We will now consider some actual problems of organisation and planning of production, and clarify the mathematical problems to which they lead.

1. Method of Machine Loading to obtain the Highest Productivity subject to Completeness (Statement of Basic Mathematical Problems)

To explain the kind of problems we have in mind, I will take a very simple example which does not require any special method since the solution is self-evident. It will serve for illustration[1] and will help to clarify the problem.

Example 1

Metal parts may be turned on various machine tools—ordinary centre lathes, turret lathes or automatic lathes. Let us assume that there are three centre lathes, three turret lathes and an automatic lathe. The product is a very simple one consisting of two components.

The production of these components is as follows: in a working day a centre lathe can produce 10 components I or 20 components II; a turret lathe—20 components I or 30 components II; and the automatic lathe can produce 30 components I or 80 components II. Taking into account the number of lathes (3 centre lathes, 3 turret lathes, 1 automatic), it is clear that we can produce in a day a total of $30+60+30 = 120$ components I, or $60+90+80 = 230$ components II (see Table 1).

TABLE 1

Productivity of Available Lathes for Two Component Parts

Type of lathe	Number	Output of each lathe		Total output	
		Component I	Component II	Component I	Component II
Centre	3	10	20	30	60
Turret	3	20	30	60	90
Automatic	1	30	80	30	80

Problem A. The problem is how to break up the day's work of these machine tools so as to achieve the highest output not simply in terms of components but of complete products, consisting as we know of two components each. Thus, we have to choose the daily work-load of each machine tool so as to produce the highest possible number of complete products.

If we try simply to produce a number (not necessarily a maximum) of complete products, we could turn out equal quantities of both components on each lathe. To achieve this it is sufficient to arrange the daily load of each type of tool so that it produces an equal number of each component. Thus, the centre lathes can produce 20 components I and 20 components II, since the turning of 20 components II is equivalent to 10 components I. Turret lathes could then produce 36 components I and 36 components II, and the automatic 21 components of each type. The total output of all tools would be 77 components I and 77 components II, or 77 complete products (see Table 2).

Let us consider how suitable this method really is. On the centre lathe one component I is equivalent to two components II; on the turret lathe this ratio is 2:3, and on the automatic 3:8. This difference may be due to various causes: a certain operation may take the same time on any type of lathe,

[1] Since this example is used only as an illustration, no attempt has been made to make it real, i.e. we did not select data and circumstances found in practice.

while another operation may be done 5 times faster on the automatic than on the centre lathe, and so forth.

A consideration of these ratios leads immediately to a solution. Component I is best made on the turret lathe, and component II on the automatic. As to centre lathes, they should be used so as to obtain an equal number of both component parts.

If we distribute the work accordingly, the load will be as follows: on centre lathes: 26 components I and 6 components II; on turret lathes: 60 components I only; on the automatic: 80 components II only. Thus we will produce 86 components I and 86 components II.

We have already achieved a substantial, if not very striking, improvement, namely 12% increase in production without any additional expense.

However this problem can be solved by such elementary considerations only in the simple case of three types of tool and of two component parts. In practice the position is usually more complicated, and it is unlikely that a solution can be found merely by using common sense.

TABLE 2

Distribution of Machine-loads

Type of lathe	Simplest solution		Best solution	
	Component I	Component II	Component I	Component II
Centre	20	20	26	6
Turret	36	36	60	—
Automatic	21	21	—	80
Number of complete products	77	77	86	86

In order to find a way to a mathematical solution of this problem let us consider it in a more general manner. The efficient production of articles each consisting of a number of components raises several mathematical problems. In the other fields mentioned above in which mathematical methods are applicable, we found that mathematical problems are identical in all cases, so that it is sufficient to state to which mathematical problem any particular question can be reduced.

Let us then consider a general case. Let n be the number of available machine tools to be used for the production of articles each consisting of m different components. Now assuming that the tool i can be used for component k, we can produce in a day α_{ik} components. This is our initial data (note that $\alpha_{ik} = 0$ if the tool i cannot be used for component k).

Now we have to distribute the manufacture of parts to the available machine tools so as to produce the maximum number of complete sets of parts. Let h_{ik} be the amount of time (in fractions of a working day) needed to produce component k on machine tool i. This amount of time is unknown; it must be determined so as to achieve a maximum overall output. The following conditions apply for the determination of h_{ik}:

First, $h_{ik} \geqq 0$; it is non-negative. This is, in practice, quite obvious, but it must be stated, since it is a mathematically important limitation.

Second, for each i, $\sum_{k=1}^{m} h_{ik} = 1$. This means that on the whole—in respect of all components—tool i will be used during the full working day.

Third, the quantity of manufactured components k will be $z_k = \sum_{i=1}^{n} \alpha_{ik} h_{ik}$, since each product $\alpha_{ik} h_{ik}$ represents the number of components k made on tool i. As we want to produce complete sets, it is essential that values z should be equal: $z_1 = z_2 = \ldots = z_m$. The common value of these numbers z will determine the number of complete sets of components; it should be the highest possible number.

Thus our question can be reduced to the following mathematical problem.

Problem A. Find the values h_{ik} ($i = 1, 2 \ldots n$; k $= 1, 2 \ldots m$) whereby:

(1) $h_{ik} \geqq 0$;

(2) $\sum_{k-i}^{m} h_{ik} = 1 \quad (i = 1, 2 \ldots n)$;

(3) h_{ik} should be so selected that in the expression $\sum_{i=1}^{n} \alpha_{ik} h_{ik} = z_k$ the values $z_1, z_2 \ldots z_m$ are equal to each other, and that their common value $z = z_1 = z_2 = \ldots = z_m$ is the maximum feasible.

Problem A also applies to the case of one component undergoing a number of operations, each of which can be done on several machine tools. The only difference is that in this case α_{ik} will indicate the output of tool i at operation k, and h_{ik} will indicate the amount of time this tool will spend on this operation.

Problem A may have several variants.

For instance, if we have to produce two different articles, there will be components of the first article and components of the second article. Let z be the quantity of the first article and y that of the second. If the ratio of these quantities is not specified and if we are only concerned with maximum monetary value of output, the price of the two articles being a and b roubles respectively, then of course we should try to make $az+by$ a maximum.

Problem B. In some cases there is a limiting factor, for instance the amount of electrical energy to be used for various processes. Assume that the process *ik* (manufacturing part k on tool i) uses up c_{ik} kWh during the working day. Total consumption of electricity will then be $\sum_{i=1}^{n} \sum_{k=1}^{m} h_{ik} c_{ik}$; this sum must not exceed a fixed amount C (available supply). In this case we arrive at the following mathematical problem:

Find the values h_{ik} of Problem A subject to conditions (1), (2), and (3), and the additional condition:

(4) $\sum_{i=1}^{n} \sum_{k=1}^{m} c_{ik}\, h_{ik} \leqq C$

Note that c_{ik} may indicate other values, for instance the number of operators for process (i, k). If we have a fixed number of man-days, the available manpower may be a limiting factor leading to Problem B. The quantity of water required for each process may also be a limiting factor if it must not exceed a certain available figure.

We now come to problem C. Let us assume that one and the same machine tool can work simultaneously on several components, oı carry out several operations on one component, and that the production process can be arranged in various ways. One variant: three components are produced simultaneously. Another variant: two components of another kind are produced simultaneously, and so forth. This problem is somewhat more complicated. Let us assume that machine tool i will produce in a working day γ_{ikl} units of component k by method l, that is simultaneously γ_{i1l} units of first component, γ_{i2l} units of second component, and so forth (some γ_{ikl} may be equal to zero).

If h_{il} is the unknown duration of work of tool i according to method l, then the quantity z_k of components k produced on all machine tools will be expressed in a more complicated manner by $z_k = \sum_{i,l} \gamma_{ikl}\, h_{il}$. Again the problem is reduced to finding the maximum number z of complete sets, whereby $z_1 = z_2 = \ldots = z_m$. Problem C can now be stated thus:

Problem C. Find the values h_{il}, whereby:

(1) $h_{il} \geqq 0$;

(2) $\sum_{l} h_{il} = 1$;

if (3) $z_k = \sum_{i,l} \gamma_{ikl}\, h_{il}$, then $z_1 = z_2 = \ldots = z_m$, and the common value z is the maximum feasible.

There may be yet another variant of this problem. When the production is aimed at a certain number of sets which are not necessarily complete, the missing components may have to be bought at a higher price; or alternatively components which are made in excess of requirements have to be charged at a lower price. In such cases the actual quantity of complete sets is very important for determining the cost of production. However, there is no need to enumerate all possible variations.

Let us consider the question of solving these problems. In practice, we find that the usual mathematical methods cannot be used. We first found some special methods which are more effective but are still too complicated. Later, however, we succeeded in finding a universal method applicable to problems A, B, C, and to other problems of this kind. This is the method of *resolving multipliers*.

Its underlying idea may be best explained with reference to Problem A. It has been found that there are multipliers $\lambda_1, \lambda_2, \ldots \lambda_m$ such that for each component their evaluation will enable the problem to be solved nearly immediately. If we consider the products $\lambda_l\alpha_{i1}, \lambda_2\alpha_{i2}, \ldots \lambda_m\alpha_{im}$ for each given i and select those k's for which the product is a maximum, then for all other k's it can be assumed that $h_{ik} = 0$. As to the few h_{ik} which have been selected, they can be easily determined by means of the conditions $\sum_{k=1}^{m} h_{ik} = 1_l$ and $z_1 = z_2 = \ldots = z_m$. The values h_{ik} produce the highest z, which gives the solution of the problem.

Thus, instead of determining a great number (nm) of unknown h_{ik} it is sufficient to find only m unknowns λ_k. In a practical case, for instance, we determine only 4 unknowns instead of 32 (see example 2 below). As to the multipliers λ_k, they can be found without much effort by means of successive approximations. The whole solution is relatively easy; it is not more difficult than a normal technical calculation. Depending on the complexity of a particular case, the solution may take from 15 minutes to 5 or 6 hours.

The solution is eminently practicable and the result can be checked very easily. When a solution has been found, the check can be made within 10 to 15 minutes.[1]

A fact of practical significance is worth mentioning: a majority of the values h_{ik} obtained in the course of solution is equal to zero. Consequently, each machine tool is occupied on only one or two components every day; i.e. a solution is not practicable if the machine tool is occupied only $\frac{1}{2}$ hour by one component and $\frac{3}{4}$ hour by another etc. In practice this is not a severe limitation: most machine tools work the whole day on only one kind of component, and only two or three tools change their job during the day. This is quite essential if it is necessary to produce an equal number of different components.

The solution of problems which have been discussed above, dealing with the achieving of a maximum output of complete sets, is applicable, I think, to a majority of enterprises in the metal-working and wood-working industries. Both these industries use a variety of machine tools of varying productivity; some of these machine tools can carry out identical operations, and consequently the problem arises as to how the work-load should be spread in the most efficient way.

Of course, the determination of the most effective distribution of work-load is possible (and sensible) only in the case of batch production. In the case of 'one-off' there is no sense in finding a solution, and in any case there will be no information as to the time taken to produce each component on

[1] A full description of this method, with numerical examples, is given in Appendix I (page 247 of this book).

each machine tool. However, batch production is the typical form of production in the metal-working and the wood-working industries.

2. Organisation of Production to secure the Most Complete Plan Fulfilment of a given Assortment of Products[1]

There is no need to stress the importance, in conditions of planned economy, of producing the required assortment of goods. Non-fulfilment of the planned assortment of required products cannot be accepted, even if the planned summary indicators (cost or tonnage) have been fulfilled. It can lead to excess stocks of some products, wasting the means of production going into them, and to an acute shortage of other products, seriously affecting the work of other enterprises which depend on the particular enterprise. Consequently, every enterprise which fulfils its total plan, or surpasses it, or even fails to fulfil it, is still in duty bound to maintain such relationship between its various products as is laid down by the state. At the present time, failure to produce the planned assortment is a fault common to many enterprises. So the question of how best to organise them for maximum output of a given assortment is of considerable importance.

Let us consider this question under the following conditions. There are n machine tools (or groups of machine tools), which can produce m different types of products. Machine tool i may produce in a day α_{ik} units of type k. We have to organise the work so as to achieve the highest possible output while maintaining the required ratios $p_1 : p_2 : \ldots : p_m$ of the different types of products. If h_{ik} is the time during which the machine tool i (or group of machine tools) is used in making the product k, then we have the following conditions for h_{ik}:

(1) $h_{ik} \geqq 0;$

(2) $\sum_{k=1}^{m} h_{ik} = 1;$

$$(3) \qquad \frac{\sum_{i=1}^{n} h_{i1}\,\alpha_{i1}^{*}}{p_1} = \ldots = \frac{\sum_{i=1}^{n} h_{im}\,\alpha_{im}^{*}}{p_m},$$

whereby the common value of last mentioned ratios is a maximum.

If we assume that $\alpha_{ik} = (1/p_k)\,\alpha_{ik}^{*}$, the last fraction will become condition (3) of problem A; thus the above problem leads to problem A, which has already been discussed.

Example 2

The very first question asked by the Central Laboratory of the Plywood Trust was related to this problem, namely the maximum output of a given

[1] A full description of the method of solving this problem is given in Appendix II (see page 267 of this book).

assortment. We have recently calculated an actual example, and given the result to the Laboratory. The problem is as follows: there are eight veneer-cutting machines and five different material specifications. The output of each machine for each specification is stated in Table 3.

TABLE 3

Machine	Material Specification				
	I	II	III	IV	V
1	4·0	7·0	8·5	13·0	16·5
2	4·5	7·8	9·7	13·7	17·5
3	5·0	8·0	10·0	14·8	18·0
4	4·0	7·0	9·0	13·5	17·0
5	3·5	6·5	8·5	12·7	16·0
6	3·0	6·0	8·0	13·5	15·0
7	4·0	7·0	9·0	14·0	17·0
8	5·0	8·0	10·0	14·8	18·0

It is required to spread the work-load so as to obtain the maximum output with the condition that material specification I forms 10% of total production, II—12%, III—28%, IV—36%, and V—14%.

This problem was solved by means of our method by A. I. Yudin.[1] The resulting values of h_{ik}—durations (in fractions of working day) of work on each material specification—are as follows:

TABLE 4

Machine	Material Specification				
	I	II	III	IV	V
1	0	0·3321	0	0	0·6679
2	0	0·9129	0·0871	0	0
3	0·5744	0	0·4256	0	0
4	0	0	0·9380	0·0620	0
5	0	0	1	0	0
6	0	0	0	1	0
7	0	0	0	1	0
8	1	0	0	0	0

The circumstances of this case were relatively unfavourable for achieving a striking improvement, since there was so little difference between the capabilities of the various machines. Even so, the use of the method of resolving multipliers has enabled the output to be increased by 5% as compared with the 'obvious' solution, while maintaining the required ratio of assortment for each machine. This method can produce more impressive results in cases in which the variation of productivity with regard to different materials is greater. However, even an increase of 5%, achieved without expense, has a practical significance.

[1] A full description of the method of solution is given in Appendix II (see p. 267 of this book).

It ought to be mentioned that our method is also useful for the co-ordination of several factories. In the example 1 above we have obtained different ratios of output of various components on a number of different machine tools. This situation may equally well apply to a number of different factories or plants. For instance, in a factory *A* the quantities of available machine tools or of components II to be produced are such that the automatic lathe is being partly used for component I, although it is more suitable for component II. At the same time in another factory *B* a turret lathe is being used to make a certain number of part II, although it is better adapted for part I. Obviously it would be an advantage so to co-ordinate the two factories, that production of component I will be partly transferred from *A* to *B*, whereas some production of component II will be transferred from *B* to *A*. In this case the solution is elementary, but in more complicated cases of co-ordination our method can be employed with success.

3. The Optimum Utilisation of Machinery

A great variety of work can be carried out by machinery of a general type. For instance, there are many methods of earth-moving, and there are many earth-moving machines such as bucket excavators, ditch-cutters, grab cranes, dozers, etc. The output of any such machine depends on the kind of soil, size of excavation, dumping requirements etc. For instance, one type of excavator may be more suitable for ditching, another for deep excavation, a third for shallow digging; one type may be better for sandy soil, and another for clay, and so forth.

Let us consider the following problem: there are a number of jobs to be tackled with the available machinery in the shortest possible time. In practice a certain job cannot always be done by the most suitable machine—for instance such a machine may be already overloaded or otherwise unavailable. Nevertheless, it is possible to use the available machinery to the best effect under the prevailing circumstances. An analysis similar to the two foregoing examples will prove that this problem can be reduced to problem A.

Let us illustrate this by two concrete examples, one relating to earth-moving and another to timber.

Example 3

There are three earth-moving jobs I, II and III, to be completed by three excavators, A, B and C. Each job involves the removal of 20,000 m^3 of soil. How are the machines to be used in the most efficient way, if each has a normal output for the various jobs as indicated in Table 5?

The best use of the available excavators, as determined by our method, is shown in Table 5, right-hand column. Thus, Excavator A should work 190 hours on job I and 94 hours on job II. The whole work can be completed in 284 hours. The left-hand column indicates, by way of comparison, a less favourable method, which would require 322 hours for the whole work, or

TABLE 5

Excavators	A			B			C			
	Duration of work (hrs)	Output norm (m³/hr)	Duration of work (hrs)	Duration of work (hrs)	Output norm (m³/hr)	Duration of work (hrs)	Duration of work (hrs)	Output norm (m³/hr)	Duration of work (hrs)	Σ
Jobs										
I	—	105	190	—	107	—	312	64	—	20,000
II	—	56	94	302	66	224	—	38	—	20,000
III	322	56	—	20	83	60	10	53	284	20,000
Total Hours	322		284	322		284	322		284	

13% more on time, and accordingly on fuel, capital, and so forth, as compared with the best method. It may be noted that the usual criteria would fail to detect the weakness of the left-hand method, since all jobs are carried out at the same time, the machines are fully used, and the normal output is achieved.

Example 4

The following jobs are to be done:

1. crosswise sawing of boards 4·5 m, 2 × 14 — 10,000 cuts
2. crosswise sawing of boards 6·5 m, 4 × 30 — 5,000 cuts
3. lengthwise sawing of boards 2 m, 4 × 15 — 4,000 running metres

Available equipment:
(*a*) 2 pendulum saws
(*b*) 1 circular saw with hand feed
(*c*) 10 circular electric saws
(*d*) 20 bow saws

The best distribution of work is given in Table 6.

TABLE 6

Equipment	Pendulum Saws (2)	Circular Saw with hand feed (1)	Circular elec. Saws (10)	Bow Saws (20)	Σ	Σ × 5·65 hours
Jobs						
1	400 × 2	—	167 × 3	59 × 9	1830	10,000
2	213 × 0	—	125 × 7	38 × 0	875	5,000
3	—	475 × 1	52 × 0	23 × 11	725	4,000

The first number in each row of Table 6 is the output norm of the equipment for the job in question (number of cuts or m/hr).[1] The multiplier of each norm is the number of tools used for this particular job, whereby zero multiplier indicates that the respective tool is not being used. As shown

[1] Normal output is taken from *Standard Norms of Output and Rates in Building*, Moscow, 1939.

in the last column, in the case of optimum work-loading all jobs can be completed in 5·65 hours.

Work-loading can be calculated not only according to kinds of work, but also according to individual operation. Having listed all operations and each tool's time for each operation (including setting-up time), the tools must be loaded so as to complete the whole work in the shortest possible time, or alternatively in a given time but at the lowest possible cost.

Other variations of the problem are possible, for instance completion of the whole work-load with the available machine tools in a given time, using a minimum amount of electricity. Similar problems may have to be solved when the electricity used must not exceed a certain amount, or when the number of operators is limited, or when the daily allowance of water for hydromechanical removal of soil is restricted, and so forth. These questions lead to problem B.

These methods can be applied not only to the utilisation of available machinery, but also to the selecting of machine tools best suited for a given work-load.

We are of the opinion that, in addition to earth-moving and other jobs encountered in constructional work, this method may be applied in the mining industry, in which we encounter ore-digging machines of various types whose output varies according to seam thickness, transport facilities, and so on. Also in the peat-cutting industry there are several methods of peat-cutting, each of which is particularly suited for a certain type of peat. Our method can find the best allocation of the available peat-cutting machines to different areas, in order to achieve the highest possible output.

In agriculture various jobs can be done by combine harvesters, threshers, binding machines etc., some machines (for instance, combine harvesters) doing a whole sequence of jobs. In this case the distribution of agricultural machinery leads to problem C.

4. Reduction of Waste

Many materials used in engineering and building are supplied as units (sheets of glass, steel, tin, plywood, paper, roofing, bars, girders, boards, fittings, billets, etc.). In order to use these standard sizes directly or as raw material for subsequent machining, it is necessary to divide them into parts of required size. As a rule there is a certain amount of waste, and in practice only a certain percentage of the material is used. There are cases in which the waste also can be utilised, but generally this either requires an additional expenditure (for welding, resmelting, etc.) and further waste, or a considerable loss in value as compared with the original material (viz. waste of building timber used as fuel). Thus a reduction of waste is important.

Our methods can be used here under the following circumstances. Suppose there is one or several sizes of material for parts of given dimensions, for which the quantities of the various parts are required in the ratio

$p_1 : p_2 : \ldots : p_m$. It is desirable to achieve the highest possible output (for instance, to produce the maximum number of glass plates for windows from a given number of standard size sheets). There are different ways of dividing a unit of material, such as a sheet of glass, into parts of the required dimensions. We have to decide how many units of material of a given size should be divided and in what manner, so as to reduce the waste to a minimum. We will show that our method can resolve this problem, as it can be reduced to problem C.

Assume that there are n sizes of material; size i comprises q_i units. We have to produce a maximum number of items each consisting of m different components, namely p_i of first component, ..., p_m of component m.

There are several ways of cutting the material of each size. Method l of cutting size i produces γ_{ikl} of component k (γ_{i1l} of first component, γ_{i2l} of second component, etc.). If there are h_{il} units of size i to be cut according to method l, then the conditions for the unknown h_{il} are that:

(1) $h_{il} \geqq 0$ and also be integers;

(2) $\sum_{l} h_{il} = q_i$;

(3) $$\frac{\sum_{i,l} \gamma_{i1l} h_{il}}{p_1} = \ldots = \frac{\sum_{i,l} \gamma_{iml} h_{il}}{p_m};$$

and their common value is the maximum feasible.

It is obvious that this problem can be reduced to problem C simply by a change of definitions.

Let us clarify these general considerations by a simple example, namely that of cutting unidimensional units of material.

Example 5

It is required to make 100 sets of logs of a length 2·9 m, 2·1 m, and 1·5 m respectively from trunks 7·4 m long.

The simplest solution is to make one set from each trunk, since $7{\cdot}4 = 2{\cdot}9+2{\cdot}1+1{\cdot}5+0{\cdot}9$, and let the end pieces 0·9 m long be wasted. By this method 100 trunks will be needed, and wastage will be $0{\cdot}9 \text{ m} \times 100 = 90$ m, that is 13·6%.

Now what is the best solution? Let us consider different ways of cutting up a trunk of 7·4 m into three parts of the length 2·9 m, 2·1 m, and 1·5 m, respectively. These are summarised in Table 7.

TABLE 7

I	II	III	IV	V	VI
2·9	2·9	2·1	2·9	1·5	2·9
1·5	2·9	2·1	2·1	1·5	2·1
1·5	1·5	1·5	2·1	1·5	1·5
1·5		1·5		2·1	
7·4	7·3	7·2	7·1	6·6	6·5

Method I does not produce any waste at all, but it cannot be used on its own, since there will be no complete sets (for instance, there will be no logs 2·1 m long).

The solution resulting in a minimum of waste has been found by our method. It is as follows: 30 trunks should be cut up according to method I, 10 according to method II, and 50 according to method IV. The total number of trunks required will be 90, as against 100 trunks needed according to the simplest solution. Wastage will be altogether $10 \times 0{\cdot}1 + 50 \times 0{\cdot}3 = 16$ m or $16/666 = 2{\cdot}4\%$. This is the minimum waste obtainable in these circumstances.

Let us consider a variation of this problem with the conditions slightly modified.

Example 6

There are 100 trunks each 7·4 m long and 50 trunks each 6·4 m long; they have to be cut up so as to produce the maximum number of sets of the same dimensions as before: 2·9 m, 2·1 m, and 1·5 m. We know already how to cut up trunks 7·4 m long; the shorter trunks of 6·4 may be cut up in the following ways: (*a*) $2{\cdot}1+2{\cdot}1+2{\cdot}1 = 6{\cdot}3$; (*b*) $1{\cdot}5+1{\cdot}5+1{\cdot}5+1{\cdot}5 = 6{\cdot}0$; (*c*) $1{\cdot}5+1{\cdot}5+2{\cdot}9 = 5{\cdot}9$; (*d*) $2{\cdot}9+2{\cdot}9 = 5{\cdot}8$, etc.

The solution in this case is as follows: 33 of the 7·4 m trunks will be cut up as per method I, 61 by method II, and 5 by method IV; all the 6·4 m trunks will be cut up according to method *a*. The result will be 161 sets, and the waste will be:

$$61 \times 0{\cdot}1 + 5 \times 0{\cdot}3 + 1 \times 0{\cdot}9 + 50 \times 0{\cdot}1 = 13{\cdot}5; \quad 13{\cdot}5 \,/\, 1060 = 1{\cdot}3\%.$$

It should be noted that the more complicated the problem, the greater the range of variations; and consequently our method can lead to a greater reduction of waste.

In my opinion this mathematical treatment of the problem of reducing waste can in many cases improve efficiency in the use of materials by some 5-10%, as compared with the present practice. In view of the shortage of many of the materials which can be treated in this manner (fittings, sawn timber, sheet metal, etc.), this saving is significant and a practical engineer should find it well worthwhile spending a couple of hours on this calculation. These comments, I think, apply particularly to the timber industry. Certainly a special effort is needed to adapt the method of resolving multipliers to these problems, but I have no doubt that it can be done.

5. Best Possible Utilisation of Composite Materials

The oil industry produces various products: petrol, benzine, paraffin, fuel oil, etc. Even a single type of oil can be treated by different cracking processes, and the final products depend on which process is used. If an oil refinery uses a number of types of crude oil, these oils must be treated by different cracking processes so as to produce the maximum output of a given assortment. It is easy to see that this question leads to problem C. The method is the same as was used for problems which have already been discussed.

A similar situation occurs in mining a variety of coals and ores for the production of different steels, since the selection of the most suitable ores and coals, and their mixture for various steel alloys present the same kind of problem. It occurs again in the chemical industry when the ore contains different metals, in the coke industry, and generally whenever a certain raw material is the source of a variety of products.

6. The Most Rational Use of Fuel

A variety of fuels—oil, hard coal, brown coal, wood, peat, shale oil—can be burnt and used in various fuel-consuming installations with varying effect. They are in use at power stations, in locomotives, ships, steam engines; also for central heating and so on. Frequently the fuel is allocated in a haphazard manner, without due consideration of the type of fuel best suited for a given installation, and even without considering whether the fuel can be used in the installation at all.

Yet the value of different fuels differs widely according to circumstances. For instance, it is possible that in a power station 2 tons of brown coal are equivalent to 1 ton of anthracite, but in a locomotive it is much more difficult to burn brown coal efficiently, so that 3 tons of brown coal may be needed to produce the effect of 1 ton of anthracite. This is only a hypothetical example, but in fact such differences do exist in practice. The same applies to various kinds of hard coal: the amount of heat produced is influenced by size, ash content, etc., and depends on the type of burner.

The problem of ascertaining the best way of distributing the available fuels to the various installations can also be solved by our methods; it leads to problem A.

The method of resolving multipliers can also be applied to another and more difficult problem, namely, how to choose the motors for a given volume of planned power delivery or output of fuels. These motors (diesel engines, gas generators, steam turbines of different types) and the relative numbers of them should be so selected that they are suitable for a certain fuel and that they are most efficient for the work assigned to them (in terms of ton-kilometres for railways and other forms of transport, kilowatt-hours for power stations, and so on). This question leads to problem C.

7. Best Possible Fulfilment of Building Plans, using Various Building Materials

We should like now to indicate a possible application of our methods to the planning of building.

At the eighteenth Congress of the Soviet Communist Party (Bolsheviks) it was mentioned that while the Second Five-Year Plan for the main industries had been more than fulfilled, the targets of the building plan had not been achieved. More precisely, part of the funds allocated for building had not been fully used. One of the main reasons was the shortage of certain materials or of certain grades of labour, which either seriously delayed the progress of building, or prevented it from starting, even although the necessary funds were available. We feel that the present method of planning for building does not make the best possible use of materials in short supply; and that the plans could be carried out better by a more advantageous distribution of materials.

It is well known that many building operations—on bridges, viaducts, industrial buildings, schools, garages, etc.—can be carried out wholly or partly in different ways; the method of construction may be decided by the use of reinforced concrete, bricks, large blocks, stone, and so on. Frequently, a number of methods are possible and almost equally practicable. The choice is usually made by the project group for each particular structure, and very often the chosen method has only a slight advantage over other possible methods. Yet the selection of the right method is a very important one, since it affects the quantities of materials required (cement, steel, bricks, mortar, etc.), and also other important limiting factors (number of workers of different grades, building machinery, transport, etc.).

A proper balance is essential if the whole programme of work for a given area or for a particular building project is to be carried out. In our view, constructional methods should be chosen neither haphazardly nor separately

TABLE 8

List of building projects in the area (in order of priority)	Limiting Factors									
	Materials						Labour (by grades)	Machinery (by kind)	Transport	Financial Allocations (by items)
	Cement	Mortar	Bricks	Metal	Timber					
1. Bridge										
Variant I										
Variant II										
Variant III										
2. School										
Variant I										
Variant II										
3. Garage										
Variant I										
Variant II										

for each building project, but rather for the whole volume of work for the area or project, according to the findings of scientific calculation. Thus maximum coherence is ensured between the quantity of required materials, labour force, building machinery, and other deciding factors which may restrict the plan.

The method of planning constructional work that we propose is roughly as follows. The building organisations select the few (two or three) variants most suitable for each project, and work out approximate requirements of building materials etc. for each variant. In this way the area planning organisation receives the data roughly as shown in Table 8.

The planning organisation then selects the best variants so that the balance of materials and other limiting factors corresponds to the production plan for the particular year, and so that this realistic building plan contains the greatest possible number of projects listed in order of priority.

This final selection of variants can be reduced to problem C with some additional conditions and can be solved by our methods even in relatively complicated cases (100-200 projects). We will not discuss here details such as co-ordination of plans of a number of organisations, allocations of materials and finance, etc. Suffice it to say that all these problems can be satisfactorily resolved.

8. Most Favourable Distribution of Crops

It is well known that the suitability of different areas and plots for agricultural crops depends on variations of soil and climatic conditions and on other natural factors. The selection of a suitable plan for land usage is most important. I should like to mention the statement made by a delegate to the eighteenth Party Congress. According to him, in the northern districts of his county the best crop is barley, whereas in the southern districts wheat grows best. Yet the County Agricultural Department automatically divides the plan for all districts according to the total areas of all cultures; it does not matter that barley would not grow in a certain district—you still have to sow barley. . . . However, a sensible distribution of crops is not quite easy to achieve.

Let us assume there are n plots of sizes $q_1, q_2, \ldots, q_n$ and m crops, which according to plan must be planted in ratio $p_1 : p_2 : \ldots : p_m$. The expected harvest of crop k on plot i may be designated α_{ik}.

Now we have to calculate how many hectares of the first plot (or district) should be used for a certain crop, how many hectares should be used for another crop, and so forth, in order to obtain the best harvest. Let h_{ik} be the number of hectares of plot i which are used for crop k. Then the whole area of plot i is $\sum_{k=1}^{m} h_{ik} = q_1$ (h_{ik} is, of course, not negative). The number of hundredweights of the expected harvest of crop k for the whole area of the plot will be $z_k = \sum_{i=1}^{n} \alpha_{ik} h_{ik}$, and the values z_k should be so chosen that they relate as $z_1 : p_1 = z_2 : p_2 = \ldots = z_m : p_m$, so as to maintain the ratio of crops as laid down by the plan and to achieve the maximum harvest z_k. This leads to problem A. Indeed, if we replace $h^*_{ik} q_i$ by h^*_{ik}, whereby $\alpha^*_{ik} = 1/(p_k q_i)\, \alpha_{ik}$, then for the magnitudes h^*_{ik} and α^*_{ik} the equations of problem A apply exactly.

We have considered the question of maximum harvest for one year. If we consider the maximum harvests for a number of years and take into account the influence of crop rotation, the question becomes more complicated; it leads to problem C.

If a part of the land is irrigated, and if the normal usage of water for crop k on plot i is c_{ik} litre/sec per hectare, then we have an additional condition $\sum_{i,k} c_{ik} h_{ik} \leqq C$, if C is the total capacity of the irrigation supply. This leads to problem B.

We have already pointed out in Chapter 3 that our methods can be used for determining the most favourable distribution of agricultural machinery according to type of work.

I ought to say that a certain caution is needed when our methods are applied to agriculture, since these data (expected harvests) are very tentative. Of course, if the basic assumptions are wrong, then the solution is likely to be wrong too. However, I believe that the adherence to the principle of best possible distribution, even on the basis of approximate data, will only occasionally lead to a wrong conclusion (if these data are faulty); usually, on the average, it will produce a definitely useful result.

9. The Best Plan of Transportation

First, let us consider the following question. A number of commodities —oil, grain, machinery etc.—can be transported from one point to another by different means: by rail or by water, or partly by rail and partly by road, and so on. Depending on type of goods, methods of loading, suitability of carriers etc., the efficiency of various means of transportation differs; for instance, oil transport by water is particularly advantageous if oil tankers are available, and so forth. Our methods can be used for choosing the best distribution of a given sum total of cargo of the different means of transportation, bearing in mind the quickest movement, or the least expenditure of fuel when the period of movement is laid down. This case leads to problems A or C. There is another problem which can also be solved by our methods, although it does not directly correspond to problems A, B or

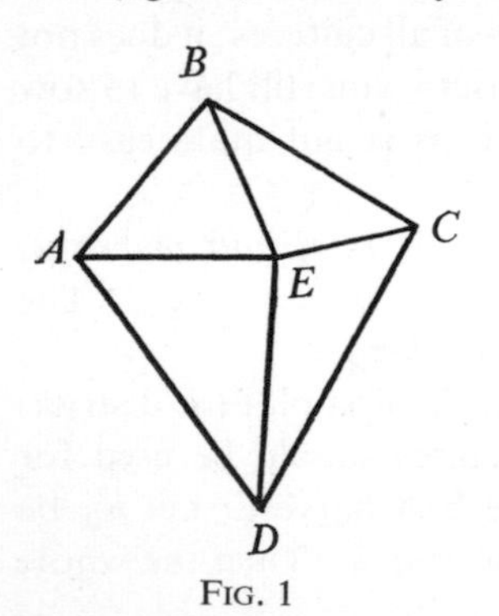

FIG. 1

C. This is route selection for transportation. Points A, B, C, D, E (see Fig. 1) may be connected by a railway network. A train from B to D may take the shortest route B E D, but it may be also directed via B C D or B A D. Suppose that a certain amount of freight is consigned, i.e. a given number of railway trucks must be moved from A to B, another from D to C, and so forth. Each route can handle at the most only a limited volume of traffic (which, however, may change with new methods of transportation). Bearing in mind the traffic capacity of each route, how are we to arrange the movement of trains so as reduce the expenditure of fuel and also the movement of empty trucks to a minimum? As already pointed out, our methods can supply the answer to this question.

This concludes our consideration of different kinds of problems.

CONCLUSION

1. General Significance of the Present Work

The real significance of the present work is this: a method has been evolved for the solution of problems involving a huge number of different factors and variants, from which the most favourable variant has to be selected. This method makes it possible to find a solution even under very difficult circumstances, when the best variant has to be chosen from millions or even billions of possible variants, whereby many additional factors have to be taken into account.

It is well known that such problems are constantly encountered in the fields of technology and economics, particularly with regard to the organisation and planning of production. Many of these problems can be directly reduced to problems A, B, C discussed above, and consequently they can be solved by our methods. Many other problems lead to different mathematical relations, but nevertheless they can also be solved by the same methods.

So far all these problems of technology and economics have been treated in a rather haphazard manner, by guesswork or by rule of thumb, and of course the solution hit upon was only occasionally the best one. Often no attempt has been made at all to find the optimum solution; on the other hand, when such an attempt was undertaken, it was usually unsuccessful. Instead of trying to find an answer by the hit-and-miss method, it is now possible to determine the optimum variant in a systematic, scientific manner.

2. Further Investigations

Of course, as it stands at present this work is in no way complete; it has not yet accomplished all the tasks it set out to achieve. This work is only a tentative outline of a future paper on this subject, which should deal fully with the very important problem which so far has been barely outlined. However, before this stage has been reached, further extensive investigations have to be carried out by joint efforts of mathematicians and production experts.

With regard to the mathematical treatment much remains to be done, although an important step forward has been made—a widely applicable and sufficiently effective method of dealing with a great variety of problems has been established. In future it will be necessary to define the field of application of this method; to point out further problems it can handle; to work out a detailed technique of its application[1]; to clarify any adaptations of this technique to various circumstances; to find simpler ways which may lead to a solution so close to the very best solution as to be practically equivalent; to improve the description of this method; and so on. Even greater efforts will be required to persuade the technicians—the specialists in the various fields of the national economy—to make actual use of this work.

First of all we should define those questions in the various fields of our national economy where the applicability of our method appears to be feasible and real. In this paper we have made some attempts to point out and to outline these questions, but it is hardly to be expected that they will be wholly successful and will not encounter any criticisms from the experts concerned. Some of these questions may be found to be unrealistic or unimportant, others may need substantial corrections and additions; and no doubt, many problems will be pointed out to us which we have overlooked altogether.

Nevertheless we thought it worthwhile to make this attempt, on the assumption that our approach and treatment will be more readily understood by the engineer if they are related to definite practical requirements. The mention of a large number and variety of these questions may help him to visualise and to circumscribe the range of problems to which our methods can be applied; and at the same time it will help him to find and to pose similar questions arising in his own sphere of activity, and thus it will assist in a creative application of these methods.

Once the fields which are suitable for an application of mathematical methods have been defined, the question of specific techniques of the methods to deal with different circumstances will arise. This will involve: a detailed investigation of factors which enable these methods to be sufficiently useful, so that their application can be demonstrated; a clarification of technical data required for the application of these methods; a presentation of these data in the form of convenient tables; detailed adaptation of this method to the specific problems of a particular field (indication of rules governing the selection of the first approximation, etc.) and so forth.

[1] We may mention here that we do not expect the refinement of this method to be carried very far; we do not believe that our method of calculation will be replaced by formulae, tables or nomograms. It is very unlikely that a solution in the way of a table or nomogram can be found, since the question may involve a great number (up to 40) of different data,

3. Reply to Some Fundamental Criticisms

As already mentioned, we quite expect that the examples we have investigated (and possibly the groups of questions we have chosen) will be criticised by experts. In individual cases these objections may well be so justified that we shall be forced to drop some of the intended fields of application. However, apart from these specific and detailed criticisms, and in spite of a generally favourable reception, we have encountered some counter-arguments of a fundamental character, which in effect amount to a denial, on principal, that mathematical methods can be applied to technical and economic problems in the field of organisation and planning. Let us examine these objections on principle.

The first argument runs thus: the actual problems are so involved and include so many subsidiary factors, that it is impossible to consider the whole situation mathematically; even if it were possible, the equations would be incapable of being solved.

To this we would reply first that our method is very powerful and very flexible, so that it provides a solution of a rather complex question on one hand and allows for different variants in its application on the other; second, if some practical details have not been taken into account at first, the solution can be corrected to include them. Moreover, as this method indicates not only the best solution but also the next-best variants, it is possible to introduce these corrections while losing but little of the effectiveness of the best possible variant.

We may add that this argument may be applied just as well to any theoretical treatment, in particular mathematical treatment, of technical problems. Yet technicians are well known to value highly a theoretical approach, however crude, since it gives guidance for experimentation, calculation and planning. How much more valuable is a method which allows a whole range of factors influencing a complicated problem to be taken into account!

The second argument points out that this method requires a great number of different data (α_{ik} in problem A, etc.); and if these data are not available, the proposed method can not be used.

To this we would reply that the data (output norms for various machine tools, quantities and properties of available materials, etc.) are anyhow required for all kinds of practical purposes—standardisation, payroll, material control, accounting reports—and that they should be available in every normally running enterprise. This information is essential for the preparing of any plan, quite as much as for constructing the best plan by our method.

Admittedly, in some cases the necessary data simply are not there. For instance, building materials are needed on site and must be used immediately on arrival, but it is not known what material will in fact arrive; or the material received may not be what is in the plan, and so on. Of course, in the few enterprises subjected to such 'primitive' misrule all planning is impossible, not to mention the best possible planning. However, if the desire to use our methods will stimulate the elimination of such inefficiency, that is itself an additional point in favour of these methods.

The third argument says that the calculation may be wrong if the basic data are doubtful or only approximate (as, for instance, expected harvest of various crops, amount of water required for hydromechanical soil preparation, and some other data of previously discussed examples).

To this we can say first of all that any other planning method also must use the same data, and there is no reason to think that doubtful or inaccurate data will be more detrimental for a plan carefully selected than for a plan picked out at random. Nevertheless, it is possible that in some cases the variant selected by our method may in fact not be the most suitable one, because of faulty data.

However, we believe that with large-scale application (of these methods) even in the case of doubtful data the selection of most suitable variants will be beneficial because of its statistical effect. This can be explained by the following simple example. If of two eggs we select the larger one, our choice may yet be wrong, as the bigger egg may be rotten. However, if from a box containing 1000 eggs we select the 500 largest, it is quite improbable that this selection is wrong.

According to the fourth argument the effect of a change from a conventional variant to the best possible variant is insignificant, being in many cases only 4-5%.

Our reply is, first, that the selection of the best variant costs no more than that of the usual method, apart from the quite negligible cost of calculation: second, that our method may be used not in a single random case but in many, possibly in most, fields of national economy; this means that a saving of one per cent, or even of one tenth of one per cent, will bring enormous results.

The fifth argument suggests that in many cases it is not possible to use our method because of various administrative difficulties connected with the approval of plans, estimates and the like; for instance, if some materials have already been allocated to various enterprises, a re-allocation cannot be effected during the current quarter, etc.

Of course this criticism is groundless. If it is generally appreciated that the application of the most suitable plan can produce a substantial gain for the national economy and that some change is required in the procedure for approval of estimates to put this plan into effect, then there can be no doubt that this change will be carried through.

* * *

APPENDIX I: METHOD OF RESOLVING MULTIPLIERS

We intend to present here a full description of the method of resolving multipliers mentioned in Section 1. In our opinion this method is most effective when applied to problems A, B, and C, and also to many other problems of a similar kind, which involve the selection of the most advantageous variant from a very great number of possible variants. In the main we will consider the basic problem A, but we will also mention other problems.

1. SOLUTION OF PROBLEM A FOR $m = 2$

Underlying idea of the method used

Let us start with an investigation of problem A for the simplest case of two components ($m = 2$). In this case the problem is to find the values h_{i1} and h_{i2} from the conditions:

(1) $h_{i1};\ h_{i2} \geqq 0;$

(2) $h_{i1}+h_{i2} = 1;$

(3) $\sum_{i=1}^{n} a_{i1}\, h_{i1} = \sum_{i=1}^{n} a_{i2}\, h_{i2}$

whereby their total value z is the maximum feasible.

Let us consider the relation $\frac{\alpha_{i2}}{\alpha_{i1}} = k_i$ for all i (ratios of output of each machine tool for components I and II). Thus, for the first machine tool one component I is equivalent to k_1 components II, for the second machine tool to k_2 components II, and so forth. We can assume that values $k_1, k_2 \ldots$ increase such that $k_1 \leqq k_2 \leqq \ldots$; if this is not the case, we can achieve it by re-numbering the tools, in ascending order and then allocate No. 1 to that machine tool which has the smallest ratio. Thus we can assume that the inequalities $k_1 \leqq k_2 \leqq \ldots$ are valid. Obviously it is most advantageous to produce component I on the first lathe, since if this tool does not produce component I, it will produce only k_1 components II, and k_1 is smaller than $k_2, k_3 \ldots$. To produce component I on the second lathe is less advantageous than on the first lathe, but more so than on other lathes. Thus it is easy to understand that the tools occurring first in the sequence should be reserved for component I and the last-occurring tools should be reserved for component II: i.e. for the former, $h_{i1} = 1$, and $h_{i2} = 0$; for the latter, $h_{i1} = 0$, and $h_{i2} = 1$; whereby the total output of both components must be equal. To satisfy these requirements, we select the value s so that:

$$\sum_{i=1}^{s-1} \alpha_{i1} < \sum_{i=s}^{n} \alpha_{i2};$$

$$\sum_{i=1}^{s} \alpha_{i1} \geqq \sum_{i=s+1}^{n} \alpha_{i2}.$$

This means that to reserve the lathe $(s-1)$ for component I is not good enough, since the output of component II will be greater, whereas to reserve the lathe s will be sufficient. Clearly we solve the problem if we take $h_{i1} = 1$, $h_{i2} = 0$; for $i = 1, 2, \ldots, s-1$; $h_{i1} = 0$, $h_{i2} = 1$ for $i = s+1, \ldots, n$, and if we derive h_{s1} and h_{s2} from conditions

$$h_{s1}+h_{s2} = 1;$$

$$\sum_{i=1}^{s-1} \alpha_{i1}+h_{s1}\,\alpha_{s1} = \sum_{i=s+1}^{n} \alpha_{i2}+h_{s2}\,\alpha_{s2}.$$

We apply this procedure to our Example 1 (page 227). The outputs of machine tool types were as follows:

TABLE 1

Component	Type of Lathe		
	centre	turret	automatic
I	30	60	30
II	60	90	80

We obtain the following ratios: $\frac{60}{30} = 2$; $\frac{90}{60} = \frac{3}{2}$; $\frac{80}{30} = \frac{8}{3}$, or in ascending order: $\frac{3}{2} < 2 < \frac{8}{3}$. We arrange the outputs in the same order (turret—centre—automatic) and obtain the following values for α_{ik}:

$$\alpha_{11} = 60; \quad \alpha_{21} = 30; \quad \alpha_{31} = 30;$$
$$\alpha_{12} = 90; \quad \alpha_{22} = 60; \quad \alpha_{32} = 80.$$

Setting $s = 2$, we have:

$$\sum_{i=1}^{s-1} \alpha_{i1} = \alpha_{s1} = 60 < \sum_{i=s}^{n} \alpha_{i2} = \alpha_{22}+\alpha_{32} = 140;$$

$$\sum_{i=1}^{s} \alpha_{i1} = \alpha_{11}+\alpha_{12} = 90 > \sum_{i=s+1}^{n} \alpha_{i2} = \alpha_{32} = 80.$$

Consequently, $h_{11} = 1$; $h_{12} = 0$; $h_{31} = 0$; $h_{32} = 1$.

To find h_{21} and h_{22} we have the equation:

$$h_{21}+h_{22} = 1;$$
$$60+30h_{21} = 80+60h_{22},$$

giving

$$h_{21} = \frac{8}{9}; \qquad h_{22} = \frac{1}{9},$$

which leads to the most advantageous work distribution stated in Table 2 (Section I, p. 228).

Now we should like to draw attention to a point arising from the procedure just described, which enables this procedure to be extended from the simplest case, $m = 2$, to any m. It is, that the complete solution is perfectly equivalent to finding k_s which corresponds to that s on which we base our selection. Indeed, if this relation $k_s = \frac{\alpha_{s2}}{\alpha_{s1}} = \frac{\lambda_1}{\lambda_2}$ (which is more convenient) is known, then the whole solution can be found immediately: component I is preferable (i.e. $h_{i1} = 1$; $h_{i2} = 0$) for those i for which $\frac{\alpha_{i2}}{\alpha_{i1}} < \frac{\lambda_1}{\lambda_2}$ (or, which is the same, $\lambda_1\alpha_{i1} > \lambda_2\alpha_{i2}$); component II is preferable (i.e. $h_{i1} = 0$; $h_{i2} = 1$) whenever $\lambda_2\alpha_{i2} > \lambda_1\alpha_{i1}$; and finally, h must be determined from $\Sigma\, \alpha_{i1}h_{i1} = \Sigma\, \alpha_{i2}h_{i2}$ for those i for which $\lambda_1\alpha_{i1} = \lambda_2\alpha_{i2}$. This resolving relation is the equilibrium indicator in the maximising allocation between the two components. In our particular example this equilibrium is established on the centre lathes, whereby $\lambda_1 : \lambda_2 = 2 : 1$. It may be noted that this resolving relation is determined by the totality of the conditions of the problem; for instance, it cannot be expressed by $k_1, k_2, \ldots$ alone. Indeed, if we had two automatic lathes instead of one, then in the case of maximum loading these would have to be partly used for component I, and not only the turret and centre lathes. Thus, the resolving relation will be $\lambda_1 : \lambda_2 = 8 : 3$. On the other hand, should the number of turret lathes be trebled, this relation would be $3 : 2$.

We use this notion of resolving relations in evolving a method applicable to any m. Instead of finding numerous values h_{ik}, one would like to find relations $\lambda_1 : \lambda_2 : \ldots : \lambda_m$ (equilibrium indicators for maximum loading) which, as in the case of $m = 2$, would enable us to pick out directly those h_{ik} which should be made zero. Indeed, this method is usable; we describe it below in full detail. Before we do this, however, we should mention an auxiliary factor.

2. Transformation of Condition (3), of Problem A

In view of the discussion that follows it is important to show that condition (3) of problem A can be presented in another form, which is equivalent to the original.

Let us recall the formulation of problem A.

From given numbers $\alpha_{ik} \leqq 0$ ($i = 1, 2, \ldots, n$; $k = 1, 2, \ldots, m$) find h_{ik} from the conditions:

(1) $h_{ik} \geqq 0$;

(2) $\sum_{k=1}^{m} h_{ik} = 1 \quad (i = 1, 2, \ldots, n)$;

(3) if we introduce the expression $z_k = \sum_{i=1}^{n} \alpha_{ik}\, h_{ik}$;

whereby $z_1 = z_2 = \ldots = z_m$ and their common value z is the maximum feasible.

When considering the conditions which must satisfy the values h_{ik}, we could proceed in a slightly different manner from that of Section 1. Thus, since the number of complete sets is determined by the component occurring in the smallest quantity, that is by the smallest value of z_k, this number is $z' = \min(z_1, z_2, \ldots, z_m)$. This number z' should be as large as possible. Thus we come to problem A'.

Problem A'. Condition (1) and (2) are the same as in problem A, but instead of (3) we have

(3') Value $z' = \min(z_1, z_2, \ldots, z_m)$ is the maximum feasible.

We will now demonstrate that problems A and A' are equivalent; or, more accurately, we will prove the following statement:

Theorem. If C is the maximum value of z in problem A, and if C' is the maximum value of z' in problem A', then $C = C'$; if thereby a certain system $\{h_{ik}\}$ is a maximum in problem A, it will also be a maximum in problem A'; conversely, if a system $\{h'_{ik}\}$ is a maximum in problem A', it can be readily transformed into a system $\{h_{ik}\}$ which is a maximum in problem A.

Proof. Assume that a system $\{h_{ik}\}$ produces a maximum in problem A; that is, $z_1 = z_2 = \ldots = z_m = z = C$. Obviously, for this system

$$z' = \min(z_1, z_2, \ldots, z_m) = \min(C, C, \ldots, C) = C.$$

Since C is a value of z' for a certain selection of h_{ik}, and C' is max z' for all possible selections, it follows that $C \leqq C'$.

To prove the reverse inequality, let us consider the basic case when all $\alpha_{ik} > 0$. For a certain system $\{h'_{ik}\}$ we have $z_k = \min(z_1, z_2, z_3, \ldots, z'_m) = C'$. We claim that in this case definitely all $z' = C'$. Indeed, let one of them be $> C'$, for instance $z' > C'$. In this case it should be possible to reduce all h_{i1} slightly, which would slightly increase all remaining h_{ik}; $z_1 > C'$ would still apply, and all $z_2, \ldots, z_m$ would be increased and would also be $> C'$. Consequently, for this new system $z' = \min(z_1, z_2, \ldots, z_m)$ would be $> C'$; this, however, contradicts the statement that C' is the greatest possible value of z'. Thus, unavoidably $z_1 = z_2 = \ldots = z_m = C'$. Consequently, h'_{ik} produces a system of values for which $z_1 = z_2 = \ldots = z_m$ with a common value $z = C'$; as C is the maximum possible value of z, it follows that unavoidably $C' \leqq C$.

This inequality leads, in combination with the previous inequality, to the conclusion that $C = C'$.

The second inequality $C' \leqq C$ is valid for the case when all $\alpha_{ik} > 0$; if some $\alpha_{ik} = 0$, this inequality is also valid, although the proof would require some additional considerations, which we prefer not to discuss here.

3. Basis of the Method of Resolving Multipliers

We will now show that the solution of problem A, which involves the finding of a system nm of values h_{ik} can be replaced by the problem of finding only m numbers $\lambda_1, \lambda_2, \ldots, \lambda_m$ (resolving multipliers).

We designate as 'resolving multipliers for problem A' such a system m of numbers $\lambda_1, \lambda_2, \ldots, \lambda_m$ ($\lambda_k \geqq 0$ and not all 0), which satisfies the following: If for each given i we consider products

$$\lambda_1\alpha_{i1};\ \lambda_2\alpha_{i2};\ \ldots;\ \lambda_m\alpha_{im},$$

designate the value of the largest product by t_i, and assume those h_{ik} to be zero for which the respective product is not a maximum $\lambda_k\alpha_{ik} < t_i$; then the remaining h_{ik} can be found from conditions:

$$(1)\quad h_{ik} \leqq 0; \qquad (2)\quad \sum_{k=1}^{m} h_{ik} = 1; \qquad (3)\quad z_1 = z_2 = \ldots = z_m$$

First of all we will show that problem A can indeed be solved once the resolving multipliers have been found. We postulate: if the resolving multipliers $\lambda_1, \lambda_2, \ldots, \lambda_m$ have been found and the numbers h^*_{ik} have been determined as explained above, then the value $z = z^*$ obtained with the help of these numbers is the highest possible value.

Indeed for a system of numbers h^*_{ik} we have:

$$\left(\sum_{k=1}^{m} \lambda_k\right) z^* = \sum_{k=1}^{m} \lambda_k z^*_k = \sum_{k=1}^{m} \lambda_k \sum_{i=1}^{n} \alpha_{ik} h^*_{ik} =$$

$$= \sum_{i=1}^{n} \sum_{k=1}^{m} (\lambda_k\alpha_{ik})\, h^*_{ik} = \sum_{i=1}^{n} \sum_{k=1}^{m} t_i h^*_{ik} = \sum_{i=1}^{n} t_2$$

(We were able everywhere to replace $\lambda_k\alpha_{ik}$ by t_i, because in those cases when $\lambda_k\alpha_{ik} < t_i$ it has been postulated that $h^*_{ik} = 0$.)

Now, let h_{ik} be another system of numbers for which $z_1 = z_2 \ldots = z_m = z$. We have then:

$$\left(\sum_{k=1}^{m} \lambda_k\right) z = \sum_{k=1}^{m} \lambda_k z_k = \sum_{k=1}^{m} \lambda_k \sum_{i=1}^{n} \alpha_{ik} h_{ik} =$$

$$= \sum_{i=1}^{n} \sum_{k=1}^{m} (\lambda_k\alpha_{ik})\, h_{ik} \leqq \sum_{i=1}^{n} \sum_{k=1}^{m} t_i h_{ik} = \sum_{i} t_i.$$

By comparing this inequality with the preceding equation we obtain:

$$\left(\sum_{k=1}^{m} \lambda_k\right) z \leqq \left(\sum_{k=1}^{m} \lambda_k\right) z^*,$$

or

$$z \leqq z^*.$$

This proves that z^* is the maximum value of z; that means that numbers h^*_{ik} determined by means of resolving multipliers indeed produce the solution of problem A.[1]

[1] In order to show the significance of the introduction of resolving multipliers, I should like to explain somewhat more fully the method of resolving the problem A, as derived from the general rules of analysis. The gist of problem A is the finding of the maximum

Thus, it comes to finding the resolving multipliers. We will now show how to find them. First of all, it should be noted that if instead of resolving multipliers we take a random set of numbers $\lambda_1^0, \lambda_2^0, \ldots, \lambda_m^0$, we could still proceed as if these were the desired resolving multipliers, namely we could consider products $\lambda_1^0\alpha_{i1}$; $\lambda_2^0\alpha_{i2}$; ...; $\lambda_m^0\alpha_{im}$ and for all those k for which the corresponding product is not a maximum we could assume $h_{ik} = 0$. However, with such a random set it will be usually found that only one product will be a maximum, so that for a given i all h_{ik} will be zero except one, which will have to be 1.

Thus, with such a random selection of λ_k the values h_{ik} can be fully determined, and also definite values of z_k : $z_1^0, z_2^0, \ldots, z_m^0$. Of course, these values will be unequal, and they cannot be made equal unless λ_k is changed. In what direction then should λ_k be modified?

We know that the problem will be solved when min $(z_1, z_2, \ldots, z_m)$ will be the maximum feasible. But this minimum is determined by the smallest value z_k.

Let a number z_s^0 be the smallest of numbers $z_1^0, z_2^0, \ldots, z_m^0$ in the resulting system. We want to make it larger; but it is obvious that it will become larger if we replace λ_s by a larger figure without changing the remaining λ_k. Indeed, in the majority of cases the product $\lambda_s\alpha_{is}$ will become a maximum in its turn, and h_{is} will be assumed to be unity, so that z_s will be greater than z_s^0, and, generally speaking, min $(z_1, z_2, \ldots, z_m)$ will have a greater value than before.

Actually this is the fundamental principle for finding the resolving multipliers, namely: by modifying λ_k we adjust z_k and thus gradually advance to the required extremum. Of course, variations are possible: instead of adjusting the lagging z_k upwards, it is possible to adjust those z_k which are too high towards the other values, by reducing the corresponding λ_k. However, if these operations are carried out haphazardly and without a definite system, they are unlikely to be ever completed: some values z_k may be increased but

value of z which represents a linear function of h_{ik} with some additional conditions. It is known that in order to find the maximum of a linear function for a certain range it is sufficient to compare the end values and to select the greater one. The same rule applies to the maximum of a linear function of many variables in a polygon—it is sufficient to compare its values at the vertices. Translating this rule into analytical language: in this case it is necessary to select systems consisting of $(n+m-1)$ numbers h_{ik}, taking the remaining h_{ik} equal to zero, and to determine the selected h_{ik} from $(n+m-1)$ equations

$$\sum_k h_{ik} = 1; \quad z_1 = z_2 = \ldots = z_m$$

and to compare the values z so obtained. When doing each test it will be necessary to solve only a small number of equations, but the total number of the tests to be done will be

$$\sum_{ij=0} (-1)^{i+j} C_{(m-i)(n-j)}^{m+n-1} \; C_m^i C_n^j \qquad (C_n^0 = 1;\ C_n^m = 0, \text{ if } m > n),$$

that is: if $n=3$, $m=3$ there will be 90 tests, if $n=m=4$ there will be 6256 tests; in the problem set by the Plywood Trust with $n=8$, $m=5$ the number of tests will be in the order of a billion. Thanks to the existence of resolving multipliers all unnecessary systems can be eliminated, so that only one system will have to be solved.

others may be decreased, and we will not get nearer to the result. Consequently, when carrying out this procedure, it is better to adhere to a definite system of calculation, which we will now describe. For the sake of clarity we will discuss this scheme by the way of an example.

4. An Example of Systematic Calculation

We will consider the problem of the best work-loading of excavators. (See Example 3, page 234.)

In order to complete the required jobs in the shortest possible time, it is necessary so to distribute the work as to achieve the maximum output per hour, on condition that all jobs advance evenly. In this case the problem corresponds exactly to problem A, whereby α_{ik} are the output data of the various excavators (see Table 2).

Table 2

Values α_{ik}

		i = 1	2	3
	1	105	107	64
k	2	56	66	38
	3	56	83	53

First of all it is advantageous to select as initial values of $\lambda_k(\lambda_k^0)$ those magnitudes which are inversely proportional to sums $\sum_i \alpha_{ik}$; $\lambda_k^0 = \frac{P}{\sum_i \alpha_{ik}}$, where P may be any number.

In our example, let $P = 1000$;

$$\lambda_1^0 = \frac{1000}{276} = 3{\cdot}62; \quad \lambda_2^0 = \frac{1000}{160} = 6{\cdot}25; \quad \lambda_3^0 = \frac{1000}{192} = 5{\cdot}21.$$

We now multiply the elements α_{ik} by λ_k^0, that is, we multiply the first column of the table by $\lambda_1^0 = 3{\cdot}62$, the second column by 6·25, and the third column by 5·21.

The resulting products $\lambda_k \alpha_{ik}$ are given in Table 4; the left-hand column shows the zero approximation. We select the maximum value for each i (for each column). For these values we set $h_{ik} = 1$, for the other values $h_{ik} = 0$. The products $\alpha_{ik} h_{ki}$ are shown on the right of Table 4. By forming the total for each row we obtain the values z_k for the zero approximation: $z_1^0 = 105$; $z_2^0 = 0$; $z_3^0 = 136$.

As z_2 is the smallest, we have to increase λ_2. This we have to do so as to ensure the first coincidence, namely: we examine the elements of the low valued second row ($\lambda_k^0 \alpha_{ik}$ in Table 4) and select that value which is nearest to the highest element of its column. This is 412, which is near to 432. Now we increase λ_2 and bring it up to the maximum; to do this we introduce 'corrective multiplier' $\lambda_2^1 : \lambda_2^0 = 432 : 412 = 1{\cdot}05$[1]; we leave λ_1 and λ_3 as they are, i.e. their corrective multiplier is unity (λ_k and all corrective multipliers for various approximations are stated in Table 3). By multiplying the values $\lambda_k^0\alpha_{ik}$ of the second row with this corrective multiplier 1·05 and transcribing the first and the third rows without change, we obtain values $\lambda_k'\alpha_{ik}$ for the first approximation. Maximum values in each row are shown in heavy print.

TABLE 3

Resolving Multipliers

	Initial Values	Corrective Multipliers 1st approximation	Corrective Multipliers 2nd approximation	Final Values
λ_1	3·62	1	0·97	3·45
λ_2	6·25	1·05	1	6·56
λ_3	5·21	1	1	5·21

Now all values h_{ik} have been determined; they equal 0 or 1, except h_{22} and h_{23} which correspond to equal products. We will try to determine them so that z_2 and z_3 are equal. Let $h_{22} = u$; bearing in mind that $h_{22}+h_{23} = 1$, we have $h_{23} = 1-u$, and since $z_2 = z_3$:

$$66\,u = 83\,(1-u)+53;$$

it follows that

$$u = 0{\cdot}913.$$

Consequently $h_{22} = 0{\cdot}913;\quad h_{23} = 0{\cdot}087.$

Substituting these values for $\alpha_{ik}h_{ik}$ in Table 4, we obtain for z_k in the first approximation $z_1 = 105$; $z_2 = z_3 = 60{\cdot}2$. It will be seen that the last two values lag behind; it is necessary to increase λ_2 and λ_3. Alternatively we can reduce λ_1, since it is the ratio of the λ_k's that matters. Thus we introduce for λ_1 a corrective multiplier <1, such that the maximum element 380 of the first row equals one of the elements of the same column. It is obvious that this corrective multiplier must be $\lambda_1'' : \lambda_1' = 368 : 380 = 0{\cdot}97$. By multiplying the elements of the first row with this multiplier and transcribing the second and third rows without change, we obtain $\lambda_k''\alpha_{ik}$ for the second approximation. Again the maximum in each column is shown in heavy type; there are two such values in the first and second column, and the corresponding h_{ik} are not determined.

If $h_{11} = x$; $h_{22} = y$, then $h_{12} = 1-x$; $h_{23} = 1-y$. Let us try to find such x and y as to achieve the equality $z_1 = z_2 = z_3$. We have the following values (Table 4).

$$z_1 = 105x;\; z_2 = 56\,(1-x)+66y \text{ and } z_3 = 83\,(1-y)+53.$$

[1] All values relating to the zero approximation are identified by ^{0} above the line, all values relating to the first approximation by $'$, and so on.

Consequently, we obtain the equations:

$$105x = 56\,(1-x)+66y = 83\,(1-y)+53 = z;$$

it follows:

$$x = \frac{1}{105}z; \qquad y = \frac{136}{83}-\frac{1}{83}z$$

Introducing these expressions into the second equation:

$$164{\cdot}2-0{\cdot}533z-0{\cdot}795z = z,$$

from which: $z = 70{\cdot}5$; further, $x = 0{\cdot}67$; $y = 0{\cdot}79$.

These values for x and y define the value h_{ik} for the second approximation, which is the solution of the problem.

TABLE 4

$\lambda_k \alpha_{ik}$			$\alpha_{ik} h_{ik}$			z_k
			Zero Approximation			
380*	387	232	105 × 1	107 × 0	64 × 0	105
350	412	238	56 × 0	66 × 0	38 × 0	0
282	**432**	**276**	56 × 0	83 × 1	53 × 1	136
			First Approximation			
380	387	232	105 × 1	107 × 0	64 × 0	105
368	**432**	250	56 × 0	66 × 0·913	38 × 0	60·2
282	**432**	**276**	56 × 0	83 × 0·087	53 × 1	60·2
			Second Approximation			
368	375	225	105 × 0·67	107 × 0	64 × 0	70·5
368	**432**	250	56 × 0·33	66 × 0·79	38 × 0	70·5
282	**432**	**276**	56 × 0	83 × 0·21	53 × 1	70·5

* In each approximation the highest value $\lambda_k \alpha_{ik}$ is printed in heavy type.

The value $z = 70{\cdot}5$ indicates the highest hourly output of all three kinds of work, on condition that these outputs are equal.

Since it is required to produce 20,000 m^3 of each type of work, the minimum time is 20,000 : 70·5 = 282 hours. By multiplying the values of h_{ik} with 282 we obtain the period of time for each machine for each kind of work as stated above (Section 3, Table 5).

In this example we have shown the basic procedure for solving the problem. Now we will comment on some aspects of putting it into effect.

5. Further Comments on the Procedure

First of all we should point out that the procedure explained in the foregoing example was particularly easy to apply. In other cases its application may lead to a difficulty which we will now consider. When changing from zero approximation to first approximation we have adjusted z_2 according to z_3. By finding suitable h_{22} and h_{23} we made z_2 equal to z_3. However, this is not always possible. To find $u = 0{\cdot}913$ we had an equation which, generally, will be:

$$a+bu = c(1-u)+d,$$

its solution being not always within the limits 0 and 1. Yet, this condition $0 \leqq u \leqq 1$ is absolutely essential for our purpose. We note that in any case, $a < (c+d)$ (this inequality means that $z_2^0 < z_3^0$, since if $u = 0$ both sides of the equation will be z and z). If we now set $(a+b) > d$, then the solution will satisfy the inequality $0 < u < 1$. However, if $(a+b) < d$ the solution will be < 1. In this case we have to assume $u = 1$, so as to bring z_2 as close as possible to z_3, even if we cannot achieve the equality $z_2 = z_3$.

This case can also be considered from another angle. Since we are interested in the greatest possible increase of min (z_2, z_3), we want to find the biggest number t which for a certain $u\,(0 \leqq u \leqq 1)$ will satisfy both inequalities

$$a+bu \geqq t; \; c(1-u)+d \geqq t.$$

Since from the first inequality

$$u \geqq \frac{t-a}{b}$$

and also $u \geqq 0$, the second inequality leads to:

$$t \leqq d+c(1-u) \begin{cases} \leqq c+d \\ \leqq c\left(1-\dfrac{t-a}{b}\right)+b \end{cases}$$

By solving these two inequalities in respect to t and choosing the lower limit, we obtain the maximum t which enables the original inequalities to be solved.

This last approach is also applicable when more than two values of z_k are involved.

For instance, if two equal values z_k have to be adjusted to a third value, then the equation to be solved will be:

$$a+bx = c+dy = e(1-x)+f(1-y)+g.$$

Solutions x and y may again be outside the limits 0 and 1. Since we are primarily interested in the maximum value of min (z_1, z_2, z_3), we have again to find the maximum t which would enable us to satisfy all inequalities,

$$a+bx \geqq t; \; c+dy \geqq t; \; e(1-x)+f(1-y)+g \geqq t.$$

It follows that

$$x \geqq \frac{t-a}{b}; \quad y \geqq \frac{t-c}{d}$$

and also $x \geqq 0$; $y \geqq 0$. Thus, the third inequality leads to:

$$t \leqq \begin{cases} e\left(1-\frac{t-a}{b}\right)+f\left(1-\frac{t-c}{d}\right)+g \\ e+f\left(1-\frac{t-c}{d}\right)+g \\ e\left(1-\frac{t-a}{b}\right)+f+g \\ e+f+g \end{cases}$$

depending on which pair of inequalities is used for x and y. By solving these inequalities in respect of t and selecting the least value obtained, we will find the required value of t, namely the maximum value which would satisfy all three original inequalities. After t has been found it is easy to determine x and y, and thus to complete this particular approximation. For the next approximation we again pick out one or several least significant z_k and increase the respective λ_k.

We should note that in practice we have to use the first of several inequalities which determine t; it gives the least value of t for the case which satisfies the equations $z_1 = z_2 = z_3$. We may also point out that the considerations used in the case of double or triple coincidence can also be used, with some modifications, in more complicated cases.

The foregoing description of the calculating procedure, taken together with the present comments, provides for a definite and rigid means for solving the problem. At every stage it is necessary to find the least significant value (or values if they are equal) of z_k and to adjust it as described. We ought to make clear that the literal use of this procedure can be recommended for simple cases (n being small) or alternatively, for complicated cases (n being large) near the end of calculation, when we have already nearly reached the solution (z_k being nearly equal). However, at the beginning of a calculation it is advisable to deviate from this scheme, for instance by adjusting upwards several low values of z_k simultaneously; by adjusting downwards those z_k which are too high (by reducing λ_k); there is no need to try scrupulously to equalise the least significant z_k by solving intermediate systems. All these simplifications are frequently helpful and can often reduce the calculation time; they do not affect the method. What is important is to find the λ_k; just how we do it does not matter.

It is useful to remember that all intermediate calculations with regard to λ_k can be done roughly with two to three decimals (on a slide rule), without affecting the result. If a precise result is required, it is quite sufficient to do only the final calculation with the desired degree of precision—the solution of the system which defines the final values of h_{ik}. It should be borne in mind, however, that if the relative error of our calculation is 0·01, then any two products $\lambda_k \alpha_{ik}$ which differ by less than 0·01 must be considered to be equal.

Finally, let us consider the following point. The difficulty of finding a solution depends very much on values n and m; the difficulty increases particularly when m goes up. For instance, we have seen that for $m = 2$ the solution is extremely easy for any n. For this reason we should try to reduce m and n. First of all, if two columns in the table of α_{ik} are proportional, for instance $\alpha_{i2} = k\alpha_{i1}$ for any i, then it is advisable to introduce new values $\alpha'_i = \alpha_{i1}(1+k)$ to replace α_{i1} and α_{i2}, i.e. to reduce n by unity. In other words, if we have two machine tools, the output of which is proportional, we assume a fictitious machine tool having the sum of their capacities. Further, if $m > n$ it is worthwhile to interchange them, i.e. to replace α_{ik} by $\alpha^*_{ik} = \alpha_{ik}$; now, however, instead of max z we have to search for a minimum, namely, such h_{ik} that $z_1 = z_2 = \ldots = z_m$ and that their common value is a minimum. More plainly, instead of trying to achieve the maximum daily output we consider the problem of producing a given output in minimum of time; evidently, the two problems are equivalent.

6. Checking the Result

In any mathematical problem, in order to verify the result, it is unnecessary to check the whole solution. For instance, to check the root of an equation it is sufficient to substitute it. Similarly, in order to verify the solution of problem A it is sufficient to consider the final values of λ_k and products $\lambda_k \alpha_{ik}$ of the last approximation and to check that $h_{ik} > 0$ correspond to maximum $\lambda_k \alpha_{ik}$, and that all z_k are equal. If this is so, then the result is correct. It is useful to have such a check, inasmuch as an engineer or an economist can do it easily in 10-15 minutes, whereas the lengthy calculation can be entrusted to a less highly qualified person.

7. Approximate Solution of Problem A

Nevertheless, when n and m are not small, the solution of problem A is tiresome and time-consuming. Thus it is desirable to find a simple method of finding, if not the correct result, then one which is approximate and yet equally effective. We will now indicate some ways which may be used to work out such a method.

If $h_{ik} > 0$, the result applies only to those pairs (i, k) which correspond to the maximum products $\lambda_k \alpha_{ik}$. Consequently, an approximate solution can be reached if values h_{ik} differing from 0 are accepted for those (i, k), for which the product $\lambda_k\alpha_{ik}$ is close to a maximum. This, the first approximate method, is as follows. In the Tables of products $\lambda_k\alpha_{ik}$ in each column except one we underline the maximum $\lambda_k\alpha_{ik}$ as well as the value nearest to the maximum. (There is no need to underline this nearest value if it is relatively furthest away from its maximum.) For the underlined (i, k) we try to determine h_{ik} from conditions $\sum_k h_{ik} = 1$ and equality $z_1 = z_2 = \ldots = z_m$. The reader may check for himself whether an application of this method to the example in section 4 leads straight to the final solution.

The other method is based on a different consideration. In the foregoing section 6 we have already pointed out that if two columns are proportionate, they can be combined into one. In order to obtain an approximate solution this combination can be carried out also in cases when the proportional relation is only approximate. By grouping together elements of nearly the same magnitude n and m can be significantly reduced and the problem simplified accordingly. Of course a solution of this simplified problem instead of the original will be only an approximation.

8. Application of Present Method to Problem B

As compared with problem A, problem B has an additional condition in that the solution must satisfy the inequality

$$\sum_{i,k} c_{ik} h_{ik} \leqq C,$$

wherein $c_{ik} \geq 0$ and C is given.

The method of resolving multipliers is applicable to this problem also. Without going into details as with problem A, we indicate the essential difference of applying this method to problem B.

Apart from λ_k which correspond to z_k we have to introduce a further resolving multiplier μ corresponding to

$$R = \sum_{i,k} c_{ik} h_{ik}.$$

In this case we will designate the numbers $\lambda_1, \lambda_2, \ldots, \lambda_k$ and μ as resolving multipliers on the following condition: if for each i the number t_i indicates the greatest value

$$\lambda_1 \alpha_{i1} - \mu c_{i1};\ \lambda_2 \alpha_{i2} - \mu c_{i2};\ \ldots;\ \lambda_m \alpha_{im} - \mu c_{im}$$

then, assuming $h_{ik} = 0$ if $\lambda_k \alpha_{ik} - \mu c_{ik} < t_i$, it should be possible to find other values h_{ik} from the conditions:

$$(1)\ \ h_{ik} \geqq 0; \qquad (2)\ \ \sum_{k=1}^{m} h_{ik} = 1; \qquad (3)\ \ z_1 = z_2 = \ldots = z_m;$$

$$(4)\ \ R = \sum_{i,k} c_{ik} h_{ik} = C.^1$$

Again we maintain that when the resolving multipliers have been found

[1] In the case of $\mu = 0$ it is sufficient that $R \leqq C$.

and h_{ik}^* determined accordingly as described above, then a solution has been obtained. Indeed, for $h_{ik} = h_{ik}^*$ found in this way we have:

$$\left(\sum_{k=1}^{m} \lambda_k\right) z^* - \mu C = \sum_k \lambda_k \sum_i \alpha_{ik} h_{ik}^* - \mu \sum_{ik} c_{ik} h_{ik}^* =$$
$$= \sum_i \sum_k (\lambda_k \alpha_{ik} - \mu c_{ik})\, h_{ik}^* = \sum_i t_i$$

If now h_{ik} are numbers (chosen in any other way) which satisfy the above conditions (1), (2), (3) and $R \leqq C$, then:

$$\left(\sum_{k=1}^{m} \lambda_k\right) z - \mu C \leqq \sum_k \lambda_k \sum_i \alpha_{ik} h_{ik} - \mu \sum_{i,k} c_{ik} h_{ik} = \sum_i \sum_k (\lambda_k \alpha_{ik} - \mu c_{ik})\, h_{ik} \leqq$$
$$\leqq \sum_i \sum_k t_i h_{ik} = \sum_i t_i$$

From a comparison of this inequality with the preceding equality it follows that $z \leqq z^*$, that means the solution of the problem is in fact obtained if $h_{ik} = h_{ik}^*$.

Thus the question is again reduced to the finding of resolving multipliers.[1] On the whole the means for finding them are the same as in problem A. Without going into detail, we will illustrate these means as well as some additional considerations by solving the following example.

Example. The table α_{ik} is the same as in the example of section 4 (Table 2). Values c_{ik} are as in Table 5; we assume $C = 43$. We cannot use the previously found solution, since the resulting values h_{ik} lead to:

$$R = 12 \times 0{\cdot}67 + 12 \times 0{\cdot}33 + 20 \times 0{\cdot}785 + 17 \times 0{\cdot}215 + 14 \cdot 1 = 45{\cdot}4 > 43$$

TABLE 5

Values c_{ik}

		i = 1	2	3
	1	12	21	15
k	2	12	20	11
	3	12	17	14

As zero starting values of λ_k^0 we take the same values as before; for μ we can take, for instance, the value

$$\mu^0 = \frac{1000}{\sum_{i,k} c_{ik}} = \frac{1000}{134} = 7{\cdot}45$$

[1] Contrary to problem A, in this case one cannot always guarantee that resolving multipliers exist. This is because the problem B is not always solvable. With reference to conditions (1), (2), (3) and (4), this problem is solvable only if $\Sigma\, c_{ik_i} \leqq C$, wherein c_{ik_i} is the least significant of numbers $c_{i1}, c_{i2}, \ldots, c_{im}$. It may be noted that problem B will be always solvable if condition (2) be replaced by condition $\sum_k h_{ik} \leqq 1$.

TABLE 6

Corrective Multipliers

Starting Values		1st approxim.	2nd approxim.	3rd approxim.	Final Values
λ_1	3·62	1	0·973	1	3·53
λ_2	6·25	1·063	1	1	6·65
λ_3	5·21	1	1	0·976	5·07
μ	7·45	1	1	0·751	5·59

For given λ_k^0 and μ^0 we calculate the values $\lambda_k\alpha_{ik}-\mu c_{ik}$ (see Table 7) and in each column we indicate by heavy type the most significant value; h_{ik} corresponding to these highest values we set equal to 1, otherwise equal to 0. As can be seen, z_2 is too low. Accidentally, R happens to be equal to $C = 43$. Now we have to increase z_2.

Procedure for Solving Problem B

TABLE 7

$\lambda_k\alpha_{ik}-\mu c_{ik}$			$\alpha_{ik}h_{ik}$ and $c_{ik}h_{ik}$			z_k	R
Zero Approximation							
381—90	388—156	231—111	105 ×1 12	107 ×9 21	64 ×9 15	105	
349—90	412—149	237— 82	56 ×0 12	66 ×0 20	38 ×0 11	0	43
292—90	**432—127**	**276—105**	56 ×0 12	83 ×1 17	53 ×1 14	136	
First Approximation							
381—90	388—156	231—111	105 ×1 12	107 ×0 21	64 ×0 15	105	
371—90	438—149	**252— 82**	56 ×0 12	66 ×0 20	38 ×1 11	38	40
292—90	**432—127**	**276—105**	56 ×0 12	83 ×1 17	53 ×0 14	83	
Second Approximation							
371—90	378—156	225—111	105 ×0·58 12	107 ×0 21	64 ×0 15	61	
371—90	438—149	252— 82	56 ×0·42 12	66 ×0 20	38 ×1 11	61	40
292—90	**432—127**	**276—105**	56 ×0 12	63 ×1 17	53 ×0 14	83	

TABLE 7—*cont.*

$\lambda_k\ \alpha_{ik}$—μc_{ik}			$\alpha_{ik}\ h_{ik}$ and $c_{ik}\ h_{ik}$			z_k	R
			Third Approximation				
371—69	378—117	225—85	105 ×0·662 12	107 ×0 21	64 ×0 15	69·6	
371—69	**438—112**	**252—61**	56 ×0·338 12	66 ×0·490 20	38 ×0·490 11	69·6	43
285—69	**421— 95**	**269—79**	56 ×0 12	83 ×0·510 17	53 ×0·510 14	69·6	

It will be seen that the value nearest to its maximum is 237-82. We increase λ_2 by providing a multiplier ε_2, which (in order to achieve coincidence) must be found from the equation

$$237\,\varepsilon_2 - 82 = 276 - 105;$$

thus $\varepsilon_2 = 253 : 237 = 1{\cdot}063$. We multiply by it the first elements of the second row, and indicate the maxima. We have to determine $h_{32} = u$ and $h_{33} = 1-u$. Since the equality $z_2 = 38u = 53\,(1-u)+83 = z_3$ cannot be satisfied if $0 \leqq u \leqq 1$, it is necessary to bring z_2 and z_3 together as closely as possible. Obviously, to achieve this we have to take $u = 1$. Thus we find the first approximation, whereby $R = 40$. To achieve the next approximation it is necessary to increase z_2 or instead to decrease z_1. To find the multiplier ε_1 for λ_1 we again form an equation $381\,\varepsilon_1 - 90 = 371 - 90$; and it follows that $\varepsilon_1 = 0{\cdot}973$. This leads to the second approximation (we omit the minor calculations required). Now we must reduce z_3; i.e. we have to supply a corrective multiplier ε_3 for λ_3. On the other hand, our R is not large enough ($R < C$); we have to increase R. For this purpose μ should be reduced, and we will supply a multiplier γ. The presence of two multipliers, ε_3 and γ, allows for two further coincidences. In any case the problem B demands one additional coincidence, since there is an additional equality $R = C$ for a definition of the remaining h_{ik}. Thus in order to find ε_3 and γ we introduce an equation in accordance with the requirement for two coincidences:

$$(1)\quad 438 - 149\,\gamma = 432\,\varepsilon_3 - 127\,\gamma$$
$$(2)\quad 252 - \ 82\,\gamma = 276\,\varepsilon_3 - 105\,\gamma$$

from which $\varepsilon_3 = 0{\cdot}976$; $\gamma = 0{\cdot}751$. Having introduced these corrective multipliers we come to the third approximation. Now there is a coincidence in each column. We introduce the unknown x, y, v.

$$h_{11} = x;\ h_{12} = 1-x;\ h_{22} = y;\ h_{23} = 1-y;\ h_{32} = v;\ h_{33} = 1-v.$$

Equations $z_1 = z_2 = z_3 = t$ and $R = C$ will be written thus:

$$105x = 56\,(1-x)+66y+38v = 83\,(1-y)+53\,(1-v) = t;$$
$$12x+12\,(1-x)+20y+17\,(1-y)+11v+14\,(1-v) = 43.$$

After simplification the latter equation produces $y = v$, and the former will be

$$105x = 56\,(1-x)+104y = 136\,(1-y) = t$$

which leads to

$$t = 69{\cdot}6;\; x = 0{\cdot}662;\; y = v = 0{\cdot}49.$$

This completes the calculation of the third approximation, which represents the final answer. Note that the maximum output with the additional condition is 69·6, i.e. slightly less than without this condition—70·8 as calculated previously.

9. Application of Present Method to Problem C

Problem C differs from problem A in that z_k is defined in a more complicated manner, namely:

$$z_k = \sum_{i,\,l} \gamma_{ikl}\, h_{ikl}$$

Again, h_{il} must be found according to conditions:

$$h_{il} \geqq 0; \quad \sum_{l} h_{il} = 1;$$
$$z_1 = z_2 = \ldots = z_m \text{ being a maximum.}$$

As in problem A, there are resolving multipliers. These are the numbers $\lambda_1, \ldots, \lambda_m$ which satisfy the following condition: if for each given i the figure t_i designates the most significant of the values

$$\sum_k \lambda_k\, \gamma_{ik1}; \quad \sum_k \lambda_k\, \gamma_{ik2}; \ldots$$

and assuming $h_{il} = 0$ when the corresponding sum $\sum_k \lambda_k\, \gamma_{ikl} < t_i$ is not a maximum, then the remaining h_{il} can be found from conditions:

$$(1)\;\; h_{il} \geqq 0; \qquad (2)\;\; \sum_l h_{il} = 1; \qquad (3)\;\; z_1 = z_2 = \ldots = z_m$$

Just as in the two previous cases, it is possible to prove that a solution can be obtained after the resolving multipliers have been found and h_{il} calculated as described above. As before, the procedure is to find the resolving multipliers, which can be done by the same methods.

Example. Let us solve by way of example the second trunk-cutting problem (page 238). A maximum number of sets of logs 1·5 m, 2·1 m, and 2·9 m long is to be cut from 100 trunks 7·4 m long and 50 trunks 6·4 m long.

Let each log be associated with a resolving multiplier: 1·5 with u; 2·1 with v; and 2·9 with w. Each value l indicates a certain method of cutting; for instance, $i = 1$, $l = 3$ refers to method III of cutting up a trunk 7·4 m long (Table 7, page 237) into rods 1·5+1·5+2·1+2·1 m long. Obviously, in this case $\sum_k \lambda_k \gamma_{ikl}$ is $2u+2v$. It may be remembered that γ_{ikl} is the number of logs k which can be obtained by cutting up trunk i according to method 1, so that in this case $\gamma_{113} = 2$; $\gamma_{123} = 2$. These sums, obtained by various methods of cutting, are stated in a general form in the first column of Table 8. As initial values u, v, w we assume log lengths $u^0 = 1{\cdot}5$; $v^0 = 2{\cdot}1$; $w^0 = 2{\cdot}9$.[1]

We calculate the sums $\sum_k \lambda_k \gamma_{ikl}$ for these data, indicating the highest value (separately for $i = 1$ and $i = 2$). Naturally, in either case the highest value is that corresponding to the first method. We set the corresponding $h_{il} = 1$ and the remaining values equal to zero. In other words, we cut up all bars according to the first method; this produces $z_1 = 300$, $z_2 = 150$, $z_3 = 100$.

Since z_3 is too small, we increase it by increasing w, to ensure the first coincidence. This w is found from $4{\cdot}5+w = 1{\cdot}5+2w$, or $w = 3$.

Now we calculate the second approximation. As a coincidence has occurred, $h_{11} = x$ must be found from the equality $z_1 = z_2$, i.e.

$$3x+1\,(1-x) = x+2\,(1-x)$$

$$\text{or } x = h_{11} = \frac{1}{3};\; h_{12} = \frac{2}{3};\; \text{consequently:}$$

$$z_1 = \frac{100}{3}\times 3+\frac{2}{3}\times 100 = 166{\cdot}6;$$

$$z_3 = \frac{100}{3}\times 1+\frac{2}{3}\,100\times 2 = 166{\cdot}6;$$

$$z_2 = 50\times 3 = 150.$$

Now z_2 must be raised. It is easy to see that $v = 2{\cdot}25$ should be taken to obtain another coincidence. So the third approximation is reached, whereby the fourth coincidence occurs. By introducing the unknown $x = 100h_{11}$, $y = 100h_{12}$, $z = 100h_{13}$, $t = 100h_{14}$ (numbers of trunks 7·4 m long cut up in various ways), the following equations are obtained:

$$3x+y+2z = 2z+2t+150 = x+2y+t;$$
$$x+y+z+t = 100$$

This system is indefinite, since there are more unknowns than equations;

[1] Generally, in problems concerned with reduction of waste, the lengths (or surface areas in two-dimensional cases) should be taken as the first approximations.

one of the unknowns cannot be selected at random, as the remainder must remain positive. In any case it is feasible to put $z = 0$; hence $t = \frac{50}{9} \cong 5$ (the value must be an integer), $x = 33$; $y = 61$. One trunk remains, for which method VI of cutting will be assumed. This determines h_{il} for the third approximation, and leads directly to the solution.

Procedure for Solving Problem C

Table 8

Trunks	Method of Cutting $\Sigma \lambda_k \gamma_{ikl}$	Zero Approximation $u = 1·5$; $v = 2·1$; $w = 2·9$		1st Approximation $u = 1·5$; $v = 2·1$; $w = 3·0$		2nd Approximation $u = 1·5$; $v = 2·25$; $w = 3·0$	
		$\Sigma \lambda_k \gamma_{ikl}$	h_{il}	$\Sigma \lambda_k \gamma_{ikl}$	h_{il}	$\Sigma \lambda_k \gamma_{ikl}$	h_{il}
7·4 ($i=1$)	$l = 1$; I $3u+w$	**7·4**	1	**7·5**	0·333	**7·5**	0·33
	$l = 2$; II $u+2w$	7·3	0	**7·5**	0·661	**7·5**	0·61
	$l = 3$; III $2u+2w$	7·2	0	7·2	0	**7·5**	0
	$l = 4$; IV $2v+w$	7·1	0	7·2	0	**7·5**	0·05
	$l = 5$; V $3u+v$	6·6	0	6·6	0	6·75	0
	$l = 6$; VI $u+v+w$	6·5	0	6·6	0	6·75	0·01
6·4 ($i=2$)	$l = 1$; I $3v$	**6·3**	1	**6·3**	1	**6·75**	1
	$l = 2$; II $4u$	6·0	0	6·0	0	6·0	0
	$l = 3$; III $2u+w$	5·9	0	6·0	0	6·0	0
	$l = 4$; IV $2w$	5·8	0	6·0	0	6·0	0
Number of logs	z_1 (1·5 each)	300		166·6		161	
	z_2 (2·1 each)	150		150		161	
	z_3 (2·9 each)	100		166·6		161	

10. Direct Application of Resolving Multipliers

So far we have considered the resolving multipliers merely as a technical means for solving the problems A, B and C, and nothing more. It may appear, therefore, that this method of solving the problems A, B, C, offers no advantage as compared with other possible methods, except possibly, that it is simple and quick. This, however, is not so; resolving multipliers have a much wider significance. Not only do they produce the result of a problem, but they also provide a series of important characteristics of this result. Thus, a solution found by the method of resolving multipliers is much more valuable than a mere statement of numerical values h_{ik}. We should like to draw attention to these further applications of the method.

The values λ_k and t_i found in the course of solving the problem may be used for a whole group of questions connected with the application of the maximum result. For the sake of clarity I will adhere to the first interpretation of problem A—production of sets of component parts. In this application the multipliers λ_k serve as indicators of equivalent work on various components, assuming a maximum output. Thus, production of λ_s components k is equivalent to production of λ_k components s. Production of one hundred components k is equivalent to the production of $100\lambda_k/\sum_k \lambda_k$ complete sets. If it is required to produce not $z = z_1 = z_2 = \ldots = z_m$ complete sets in a day, but rather $(z+\Delta z_1)$ first components, $(z+\Delta z_2)$ second components, and so forth (Δz_n not being excessively large), then it is possible to calculate the time needed, namely:

$$1+\left(\sum_k \lambda_k \, \Delta z_k\right) \Big/ z \sum_k \lambda_k \text{ days.}$$

Generally speaking, this solution is possible if the Δz_k are small, h_{ik} not being 0, as in the original problem.

Thus, if λ_k are known, questions connected with minor variations of the programme may be answered. Further, they assist in deciding the usefulness of co-operation. For instance, if for a certain group of machine tools the ratio of components k and s at maximum output is $\frac{\lambda_k}{\lambda_s}$, this ratio being $\frac{\lambda'_k}{\lambda'_s}$ for another group, whereby $\frac{\lambda'_k}{\lambda'_s} > \frac{\lambda_k}{\lambda_s}$, then a co-operation is useful: it is worthwhile to transfer some components k from the first group of machine tools to the second group, and conversely to transfer some of components s from the second group to the first. This transfer will increase the overall output. Similarly, factors t_i serve as indicators of equivalent output of machine tools under maximum work-loading. Here it can be shown, for instance, that the daily output of the machine tool ith in terms of complete sets equals $\frac{t_i}{\sum_i t_i} z$, where z is the total of sets produced on all machine tools. This fact may be made use of in various ways when considering variations of work-spreading, losses due to a deviation from the most favourable variant, and so forth.

Similar considerations regarding the use of resolving multipliers apply also to Problems B and C.

Finally, we should like to mention here that one may try to use the method of resolving multipliers on problems which bear very little similarity to problems A, B, C. In particular, this method can be used for various questions connected with production scheduling. Thus our attention has been drawn to the following real problem. The yearly production plan for an engineering factory includes a number of batches of products. The loading of various machine tool groups (lathes, millers, etc.) is different for every batch. On the average over the year this loading corresponds to the capacity of equipment. How are peak loads to be avoided—temporary overloading of some types of equipment? To avoid this it is obviously necessary to spread the various jobs over half-year, then over the quarters and months, while maintaining for each period the yearly average loading, approximately. In our opinion, resolving multipliers can be used to find this optimum work-loading. It will be necessary to introduce multipliers corresponding to each type of work (turning, milling, etc.) and to vary them so as to achieve a smooth distribution of work-load.

* * *

APPENDIX II: SOLUTION OF PROBLEM A IN A COMPLICATED CASE

(*The Problem of the Plywood Trust*)

This appendix contains the calculation of the most favourable work-loading of veneer-cutting machines. This calculation was carried out according to the method of resolving multipliers by A. I. Yudin, using data supplied by the Laboratory of the All-Union Plywood Trust (see Example 2, page 232).

1. CONDITIONS OF PROBLEM

TABLE 1

Machine Tools	Nomenclature of Materials				
	1	2	3	4	5
1	4·0	7·0	8·5	13·0	16·5
2	4·5	7·8	9·7	13·7	17·5
3	5·0	8·0	10·0	14·8	18·0
4	4·0	7·0	9·0	13·5	17·0
5	3·5	6·5	8·5	12·7	16·0
6	3·0	6·0	8·0	13·5	15·0
7	4·0	7·0	9·0	14·0	17·0
8	5·0	8·0	10·0	14·8	18·0

Table 1 contains the data of the productivity of eight veneer-cutting machines with regard to five different material nomenclatures, as given by the Central Laboratory of the All-Union Plywood Trust. An additional requirement was the following ratio of the quantity of material of a given nomenclature to the total quantity of all materials (Table 2).

TABLE 2

1	2	3	4	5
10%	12%	28%	36%	14%

2. TRANSFORMATION OF CONDITIONS OF PROBLEM

Following the rule given in Section 2 for reducing the production of a given assortment to problem A, in order to obtain values α_{ik} from values of Table 1, we have to divide all figures of the first column by 10, all figures of the second column by 12, and so forth (see Table 2). In order to simplify the calculation we first of all multiply all figures by 1260. Obviously the products may also be considered as α_{ik}. To carry out this calculation we multiply the figures of the consecutive columns by 126, 105, 45, 35 and 90 respectively. The resulting products are shown in Table 3.

TABLE 3

Machine Tools	Nomenclature				
	1	2	3	4	5
1	504·0	735·0	382·5	455·0	1,485·0
2	567·0	819·0	436·5	479·5	1,575·0
3	630·0	840·0	450·0	518·0	1,620·0
4	504·0	735·0	405·0	472·5	1,530·0
5	441·0	682·5	382·5	441·5	1,440·0
6	378·0	630·0	360·0	472·5	1,350·0
7	504·0	735·0	405·0	490·0	1,530·0
8	630·0	840·0	450·0	518·0	1,620·0

Remark. Since the multiplication of a whole column (or sometimes of several columns) by a common multiplier will occur repeatedly, it is convenient to set up this multiplier on a desk calculator (as a multiplicand) and to multiply it sequentially by all figures of the column or columns. This applies also to a slide rule.

Since the productivities of machine tools 3 and 8 coincide for all materials, they may be replaced by another machine tool of a productivity twice as high (see Table 4).

Productivities α_{ik} are expressed in Table 4 in some assumed units of output; the following solution of the mathematical problem will be based on this table, whereby the same units will be used to express the various productivities.

TABLE 4

Machine Tools	Nomenclature				
	1	2	3	4	5
1	504·0	735·0	382·5	455·0	1,485·0
2	567·0	819·0	436·5	479·5	1,575·0
3	1,260·0	1,680·0	900·0	1,036·0	3,240·0
4	504·0	735·0	405·0	472·5	1,530·0
5	441·0	682·5	382·5	444·5	1,440·0
6	378·0	630·0	360·0	472·5	1,350·0
7	504·0	735·0	405·0	490·0	1,530·0
Σ	4,158·0	6,016·5	3,271·5	3,850·0	12,150·0
$\frac{20{,}000}{\Sigma}$	4·810	3·324	6·113	5·195	1·646

3. Calculating Procedure

When using the method of resolving multipliers (Appendix I, sections 3, 4) for the solution of this problem, we have to find the values λ_1, λ_2, λ_3,

λ_4, λ_5. For the first approximation λ^0 we take the values (Table 4, row 9) inversely proportionate to the sums of productivities (Table 4, row 8).

Remark. Assuming the multipliers λ to be accurate to three places of decimals, we shall in future consider two numbers as equal if their difference does not exceed one thousandth of their value.

If $\lambda_k \alpha_{ik} > \lambda_s \alpha_{is}$ for a certain k, it should be assumed that $h_{is} = 0$; consequently for each approximation to λ we shall select from products $\lambda_s \alpha_{is}$ those values (for each i) which are the greatest.

If the values λ are taken at random, then generally speaking each row will contain only one selected (non-zero) value of h, i.e. there will be n (in our case 7) selected values, while the equations $\sum_k h_{ik} = 1$ and $z_1 = z_2 = \ldots = z_m$ impose $n+m-1$ (i.e. eleven) conditions on h_{ik}. Because of this, λ_k should be so selected that in each of four rows there are two maximum products. This will result in eleven non-zero values h_{ik}, which can be found from the eleven equations just mentioned.

The choice of λ_k is further complicated by the limitation $h_{ik} \geqq 0$ imposed on h_{ik}.

4. Calculation

As stated, we take the figures of row 9, Table 4, and row 1, Table 5, as the first approximation.

TABLE 5

Rows		1	2	3	4	5
1	λ^0	4·810	3·324	6·113	5·195	1·646
2	ε^1	1	1	1·017	1	1
3	ε^2	1	1·083	1·083	1	1
4	ε^3	1	1	1	1	1·082
5	ε^4	1	1	1	1·111	1
6	ε^5	1·003	1	1·003	1·003	1
7	λ	4·824	3·600	6·753	5·789	1·781

We calculate the products $\lambda_k^0 \alpha_{ik}$ (Table 6.1).

TABLE 6.1

	1	2	3	4	5
1	2,424·2	**2,443·1**	2,338·1	2,363·7	**2,444·3**
2	**2,727·3**	2,722·4	2,668·3	2,491·0	2,592·0
3	**6,060·6**	5,584·5	5,501·7	5,382·0	5,333·0
4	2,424·2	2,443·1	2,475·8	2,454·6	**2,518·4**
5	2,121·2	2,268·6	2,338·2	2,309·2	**2,370·2**
6	1,818·2	2,094·1	2,200·7	**2,454·6**	2,222·1
7	2,424·2	2,443·1	2,475·8	**2,545·6**	2,518·4
	1,827·0	0	0	962·5	2,970·0
		735·0			1,485·0

In each row we mark the highest value (heavy print). As noted before, in row 1 the values 2,443·1 (2nd column) and 2,444·3 (5th column) are considered to be equal.

At the foot of column k we write the total output of machine tools related to products $\lambda_k \alpha_{ik}$ marked in heavy print; for instance, at the foot of column 1 the output for material 1 (Table 4) of machine tools 2 and 3, i.e. 567·0+1,260·0 = 1,827·0; below column 3 will be a zero, since this column does not contain a marked value. In row 8 we note the output of those machine tools for which only one value has been marked. Row 1 contains two marked figures, and we note the corresponding outputs below row 8, namely in row 9. With reference to the following tables, should any one row contain more than two marked figures, we would write the corresponding outputs even lower down, say in row 10, and so on. This method of notation is convenient because it is necessary to select two figures for each of four rows; values of h_{ik} corresponding to the selected figures must be positive and must not exceed unity, whereas the total outputs for all columns must be equal. Consequently it is important to know the outputs for each column. If the marked figure is the highest in its row, the corresponding output is wholly contained in the output figure for the respective material (in this case $h_{ik} = 1$); if the row contains figures equal to the marked value, then the corresponding output is only partly included in the output figure for the row ($h_{ik} \leqq 1$).

The outputs according to Table 6.1 are as follows:
1st column—1,827·0 assumed units; 2nd column—between 0 and 735 units; 3rd column—0; 4th column—962·5 units; 5th column—between 2,970 and 4,455 units. Thus the outputs cannot be equal.

We will now adjust the lagging columns upwards. For this purpose we introduce for λ_k^0 the corrective multipliers ε_k^1. We start with the 3rd column.

Referring to Table 6.1 we note that if the figures of the 3rd column are increased, the figure of row 5 will be the first to reach a maximum. But since the productivity of machine tool 5 with regard to material 3 is only 382·5

TABLE 6.2

	1	2	3	4	5
1	2,424·2	**2,443·1**	2,377·9	2,363·7	**2,444·3**
2	**2,727·3**	2,722·4	2,713·7	2,491·0	2,592·5
3	**6,060·6**	5,584·3	5,595·2	5,382·0	5,333·0
4	2,424·2	2,443·1	**2,517·9**	2,454·6	**2,518·4**
5	2,121·2	2,268·6	**2,377·9**	2,309·2	2,370·2
6	1,818·2	2,094·1	2,238·1	**2,454·6**	2,222·1
7	2,424·2	2,443·1	2,517·9	**2,545·6**	2,518·4
	1,827·0	0	382·5	962·5	0
		735·0			1,485·0
			405·0		1,530·0

units, which is even less than that for material 2, it is clearly necessary to augment the figures of the 3rd column so that the maximum is reached in yet another row (row 4). In order to find ε_1^1 we divide the highest figure of row 4 (2,518·4) by 2,475·8, and assume the remaining ε_k^1 to be unity (see row 2 of Table 5).

By multiplying the figures of Table 6.1, 3rd column, by ε_k^1 we obtain Table 6.2.

Now, the smallest (approximately equal) outputs are associated with materials 2 and 3. Consequently we will adjust them together, i.e. we will assume for the second corrective multipliers $\varepsilon_3^2 = \varepsilon_3^2 = \varepsilon$.

While choosing ε we note that the figure of row 7 in 3rd column will be the first to reach the maximum; this, however, does not satisfy us; just as unsatisfactory is the maximisation of the figure of row 2 in 2nd column. We must maximise the figure of row 3 in 3rd column.

We calculate 6,060·6 : 5,595·2 = 1·083. The remaining $\varepsilon_k^2 = 1$ (Table 5, row 3). Further multiplication using these multipliers produces $\lambda_k \, \alpha_{ik}$ for the third approximation (Table 6.3).

By increasing the figures of the 5th column (row 4, Table 3), the corresponding values of the fourth approximation are obtained (Table 6.4).

TABLE 6.3

	1	2	3	4	5
1	2,424·2	**2,645·9**	2,575·3	2,363·7	2,444·3
2	2,727·3	**2,948·4**	2,938·9	2,491·0	2,592·5
3	**6,060·6**	6,047·8	**6,059·6**	5,382·0	5,333·0
4	2,424·2	2,645·9	**2,726·9**	2,454·6	2,518·4
5	2,121·2	2,456·9	**2,575·8**	2,309·2	2,370·2
6	1,818·2	2,267·9	2,423·9	**2,454·6**	2,222·1
7	2,424·2	2,645·9	**2,726·9**	2,545·6	2,518·4
	0	1,554·0	992·5	472·5	0
	1,260·0		900·0		

TABLE 6.4

	1	2	3	4	5
1	2,424·2	**2,645·9**	2,575·3	2,363·7	**2,644·8**
2	2,727·3	**2,948·4**	2,938·9	2,491·0	2,805·1
3	**6,060·6**	6,047·8	**6,059·6**	5,382·0	5,770·3
4	2,424·2	2,645·9	**2,726·9**	2,454·6	**2,724·9**
5	2,121·2	2,456·9	**2,575·3**	2,309·2	2,564·6
6	1,818·2	2,267·9	2,423·9	**2,454·6**	2,404·3
7	2,424·2	2,645·9	**2,726·9**	2,545·6	2,724·9
	0	819·0	382·5	472·5	0
	1,260·0		900·0		
					1,485·0
		735·0	810·0		3,060·0

We note that although there are eleven non-zero values h_{ik} in Table 6.4, nevertheless the outputs of all columns cannot be made equal as long as h_{ik} remains within limits 0 to 1. (We also note that the coincidence of maximum values in rows 4 and 7, columns 3 and 5, is accidental.)

By an adjustment of the 4th column we achieve a maximisation of figures of this column not only in row 7, but also in row 4 (Table 6.5).

All remarks concerning Table 6.4 apply equally to Table 6.5, but it is much more difficult in the latter case to detect that positive solutions for all h_{ik} are impossible (a system of equations must be solved in order to establish this fact).

We increase the figures of columns 1, 3 and 4 simultaneously. Because of the increase being simultaneous, we retain two marked values in each of two rows (3 and 4); furthermore, there are still two maximum values in row 1. By increasing the figures of three columns we will get two maxima in yet another row.

TABLE 6.5

	1	2	3	4	5
1	2,424·2	**2,645·9**	2,575·3	2,626·1	**2,644·8**
2	2,727·3	**2,948·4**	2,938·9	2,767·5	2,805·1
3	**6,060·6**	6,047·8	**6,059·6**	5,979·1	5,770·3
4	2,424·2	2,645·9	**2,726·9**	**2,727·1**	**2,724·9**
5	2,121·2	2,456·9	**2,575·3**	2,565·5	2,564·6
6	1,818·2	2,267·9	2,423·9	**2,727·1**	2,404·3
7	2,424·2	2,645·9	2,726·9	**2,828·2**	2,724·9
	0	819·0	382·5	962·5	0
	1,260·0		900·0		
		735·0			1,485·0
			405·0	472·5	1,530·0

TABLE 6.6

	1	2	3	4	5
1	2,431·5	**2,645·9**	2,583·0	2,634·0	**2,644·8**
2	2,735·5	**2,948·4**	**2,947·7**	2,775·8	2,805·1
3	**6,078·8**	6,047·8	**6,077·8**	5,997·3	5,770·3
4	2,431·5	2,645·9	**2,735·1**	**2,735·3**	2,724·9
5	2,127·6	2,456·9	**2,583·0**	2,573·2	2,564·6
6	1,823·7	2,267·9	2,431·2	**2,735·2**	2,404·3
7	2,431·5	2,645·9	2,735·1	**2,836·7**	2,724·9
	0	0	382·5	962·5	0
	1,260·0		900·0		
		735·0			
		819·0	436·5		1,485·0
			405·0	472·5	

The first to reach a maximum is the figure in row 2, column 3; for this purpose it is to be multiplied by $\varepsilon_3^5 = 2{,}948{\cdot}4 : 2{,}938{\cdot}9 = 1{\cdot}003$ (see row 6, Table 5).

According to Table 6.6 the output of the 1st column varies between 0 and 1,260·0 units, that of the 2nd column from 0 to 1,554 units, that of the 3rd column from 382·5 to 2,124·0 units, that of the 4th column from 962·5 to 1,435·0 units, and finally the output of the 5th column from 0 to 1,485 units. There are eleven outputs of one class for all columns, and eleven non-zero values of h_{ik}.

5. CALCULATION OF h_{ik}

Setting $h_{ik} = 0$ if the figure of row i, column k in Table 6.6 is not marked in heavy type, we receive the following equations for the remaining h_{ik}:

$$1{,}260h_{31} = 819h_{22}+735h_{12} = 436{\cdot}5h_{23}+900h_{33}+405h_{43}+$$
$$+382{\cdot}5h_{53} = 472{\cdot}5h_{44}+472{\cdot}5h_{65}+490h_{74} = 1{,}485h_{15}$$
$$h_{12}+h_{15} = 1; \quad h_{22}+h_{23} = 1; \quad h_{31}+h_{33} = 1;$$
$$h_{43}+h_{44} = 1; \quad h_{53} = 1; \quad h_{64} = 1; \quad h_{74} = 1$$

We introduce the unknowns:

$$x_1 = h_{31}; \quad x_2 = h_{15}; \quad x_3 = h_{25}; \quad x_4 = h_{44}$$

By means of the last seven equations we transform the first four equations into:

$$1{,}554-819x_3 = 2{,}220x_2;$$
$$1{,}260x_1 = 1{,}485x_2;$$
$$1{,}687{\cdot}5+436{\cdot}5x_3-900x_1-405x_4 = 1{,}485x_2;$$
$$962{\cdot}5+472{\cdot}5x_4 = 1{,}485x_2;$$

or, after simplification:

$$740x_2 = -273x_3+518,$$
$$33x_2 = 28x_1;$$
$$33x_2 = -20x_1+9{\cdot}7x_3-9x_4+37{\cdot}5;$$
$$297x_2 = 94{\cdot}5x_4+192{\cdot}5$$

By solving this system of equations, the following values of x are obtained:

$$x_1 = 0{\cdot}7872;$$
$$x_2 = 0{\cdot}6679;$$
$$x_3 = 0{\cdot}0871;$$
$$x_4 = 0{\cdot}0620$$

Note. We are entitled to calculate x (and consequently λ_{ik}) to the 4th decimal place in spite of the fact that λ_k have been worked out only to the 3rd decimal, because λ_k are only of subsidiary importance, and any error in their calculation does not affect the accuracy of calculation of h_{ik}.

Evaluating h_{ik} according to x_{ik}, the figures of Table 7 are obtained.

TABLE 7

	1	2	3	4	5
1	0	0·3321	0	0	0·6679
2	0	0·9129	0·0871	0	0
3 (8)	0·7872	0	0·2128	0	0
4	0	0	0·9380	0·0620	0
5	0	0	1	0	0
6	0	0	0	1	0
7	0	0	0	1	0

The values in row 3 designate the machining time for the given material for both machine tools 3 and 8 (see Tables 1 and 3); it is obvious, however, that it can be varied within certain limits. Total output for each material is 991·8 assumed units.

6. Checking

In order to check that z is a maximum, we ascertain (see sections 4 and 6) that the non-zero values λ_{ik} have been separated correctly. For this purpose we list the values $\lambda_k \alpha_{ik}$ (that is, we multiply the columns of Table 4 by the 7th row of Table 5), and mark the maximum value in each row (see Table 8).

TABLE 8

	1	2	3	4	5
1	2,431·3	**2,646·0**	2,583·0	2,631·0	**2,644·8**
2	2,735·0	**2,948·4**	**2,947·7**	2,775·8	2,805·1
3	**6,078·2**	6,048·0	**6,077·7**	5,997·4	5,770·4
4	2,431·4	2,646·0	**2,735·0**	**2,735·3**	2,724·9
5	2,127·4	2,457·0	**2,583·0**	2,573·2	2,564·6
6	1,823·5	2,268·0	2,431·1	2,735·2	2,404·4
7	2,431·3	2,646·0	2,735·0	**2,836·6**	2,724·9

In order to check h_{ik} we calculate the output for each material:

1st material $1{,}260 \times 0{\cdot}7872 = 991{\cdot}9$ units

2nd material $735 \times 0{\cdot}3321 + 819 \times 0{\cdot}9129 = 991{\cdot}8$ units

3rd material $436{\cdot}5 \times 0{\cdot}0871 + 900 \times 0{\cdot}2128 + 405 \times 0{\cdot}9380 + 382{\cdot}5 =$
$= 991{\cdot}9$ units

4th material $472 \times 5 \times 0{\cdot}0620 = 962{\cdot}5 = 991{\cdot}8$ units

5th material $1{,}485 \times 0{\cdot}6679 = 991{\cdot}8$ units

7. Productivity of Machine Tools

We calculate the productivity with regard to various materials directly from data supplied by the Central Laboratory of the All-Union Plywood Trust (Table 1). The results are listed in Table 9.

TABLE 9

	1	2	3	4	5
1	0	2·32	0	0	11·02
2	0	7·12	0·84	0	0
3	3·94	0	2·13	0	0
4	0	0	8·44	0·84	0
5	0	0	8·50	0	0
6	0	0	0	13·50	0
7	0	0	0	14·00	0
8	3·94	0	2·13	0	0
Total	7·88	9·44	22·04	28·34	11·02

8. Comparison with the Simplest Solution

In order to ascertain the economy achieved by the foregoing calculation, we compare the resulting output with that which would be obtained if the various materials were machined in a given ratio on all machine tools. This calculation is based on the data of Table 4; it is necessary to machine an equal quantity of each material on each machine tool. Let us see how much of each material is machined on the ith tool, y_i being the quantity in assumed units.

$$y_i = \alpha_{i1} h_{i1} = \alpha_{i2} h_{i2} = \alpha_{i3} h_{i3} = \alpha_{i4} h_{i4} = \alpha_{i5} h_{i5}$$

and since

$$h_{i1}+h_{i2}+h_{i3}+h_{i4}+h_{i5} = 1,$$

it follows that

$$y_i = \frac{1}{\frac{1}{\alpha_{i1}}+\frac{1}{\alpha_{i2}}+\frac{1}{\alpha_{i3}}+\frac{1}{\alpha_{i4}}+\frac{1}{\alpha_{i5}}}$$

Using Barlow's Table of Reciprocals, we obtain the following values for y_i:

$$y_1 = 113{\cdot}2 \qquad y_5 = 107{\cdot}6$$
$$y_2 = 125{\cdot}0 \qquad y_6 = 101{\cdot}3$$
$$y_3 = 264{\cdot}9 \qquad y_7 = 117{\cdot}5$$
$$y_4 = 116{\cdot}5$$

and the total output is 946·0 units.

The maximum productivity in relation to the figure just obtained is 104·8%.

Note. This relatively low percentage of increase is explained by the fact that the productivities of various machine tools are nearly proportional, according to the data given by the Laboratory.

* * *

Appendix III: THEORETICAL PROOF OF THE EXISTENCE OF RESOLVING MULTIPLIERS

It has been established in Appendix I that the determination of values h_{ik} by means of resolving multipliers does lead to a solution, and the procedure for finding these resolving multipliers has been stated. This is probably sufficient for all practical purposes; however, to complete the description it is important to establish the fact that resolving multipliers always exist. This will demonstrate that the method of resolving multipliers is definitely applicable for any problem. We decided to present this proof in a separate appendix, since the ignorance of the proof does not in any way affect the study and the application of the method; and also because somewhat finer mathematical means are required for this proof.

For the sake of brevity, in presenting the proof of existence of resolving multipliers we will consider only the Problem A.[1] It is useful to present an analytical proof as well as a geometrical one.

1. Analytical Proof

Let us consider the systems of numbers $(\lambda_1, \lambda_2 \ldots \lambda_m)$ governed by conditions $\lambda_k \geqq 0$; $\lambda_1 + \lambda_2 + \ldots = \lambda_m = 1$. For each given system $(\lambda_1, \lambda_2, \ldots, \lambda_m)$ we will consider the products $\lambda_1 \alpha_{i1}$; $\lambda_2 \alpha_{i2}$; ... ; $\lambda_m \alpha_{im}$; we will set $h_{ik} = 0$ for those k, for which the product $\lambda_k \alpha_{ik}$ is not a maximum of its series, and the remaining h_{ik} we will try to select so that min $(z_1, z_2, \ldots, z_m)$ is as large as possible. Let the maximum value of this minimum be $C(\lambda_1, \lambda_2, \ldots, \lambda_m)$. Obviously, this is a finite function. For instance, clearly $C(\lambda_1, \lambda_2, \ldots, \lambda_m) \leqq \sum_{i,k} \alpha_{ik}$. This function has a definite higher limit, which may be designated C^*. There is a sequence of systems $\lambda_1^{(s)}, \lambda_2^{(s)}, \ldots, \lambda_m^{(s)}$, for which the value $C(\lambda_1, \lambda_2, \ldots, \lambda_m)$ approaches C^*.

$$\lim_{s \to \infty} C(\lambda_1^{(s)}, \lambda_2^{(s)}, \ldots, \lambda_m^{(s)}) = C^*$$

From the sequence of systems $\lambda_1^{(s)}, \lambda_2^{(s)}, \ldots, \lambda_m^{(s)}$ $(s = 1, 2, \ldots)$ it is possible to select one which is partly asymptotic; obviously, without any loss of generality, this may well be the very first sequence, that is $(\lambda_1^{(s)}, \lambda_2^{(s)}, \ldots, \lambda_m^{(s)}) \to (\bar{\lambda}_1, \bar{\lambda}_2, \ldots, \bar{\lambda}_m)$.

Further, for every s there is a definite system of numbers $\{h_{ik}\}$ which leads to the value $C(\lambda_1^{(s)}, \lambda_2^{(s)}, \ldots, \lambda_m^{(s)})$. These systems of numbers may be also considered, if necessary, by changing to partial sequence, as being asymptotic to a definite system.

$$\lim_{s \to \infty} h_{ik}^{(s)} = \bar{h}_{ik} \quad (i = 1, 2, \ldots, n; \quad k = 1, 2, \ldots, m)$$

[1] A fuller mathematical treatment of this question will be given in a special paper (see L. V. Kantorovich, 'Regarding an effective method of solving some types of extremal problems'. *Proceedings of the Academy of Science, USSR*, Vol. 28, No. 3, pp. 212-15, 1940. Editor's note).

Since for each s the necessary conditions for $h_{ik}^{(s)}$ have been satisfied, these must also be satisfied within limits for $\bar{h}_{ik}$. For the system $h_{ik} = \bar{h}_{ik}$ we obtain:

$$\min(\bar{z}_1, \bar{z}_2, \ldots, \bar{z}_m) = \lim_{s\to\infty} \min(z_1^{(s)}, z_2^{(s)}, \ldots, z_m^{(s)}) =$$
$$= \lim C(\lambda_1^{(s)}, \ldots, \lambda_m^{(s)}) = C^*,$$

and consequently $C(\bar{\lambda}_1, \bar{\lambda}_2, \ldots, \bar{\lambda}_m) \geqq C^*$. On the other hand, since the reversed inequality is valid:

$$\min(\bar{z}_1, \bar{z}_2, \ldots, \bar{z}_m) = C(\bar{\lambda}_1, \bar{\lambda}_2, \ldots, \bar{\lambda}_m) = C^*$$

By modifying λ_k we can make all z_k equal to C^*. Indeed, since some $z_k > C^*$, by reducing the corresponding λ_k and by proportionately increasing the remaining λ_k, we can achieve a coincidence of $\lambda_k \alpha_{ik}$, on account of which this z_k may be reduced. Since the remaining z_k cannot all at the same time exceed C^*, as this would contradict the definition of C^*, we can gradually arrive at values $\lambda_1^*, \lambda_2^*, \ldots, \lambda_m^*$, for which it is possible to choose h_{ik} so that $z_1 = z_2 = \ldots = z_m = C^*$. After we have achieved this result, the existence of resolving multipliers can be considered to be proved.

2. Geometrical Proof

Let us consider all possible systems $\{h_{ik}\}$ which satisfy the conditions $h_{ik} \geqq 0;\ \sum_{k=1}^{m} h_{ik} = 1$. A definite system of numbers $z_k = \sum_i \alpha_{ik} h_{ik}$ corresponds to each system of numbers h_{ik}. These systems $(z_1, z_2, \ldots, z_m)$, taken

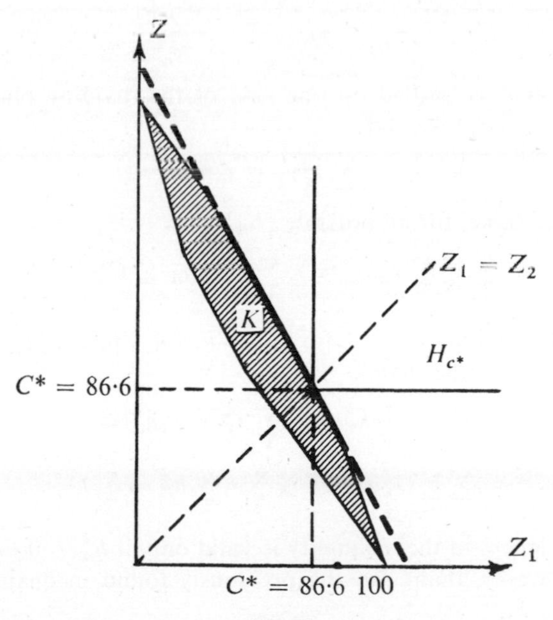

Fig. 2

for all feasible $\{h_{ik}\}$, fill a convex region K (see Fig. 2)[1] in an m-dimensional space of points $(z_1, z_2, \ldots, z_m)$. Let us also consider another convex set H_C consisting of points which satisfy the conditions $z_1 \geqq C, \ldots, z_m \geqq C$ or, which is the same, $\min(z_1, z_2, \ldots, z_m) \geqq C$.

As before, we designate by C^* the common maximum value z and z' of problems A and A′ (see Appendix I, paragraph 2). Since C^* is the maximum value of $\min(z_1, z_2, z_3, \ldots z_m)$, we have for all points of region K $\min(z_1, z_2, \ldots, z_m) \leqq C^*$. For this reason the region K has no interior points common with the set H_{C^*}, since, for all interior points of the latter, $\min(z_1, z_2, \ldots, z_m) \geqq C^*$.

Consequently, K and H_{C^*} have only boundary points in common, one of which is $(C^*, C^*, \ldots, C^*)$. According to Minkowski's theorem there exists a plane which passes through this point; this plane divides these convex sets, and is expressed by an equation of the type

$$\lambda_1^* z_1 + \lambda_2^* z_2 + \ldots + \lambda_m^* z_m = C^*,$$

where $\lambda_1^* + \lambda_2^* + \ldots + \lambda_m^* = 1$ (which can always be achieved); whereas the free member is equal to C^*, since the point $(C^*, C^*, \ldots, C^*)$ is located in this plane. Further, it is evident from the geometrical appearance of the region H_{C^*} that, necessarily, $\lambda_k^* \geqq 0$.

The coefficients of this dividing plane (which is shown in Fig. II as a heavy and heavily dotted line) are in fact the resolving multipliers. Indeed, let $\{h_{ik}^*\}$ be a system of numbers, for which $z_1 = z_2 = \ldots = z_m = C^*$. As before, let t_i be the greatest of products

$$\lambda_1^* \alpha_{i1};\ \lambda_2^* \alpha_{i2};\ \ldots;\ \lambda_m^* \alpha_{im}.$$

Since region K is located on one side of the dividing plane, for all its points $(z_1, z_2, \ldots, z_m)$ is valid:

$$\sum \lambda_k^* z_k \leqq C^*$$

or, which is the same, for all possible $\{h_{ik}\}$

$$\sum_k \lambda_k^* \sum_i \alpha_{ik} h_{ik} = \sum_i \sum_k \lambda_k^* \alpha_{ik} h_{ik} \leqq C^*$$

In particular, taking $h_{ik} = 1$ for those k, for which $\lambda_k^* \alpha_{ik} = t_i$, we find $\sum_i t_i \leqq C^*$. On the other hand,

$$C^* = \sum_k \lambda_k^* z_k^* = \sum_k \lambda_k^* \sum_i \alpha_{ik} h_{ik}^* =$$

$$= \sum_i \sum_k (\lambda_k^* \alpha_{ik})\, h_{ik}^* \leqq \sum_i t_i \sum_k h_{ik}^* = \sum_i t_i$$

Here, the sign $=$ in the inequality is valid only if $h_{ik}^* = 0$ every time that $\lambda_k^* \alpha_{ik} < t_i$; however, thanks to the previously found inequality, $\Sigma\, t_i \leqq C^*$

[1] The drawing is plotted according to the data of Example 1.

the sign of equality must necessarily apply here, and consequently the above requirement for h_{ik}^* is indeed fulfilled. Thus it is evident that for $h_{ik} = h_{ik}^*$, the condition of being equal to zero is satisfied for all those values which do not correspond to maximum products; all other values are such that $z_1 = z_2 = \ldots = z_m$. This shows that λ_k^* are indeed the resolving multipliers, and proves the existence of resolving multipliers in problem A in all circumstances.

Further Development of Mathematical Methods and the Prospects of their Application in Economic Planning[1]

L. V. Kantorovich

The subject of this paper is the application of mathematical methods developed in connexion with some problems of industrial production planning (these methods became known later as 'linear programming') to a wider range of questions in the field of planning and economic analysis. The central problem is the construction of optimum plans which would guarantee the best possible utilisation of available resources and the most useful result. In this connexion the formulation of suitable tasks is considered, the methods of investigation are discussed, and the economic value of the results achieved by an analysis of these problems is examined. Finally the paper discusses the possible practical application of these results and of computing procedures.

This analysis is applied to a problem of production planning which generalises the problems A, B and C, considered in the previous paper. This general problem may be considered as a mathematical model of the problem of current planning. Sections 1-5 present a study of this mathematical model. Questions of economic planning and illustrative examples considered in these sections have been initially taken in their abstract form which ensures their adequate description by means of this model. Consequently there is no reason to doubt the reliability of conclusions drawn from the investigation of them. The application of this analysis to actual problems of economic planning, however, is not quite so obvious and free of doubts. This question has been investigated in section 8 (and elsewhere), in surveying the planning

[1] This paper is a continuation of an earlier paper published in 1939. In the following years (1940-1943) the author and his collaborators further developed and improved the method of resolving multipliers, and clarified the possibilities of its application to other problems and also to general questions in the fields of planning and economics. During 1948-1950 some further work was done on this method in connexion with the problem of economic cutting-up, and an experimental application to production practice has been carried out (see L. V. Kantorovich and V. A. Zalgaller, *The calculation of economic methods of cutting-up industrial materials*, Leningrad, 1951. The present paper touches to some extent on all these questions. For detailed annotation of this paper see postscript on p. 369 of this book. (Editor's note)

problems at different levels of the socialist economy; to these, in our opinion, the methods of linear programming are applicable.

1. The General (Basic) Problem of Working Out an Optimum Plan

When working out a production plan we constantly encounter problems which demand a plan to guarantee a required volume of production, using available resources and manufacturing facilities and taking into account various production methods. Thereby, the production plan is determined by a given degree of utilisation of each technological process (number of units of output or factor to which it is applied). It appears that, despite a number of limiting conditions, there is usually a very considerable number of possible solutions; that is, a variety of possible production plans. The problem is not to form a plan, but to select from a number of possible plans the one which is an optimum in a certain respect, for instance because it offers the maximum output, or the minimum cost, etc. Problems of this kind are most important; they are typical in conditions of socialist production.

The basic problem may be put thus. There are several kinds of products to be made, and a series of elements used in the course of manufacture (productive factors). These may be: labour, equipment, raw materials, manufactured materials and the like. Suitable technological processes have been specified. A plan is required which ensures that:

1. the total expenditure of each productive factor does not exceed the available reserves;
2. the products are manufactured in the required proportions;
3. the products are manufactured in the greatest possible quantity.

We will call this required plan the *optimum* plan. A plan which satisfies only conditions (1) and (2) will be called a *feasible* plan. In some cases the conditions (1), (2) and (3) which define the optimum plan and the feasible plans have to be slightly modified.

We illustrate the formulation of this problem, which may be designated as the general or basic problem, by a numerical example. In Table 1 are

Table 1

Technical Process	Output and Expenditure				Planned Utilisation of Processes	
	Products		Productive Factors			
	I	II	I	II	Plan A	Plan B
1	5	2	−1	−3	2	0
2	5	2	−3	−1	0	2
3	2	7·75	−7·25	−1	2	0
4	2	6	−1	−4	0·5	1
5	2	7	−5	−2	0	2
Plan A	15	22·5	−17	−10		
Plan B	16	24·0	−17	−10		

listed the production data for possible technological processes (the negative values represent expenditure). For instance, process 1 achieves an output of five units of product I and two units of product II at the expenditure of one unit of factor I and three units of factor II.

A plan is to be evolved which would ensure that: (*a*) expenditure does not exceed seventeen units of factor I and ten units of factor II, (*b*) the quantities of completed products I and II are in ratio 2:3, and (*c*) the volume of output of these products is a maximum.

A direct consideration of processes does not enable one to decide which one is the most rational under the circumstances; yet the output depends essentially on the selection of the most suitable process.

Thus the two plans mentioned in Table 1 both satisfy the conditions 1 and 2, i.e. they are feasible. Indeed, according to plan A, process 1 is used twice (for ten units of product I), process 3 is used twice (for four units of product I), and process 4 is used in ratio 0·5 (for one unit of product I); the total output of product I is:

$$2\times 5+2\times 2+0{\cdot}5\times 2 = 15 \text{ units}.$$

Outputs and expenditures are stated for both plans in the two bottom rows of Table 1. The output of each product according to plan B is higher than for plan A.

Having given this explanation, we will now give a general mathematical formulation of the problem.

The mathematical model of the basic problem of production planning is this: there are m products $(1, 2, \ldots, m)$ and n productive factors $(1, 2, \ldots, n)$. There is a number of technological processes $s = 1, 2, \ldots, S$, whereby for each process s the output of each kind is known; that means the vector of production is known:

$$X_s = (x_1^s, x_2^s, \ldots, x_m^s)$$

with components x_1^s = output of kind 1, x_2^s = output of kind 2, etc. The vector which defines the expenditure for this particular process is also known:

$$Z_s = (z_1^s, z_2^s, \ldots, z_n^s)$$

wherein z_1^s = expenditure of factor 1, z_2^s = that of factor 2, etc.

The plan is determined by the index of the intensity of utilisation of each process, that is by values $p_1, p_2, \ldots, p_S$; $p_s \geqq 0$ $(s = 1, 2, \ldots, S)$; $(p_s = 0$ if the plan makes no use of process $s)$.

The outputs and the expenditures according to this plan are defined by vectors X and Z, the components of which give respectively the volume of output of each kind, and the consumption of each factor for a given plan:

$$X = \sum_{s=1}^{S} p_s X_s = (x_1, x_2, \ldots, x_m); \quad x_i = \sum_{s=1}^{S} p_s X_i^s \quad (i = 1, 2, \ldots, m);$$

$$Z = \sum_{s=1}^{S} p_s Z_s = (z_1, z_2, \ldots, z_n); \quad z_j = \sum_{s=1}^{S} p_s z_j^s \quad (j = 1, 2, \ldots, n).$$

These data can be arranged in a table similar to Table 1.

TABLE 2

Techno-logical processes	Outputs and expenditures for a given process								Planned intensity of utilisation of processes
	Products				Productive Factors				
	1	2	....	m	1	2	....	n	
1	x_1^1	x_2^1	....	x_m^1	z_1^1	z_2^1	....	z_n^1	p_1
2	x_1^2	x_2^2	....	x_m^2	z_1^2	z_2^2	....	z_n^2	p_2
.									
.									
.									
.									
.									
S	x_1^S	x_2^S	....	x_m^S	z_1^S	z_2^S	....	z_n^S	p_S
Total as planned	x_1	x_2	....	x_m	z_1	z_2	....	z_n	

It may be stated that the problem of selecting the optimum plan is defined by the following conditions:

(*a*) expenditure of productive factors must not exceed the given values (available resources)

$$Z \geqq Z^0 \, (z_j \geqq z_j^0, \; j = 1, 2, \ldots, n)$$

(The inequality $\geqq$ is used because the expenditure figures are preceded by the minus sign; in the foregoing example $z_1 \geqq -17$);

(*b*) The output must have a given composition

$$\frac{x_1}{k_1} = \frac{x_2}{k_2} = \ldots = \frac{x_m}{k_m}$$

wherein $k_1 : k_2 : \ldots : k_m$ are the ratios determining this composition;

(*c*) the volume of production must be as large as possible.

The plan which satisfies all these conditions is the optimum plan, whereas a plan satisfying the conditions (*a*) and (*b*) only is known as a feasible plan.

Note 1. Sometimes condition (*b*) is inconvenient, as an excess of a certain product cannot be avoided. In such cases it is evident that, without departing from the spirit of the problem, conditions (*b*) and (*c*) may be replaced by the demand that the number of produced sets (according to the assortment)

$$x = \min_i \frac{x_i}{k_i}$$

should be a maximum.

Note 2. A very special case of the basic problem of production planning is Leontief's model (a scheme for the analysis of a balance of inputs and outputs which is confined to only one manufacturing process for each product. It is not related to the finding of extreme solutions, and amounts to a solution of systems of algebraic linear equations.

The problems discussed previously, including A, B and C, can be considered as particular cases of the general problem of production planning. Of these, the following may be mentioned:

1. *Machine tool loading*, i.e. allocation to the available machine tools of jobs to be done, so as to ensure a maximum output (problem A, p. 229). The technological process in this case consists in a given job being carried out on a certain machine tool, and may be assumed to require one unit of time of this tool (for instance, one tool-hour), during which time a certain number of units of the given article is produced. Thus, this problem can be reduced to the basic problem.

2. *Rational cutting up*. Serial production of articles made of a material available as sheets (strips, billets) of a certain size requires a variety of cut-off pieces. There is a number of technically possible ways of cutting up a sheet of material. A plan is required to produce complete sets of cut-off pieces, using a minimum of material per set (see jobs mentioned in the footnote on p. 317).

In this case the output comprises the cut-off pieces, the expendable factor is the sheet material (of one or several kinds), and the technological processes are the various layouts for cutting. Obviously the problem of best use of complex raw materials is similar if there are various treatments, each resulting in a number of different products (each process giving a different output per unit of material).

3. *Mixing*. There are given quantities of a number of substances. It is possible to mix these substances in different ways. The price per unit of each mixture is known. It is required to calculate the quantities of various mixtures so that they can be made up from available substances, the total price being as high as possible.

Obviously, this problem can also be reduced to the basic scheme if the cost of final mixtures is taken as the product, and the initial substances take the place of productive factors; every kind of mixture may be considered as a technological process.

The problems relating to the choice of constructional methods using available resources of materials, or of a production programme using available equipment of various kinds, and so on, are of a similar nature (see pp. 232-59).

4. *Transportation.* A certain product is being manufactured at a number of production establishments for distribution to various locations. The cost of transportation of one unit of the product from each production establishment to any destination is fixed. A transport plan is required to reduce the total cost of transportation to a minimum.

The product at each destination may be considered as one of several kinds of products; the product at each production establishment as well as the transport cost may be considered as equivalent to productive factors.

2. Characteristics of the Optimum Plan

A natural question arises: how are we to select the optimum plan from the many feasible plans? Given a plan, how are we to know whether it is in fact the optimum plan? There is a very effective answer to this question —by the method of ratings (resolving multipliers) or specific indicators associated with the optimum plan.

It is more convenient to explain this method initially with reference to the problem of machine tool loading, and not to the general problem of production planning.

Let us consider the table of output norms and two plans (A and B) for this problem (see Table 3). The plans are indicated by the fraction of time that each machine tool is to be used for a certain job.

It can be seen that plan B ensures a greater volume of production. Let us analyse this plan.

Table 3

Jobs / Machine tools	I			II			III		
	Time Fraction *A*	Output Norm	Time Fraction *B*	Time Fraction *A*	Output Norm	Time Fraction *B*	Time Fraction *A*	Output Norm	Time Fraction *B*
1	—	72	0·5	1·0	20	—	—	48	0·5
2	0·5	64	—	0·5	24	0·75	—	48	0·25
3	—	48	—	—	18	1·0	1·0	32	—
Output as per plan *A*	32			32			32		
plan *B*			36			36			36

In order to compare the various jobs, let us assign ratings to them. Let 1 ($\lambda_1 = 1$) be the rating of one unit of job I. The productivity of machine tool 1 with regard to this job is then $1 \times 72 = 72$ ($\mu_1 = 72$ assumed units). Accordingly, the rating of one unit of job III is $\lambda_3 = 72 : 48 = 1{\cdot}5$. Since machine tool 2 has the same productivity job for III as machine tool 1, $\mu_2 = 48 \times 1{\cdot}5 = 72$. Bearing in mind that 24 units of job II are produced on machine tool 2, $\lambda_2 = 72 : 24 = 3$. It follows that the productivity of machine tool 3 is $\mu_3 = 18 \times 3 = 54$ assumed units.

This procedure can be shown schematically thus:

(I) $\lambda_1 = 1$ → $\mu_1 = 72 \times 1 = 72$ (1)

(II) $\lambda_2 = 72 : 24 = 3$ → $\mu_2 = 48 \times 1{\cdot}5 = 72$ (2)

(III) $\lambda_3 = 72 : 48 = 1{\cdot}5$ → $\mu_3 = 18 \times 3 = 54$ (3)

If we calculate the productivity of machine tools for each job from these ratings λ_i, we arrive at the figures of Table 4. They show that on the basis of these ratings each machine tool is used on the job for which it is best suited.

TABLE 4

	Jobs		
Machine tools	I	II	III
1	72*	60	72
2	64	72	72
3	48	54	48

* We quote the valuations of productivity used in plan *B*.

A simple consideration will suffice to show that the very existence of ratings of this nature ensures that plan *B* is the optimum plan. Indeed, let us assume that another plan results in a higher total output, and let us rate it in the same units. The total output of all machine tools is based on the ratings of various jobs. For the total output to be higher than per plan *B* it is necessary that at least one machine tool should produce more. This, however, is impossible, since according to the ratings used in plan *B* every machine tool is loaded to capacity. Consequently a better plan than *B* is not feasible, and *B* is in fact the optimum plan.[1]

Evidently, such ratings do not exist for plan *A*. Should we attempt to rate it on the same basis as before, we would arrive at:

$$\lambda_1 = 1; \quad \mu_2 = 64; \quad \lambda_2 = 64 : 24 = 2{\cdot}67; \quad \mu_1 = 20 \times 2{\cdot}67 = 53{\cdot}3$$

According to plan *A* the first machine tool is used for job II, which results in a lesser productivity: $53{\cdot}3 < 72$. Thus, plan *A* is not an optimum (it does not achieve the required ratings). It is important to note that we have

[1] A formal mathematical proof of this proposition is given below.

arrived at this conclusion by means of a direct analysis of plan A, and not by a comparison with plan B.

Thus, an analysis of the optimum plan has led logically to a definite system of corresponding internal ratings, which can be considered to be objectively based. The presence of these ratings is a characteristic of the optimum plan; they do not exist for non-optimum plans.

This characteristic of the optimum plan can be modified, if in addition to output ratings we apply ratings of productivity of machine tools. For each technological process (the use of a certain machine tool for a certain job), the algebraic sum of ratings of output and expenditure is 0; in other words, the expenditure is 'justified'. For instance, with machine tool 3 used on job II we have: $18 \times 3 + 54(-1) = 0$. It is not possible to find such ratings for plan A, since for methods not used in plan B the corresponding sums $\leqq 0$. For example, with machine tool 1 used on job II: $20 \times 3 + 72(-1) = -12 < 0$.

This characteristic of the optimum plan can be directly applied to the general problem of production planning, and we are now able to formulate two propositions:

Proposition 1. If for a certain (acceptable) plan such (non-negative) ratings (multipliers) of each kind of product and productive factors can be found that, for the technological processes used according to this plan, the algebraic sum of ratings of output and expenditure is 0, while for processes not used according to this plan the said sum is less than or equal to 0, then this plan is the optimum plan. In other words, there cannot be any other plan which would produce a higher output of every kind than the present plan, when using the same resources and processes.

Proposition 2. Conversely, if a plan is an optimum plan, it always possesses ratings of the kind stated above. Thus, if such ratings cannot be found for a certain plan, then it is not the optimum plan; consequently, another plan can be evolved which will ensure more output of every product, using the same resources and processes.

We will now demonstrate the application of these propositions on the basis of the foregoing general problem (Table 1).

For plan B these multipliers are $\lambda_1 = 1$, $\lambda_2 = 2$, $\mu_1 = 2$, $\mu_2 = 4$. They can be found, with the accuracy of the proportionality multiplier from equations formed according to data of Table 1:

$$\begin{array}{ll} \text{second process:} & 5\lambda_1 + 2\lambda_2 - 3\mu_1 - 1\mu_2 = 0 \\ \text{fourth process:} & 2\lambda_1 + 6\lambda_2 - 1\mu_1 - 4\mu_2 = 0 \\ \text{fifth process:} & 2\lambda_1 + 7\lambda_2 - 5\mu_1 - 2\mu_2 = 0 \end{array}$$

which justifies the use of processes 2, 4 and 5. It is easy to check that the corresponding sum < 0 for processes not used in this plan, for instance for process 1:

$$5 \times 1 + 2 \times 2 - 1 \times 2 - 3 \times 4 = -5 < 0$$

If we attempt to define these ratings for plan A, we will find from equations

$$5\lambda_1+2\lambda_2-1\mu_1-3\mu_2 = 2\lambda_1+7{\cdot}75\lambda_2-7{\cdot}25\mu_1-1\mu_2 =$$
$$= 2\lambda_1+6\lambda_2-1\mu_1-4\mu_2 = 0$$

that the ratings must necessarily be (within the accuracy of the multiplier) $\lambda_1 = 0{\cdot}485$, $\lambda_2 = 0{\cdot}614$, $\mu_1 = 0{\cdot}652$, $\mu_2 = 1$. However, with these multipliers the sum for the unused process 2 is:

$$5\times 0{\cdot}485+2\times 0{\cdot}614-3\times 0{\cdot}652-1\times 1 = 0{\cdot}697 > 0$$

instead of $\leqq 0$. It follows that it is impossible to find multipliers for plan A; consequently it is not the optimum plan.

We now present a general mathematical formulation of these criteria:

Theorem 1. A given (feasible) plan is the optimum plan, if such ratings (multipliers) applicable to all products $\lambda_1, \lambda_2, \ldots, \lambda_m$ ($\lambda_i \geqq 0$; $\Sigma\lambda_i > 0$) and productive factors $\mu_1, \mu_2, \ldots, \mu_n$ ($\mu_i \geqq 0$) can be found that for processes used in this plan the sum of ratings $= 0$, and, for processes not used, this sum $\leqq 0$; that is

$$\sum_i \lambda_i x_i^s + \sum_j \mu_j z_j^s = 0, \text{ if } p_s > 0 \qquad \ldots[1]$$

$$\sum_i \lambda_i x_i^s + \sum_j \mu_j z_j^s \leqq 0, \text{ if } p_s = 0 \qquad \ldots[2]$$

Theorem 2. If a given plan is an optimum plan, there exist non-negative ratings $\lambda_1, \ldots, \lambda_m$; $\mu_1, \ldots, \mu_n$, such that the conditions [*1*] and [*2*] are satisfied.

We will present the proof of the first theorem, which actually repeats the consideration on which was based the proposition relating to the problem of machine tool loading.

We assume the opposite, namely that the plan is not an optimum. If so, there must be another plan (characterised by vector $\{p_s'\}$) for which the expenditure of productive factors is not greater, but the output is higher:

$$x_i' > x_i \; (i = 1, 2, \ldots, m); \quad z_j' \geqq z_j \; (j = 1, 2, \ldots, n)$$

Then on one hand

$$\sum_i \lambda_i x_i' + \sum_j \mu_j z_j = \sum_i \lambda_i \sum_s p_s' x_i^s + \sum_j \mu_j \sum_s p_s' z_j^s =$$
$$= \sum_s p_s' \left(\sum_i \lambda_i x_i^s + \sum_j \mu_j z_j^s\right) \leqq 0$$

and on the other hand

$$\sum_i \lambda_i x_i' + \sum_j \mu_j z_j' > \sum_i \lambda_i x_i + \sum_j \mu_j z_j =$$
$$= \sum_s p_s \left(\sum_i \lambda_i x_i^s + \sum_j \mu_j z_j^s\right) = 0$$

Thus, there is a contradiction. It means that no such alternative plan exists and consequently the given plan is the optimum plan.

We will not give the proof for the second theorem; it can be evolved in the same way as a similar proof for the specific case of machine tool loading (see pp. 277-79).

The two propositions regarding the characteristics of the optimum plan on one hand give rise to a number of effective methods for developing an optimum plan (described in Section 3); on the other hand they represent important economic indicators with a wide field of application (see Section 4).

In conclusion, we should like to mention possible variations of these propositions and to note peculiarities of their application in various circumstances.

1. If a given plan does not fully satisfy the requirements in the matter of assortment (there are 'surpluses' of some products, see note 1, p. 285), then its being an optimum plan means that no plan exists for which $x_i' > x_i$ for all i without a 'surplus'. In this case the condition of theorem 1 changes: multipliers λ_i no longer being equal to 0 for those i where a surplus exists. This applies to theorem 2 as well.

2. We did not consider here the question of the existence of an optimum plan. In practice, an optimum plan in a general sense (allowing for 'surpluses') exists always.[1]

3. The way we posed the problem—achievement of maximum output of a given assortment—is not the only possible one. For instance, the requirement may be to produce definite quantities of all products, except one which is to be produced in the greatest possible quantity; or it may be desirable to produce a given range of goods for a minimum of expenditure, and so on. In all these cases there will exist ratings for the plan, and theorems 1 and 2 will remain valid.

4. In some cases there are no rigid conditions for the composition of production; for instance, it is possible to replace some products by others, in a certain proportion. In a number of such cases, the problem can be reduced to one that has been discussed; in particular, in the case just mentioned it is sufficient to introduce this change as a new technological process.

5. We should note that the division of production components into products and productive factors is in a sense fictional, since we allow for x_i^s and z_j^s to be either positive or negative. This division depends mainly on how these components enter the problem mathematically (as limiting conditions or proportionality conditions); as already pointed out, however, this division is not very significant. Indeed, this was why we did not specially introduce some intermediate products. They can be introduced as factors for which $z_j = 0$ (that means, their intakes are equal to 0).

6. It is necessary to separate the cases when each technological process involves only one kind of productive factors. In these cases the definition of

[1] Compare L. V. KANTOROVICH, 'Methods of analysis of some extremal problems of production planning', *Proceedings of the Academy of Science of the USSR* **115**, No. 3, pp. 441-4. 1951.

an optimum plan can be simplified by introducing no other ratings than those for output. This simplification is due to the total rating of output being identical for all used processes which expend a unit of the given factor (and being equal to the rating for this unit). An example of this kind of problem is the question of rational cutting up (complex usage of materials). A similar situation arises when each process involves only one kind of product (mixing problem); in this case the ratings of factors are sufficient for a definition of the optimum plan. Machine loading may be considered as a problem of the former or the latter type, as desired.

7. In the transportation problem we have ratings for product at all production establishments A_i, equal to $U(A_i)$, and at all destinations B_j, equal to $U(B_j)$. If the expenditure of moving one unit of product from A_i to B_j is r_{ij}, then the characteristics of the optimum plan are as follows:

$$U(B_j) - U(A_i) = r_{ij} \quad \text{for methods to be used}$$
$$U(B_j) - U(A_i) \leqq r_{ij} \quad \text{for methods not to be used.}$$

This is the criterion for this problem; the value U is known as the freight potential.

8. The mathematical model of the problem of production planning is based on the assumption of linearity—if the output is doubled, the expenditure is also doubled. This assumption is known not to be fully valid in actual practice. Nevertheless, we consider the methods and results of this analysis to be of a sufficiently broad applicability. First, in a number of cases the hypothesis of linearity nearly meets the practice; for instance, it can be assumed that doubling the output would double the working time or the equipment used, and thus double the expenditure, and so forth. Secondly, in cases which are not strictly linear the problem can be reduced to a linear one. For instance, if a further increase of output demands a higher expenditure per unit of production, this additional output at higher cost can be included as an additional technological process which, naturally, may be incorporated in the plan after the possibilities of the first process have been exhausted.

Lastly, in a number of cases the methods of linear programming are used not for the preparation of the plan, but for its modification. In these cases the assumption of linearity is justified even more fully.

3. Methods of Determining the Optimum Plan and its Indicators

Some effective methods of determining the optimum plan by the use of resolving multipliers have been stated in the previous paper. Consequently it will suffice here to list the improvements of these methods which have been achieved in the course of our subsequent work.

(*a*) *Checking that the plan is an optimum.* In order to prove that a plan is an optimum, it is sufficient to show that the associated resolving multipliers exist. Generally, the system of equations and inequalities [*1*], [*2*] which determines them should be written down. If this system can be solved (for instance, if the roots of equations [*1*] satisfy the inequalities [*2*], then the plan is an optimum. On the other hand, if the conditions for finding the resolving multipliers are found to be contradictory, then the plan is not an optimum; at the same time a way of improving the plan will be seen.

(*b*) *Progressive improvement of the plan.* This method consists of the introduction of a more effective plan which so far has not been used but which has been discussed in the course of finding the multipliers; this new method will increase the output. In the example considered previously for plan *A* (see p. 286) this new method was the use of machine tool 1 for job I.

Before doing this it is advisable to complete the system of ratings by assuming that, say, machine tool 1 is used on job III during 0 time. Then

$$\lambda_3 = 53{\cdot}3 : 48 = 1{\cdot}11; \quad \mu_3 = 48 \times 1{\cdot}11 = 53{\cdot}3$$

Let α be the length of time that machine tool 1 is used on job I. The use of this machine tool during one unit of time results in a gain of $72-53{\cdot}3 = 18{\cdot}7$ assumed units, which corresponds to $18{\cdot}7 : (1+2{\cdot}67+1{\cdot}11) = 3{\cdot}91$ completed sets; during a period α the gain is $3{\cdot}91\alpha$ completed sets. Due to the use of machine tool 1 the output of job I is increased by 72α. However, job I should be increased only by $3{\cdot}91\alpha$; the remaining $68{\cdot}09\alpha$ allow for the load on machine tool 2 to be reduced in ratio $68{\cdot}09\alpha : 64 = 1{\cdot}06\alpha$. Consequently, it can be used on job II to the extent of $24 \times 1{\cdot}06\alpha = 25{\cdot}4\alpha$. As an increase of $3{\cdot}9\alpha$ has been provided for, in view of $25{\cdot}4\alpha - 3{\cdot}9\alpha = 21{\cdot}5\alpha$ of job II the machine tool 1 can be released for other use for a period $21{\cdot}5\alpha : 20 = 1{\cdot}08\alpha$. The saving on working time of tool 1 is $1{\cdot}08\alpha - 1\alpha = 0{\cdot}08\alpha$; it allows for job III being done on this machine tool to the extent of $0{\cdot}08\alpha \times 48 = 3{\cdot}84\alpha$. It can be readily seen that the maximum value of α for non-negative working time can be found from the condition $0{\cdot}5 - 1{\cdot}06\alpha = 0$; $\alpha = 0{\cdot}47$. This results in an improved plan *A* (Table 5).

TABLE 5

Jobs	I		II		III	
Machine tools	Fraction of time	Output norm	Fraction of time	Output norm	Fraction of time	Output norm
1	$0{\cdot}47\ (\alpha)$	72	$0{\cdot}41\ (1-1{\cdot}08\alpha)$	20	$0{\cdot}04\ (0{\cdot}08\alpha)$	48
2	$0\ (0{\cdot}5-1{\cdot}06\alpha)$	64	$1{\cdot}0\ (0{\cdot}5+1{\cdot}06\alpha)$	24	—	48
3	—	48	—	18	1·0	32
Total output	33·9		33·9		33·9	

In this manner an improvement of the work plan has been achieved. A check of this plan and a definition of the resolving multipliers will show again that this is not the optimum plan. However, a few similar improvements will lead to plan *B*.

Generally, this gradual improvement is done algebraically. For instance, in the example of basic problem (Table 1) of plan *A* we can add to the processes 1, 3, 4 used in plan *A* the more effective process 2 which has not been used; corrections Δp_1, Δp_2, Δp_3, Δp_4 can be found from conditions of equal expenditure and proportionally increased output by means of equations:

$$1\Delta p_1+3\Delta p_2+7{\cdot}25\Delta p_3+1\Delta p_4 = 0$$
$$3\Delta p_1+1\Delta p_2+1\Delta p_3+4\Delta p_4 = 0$$
$$3\,(5\Delta p_1+5\Delta p_2+3\Delta p_3+2\Delta p_4) = 2\,(2\Delta p_1+2\Delta p_2+7{\cdot}75\Delta p_3+6\Delta p_4)$$

On the basis of these equations Δp_1, Δp_3, and Δp_4 can be expressed by Δp_2, and it will be seen that the maximum value which would permit the introduction of process 2 is $\Delta p_2 = 1{\cdot}99$. As a result we arrive at an improved plan, which again should be subjected to a test.

This method is particularly suitable for the transportation problem. It is similar to the simplex method which does not make use of resolving multipliers.

(*c*) *Progressive improvement of ratings.* This method has been presented in the previous paper. Generally, it assumes some approximate rating values, from which the most promising processes are defined. From the available resources we then attempt to develop a plan to fulfil the given task to the greatest extent. Thereby an excess or shortage of a certain product calls for a reduction or increase of its rating, respectively. The productive factors are treated similarly. In this manner we gradually approach the best plan. In a sense this process resembles the process of changing market prices with changes of supply and demand ratio (overproduction leads to price reduction, etc.). In our case, however, the competitive fight between different processes takes place merely within the framework of planning, without losses and without crises. Naturally, this is possible on a large scale only under the conditions of a planned socialist economy.

This method is particularly suitable when the number of productive factors or of various products is not large.

(*d*) *Finding the first approximation.* The speed of achieving the required result depends on how good is the first approximation. This approximation is found on the basis of rough ratings, which are easily defined for individual types of problems. In the machine loading problem these ratings are the inverse values of total productivities, in the cutting-up problem they are the areas or lengths of cut off pieces.

After these ratings have been found, it is advisable to note the most promising and the next best processes, and to try to attain the production of the planned assortment by means of these processes. A plan worked out in this manner may prove to be the optimum plan right away, or it may come close to the optimum. If it is the latter, it may be progressively improved.

For instance, in the previously discussed machine-loading problem (Table 3) the ratings for individual jobs I, II and III, may be assumed as:

$$\lambda_1^0 = \frac{1{,}000}{72+64+48} = 5{\cdot}43, \quad \lambda_2^0 = \frac{1{,}000}{20+24+18} = 16{\cdot}13,$$

$$\lambda_3^0 = \frac{1{,}000}{48+48+32} = 7{\cdot}8$$

For these ratings, the productivities of available machine tools on different jobs are (in assumed units) as in Table 6.

TABLE 6

Machine tools	Jobs I	II	III
1	**391**	323	375
2	348	**387**	375
3	261	**290**	250

If we assume the productivity of each machine tool to be equal to the maximum value in each horizontal row: $\mu_1^0 = 391$, $\mu_2^0 = 387$, $\mu_3^0 = 290$, then the achievable maximum—the number of complete sets—can be assumed to be equal to $\dfrac{391+387+290}{5{\cdot}43+16{\cdot}13+7{\cdot}8} = 36{\cdot}4$.

Now we work out the programme for achieving this planned target. It seems reasonable to use machine tool 1 for job I, since it has the highest rating for this job. Its loading for this job will be approximately 0·5 (this fraction of its operating time may be designated x). Further, it is reasonable to use machine tool 1 for job III, whereby it will produce roughly $0{\cdot}5\times 48 = 24$ assumed units. The remainder of job III can be carried out on machine tool 2, with a rating of productivity nearing the maximum (the fraction of its operating time taken up by job III may be designated y). The remainder of working time of tool 2 and the whole time of tool 3 will be used for job II.

The requirement of equal volumes of all jobs leads to the equations:

$$72x = 24\,(1-y)+18 = 48\,(1-x)+48y;$$

consequently $x = 0{\cdot}5$; $y = 0{\cdot}25$.

As an immediate result we obtain an optimum plan. This can be easily ascertained by finding its multipliers. Actually this is the plan B already known to us.

It is easy to show that a similar procedure in dealing with Plywood Trust problem[1] would also lead to the optimum plan, either directly or after one or two improvements.

[1] See p. 232 of this book.

(*e*) *Rating limits.* This method is based on finding, even before the optimum plan has been fully defined, the upper and lower limits between which the true values of ratings must necessarily lie; approximate ratings so obtained are then used to work out the optimum plan.

Let us illustrate this approach by a reference to the machine loading problem. For example, let $\lambda_1 = 1$. It follows from a comparison of productivities of machine tools for jobs I and II: $\frac{72}{20}$; $\frac{64}{24}$; $\frac{48}{18}$; that λ_2 lies somewhere between the largest and the smallest of these ratios, which can be taken as limits for λ_2:

$$\lambda_2^- = \frac{64}{24} = 2{\cdot}67 \leqq \lambda_2 \leqq \lambda_2^+ = \frac{72}{20} = 3{\cdot}6$$

Similarly, $\lambda_3^- = 1{\cdot}33 \leqq \lambda_3 \leqq \lambda_3^+ = 1{\cdot}5$. It is just as easy to find the approximate ratings for μ_i, for instance:

$$\mu_2^+ = \max(64\lambda_1^+, 24\lambda_2^+, 48\lambda_3^+) = 86{\cdot}4$$

$$\mu_2^- = \max(64\lambda_1^-, 24\lambda_2^-, 48\lambda_3^-) = 72$$

since the rating of each machine tool is limited by the maximum rating of its productivity. It is also advisable to introduce rating limits for complex productivity, expressed in assortments of products. To make the ratings more accurate, approximations to the plan may be used, particularly solutions of some simplified problems.

This method can be useful in cases when even the initial data (productivities) are merely approximate. It can also be applied to involved combined problems, where the data must be clarified and the solutions must be improved progressively in a series of stages.

(*f*) *Analogue methods.* Problems of linear programming can be solved, apart from calculating procedures, by various analogue devices. For instance, as long ago as 1940 the following analogue solution of the transportation problem was suggested to us. Each point of production or consumption may be likened to a reservoir. A volume of fluid corresponding to the respective volume of production may flow into each reservoir representing a production point; conversely, a fluid may flow from each reservoir representing a destination point in proportion to its consumption. The various reservoirs may be connected by a pipework which would be opened when the difference of levels reaches a value $\geqq r_{ij}$ (transport cost). The state of the liquid in the pipework system provides a solution of the problem; for the flow in a pipe will indicate a rational route and the levels will correspond to transport potentials. An electrical analogue of this problem is also feasible. Similar analogue models, either electrical or mechanical, may be devised for other problems of linear programming.

It is interesting to note that such models can be developed, apart from physical make-up, purely by means of calculation.

(g) *Use of electronic computers.* Methods of linear programming, those mentioned above as well as others, are adequate as long as the number of products and of factors of production is relatively low. If this number is high, however, the calculations involved become rather cumbersome. All these methods can be carried out by means of programme-controlled digital computers. Frequently, after the standard programmes have been developed the computer can produce a solution within a few minutes. The experience of computer solution of the transportation problem has been described by M. A. Yakovleva. Such methods have also been tried out at the Leningrad branch of the Mathematical Institute. Thus the use of computers considerably simplifies the solution of problems of optimum programming and in consequence it significantly increases the efficiency of these methods.

It is essential to stress the importance of using the electronic computers in combination with the methods of optimum planning. The use of electronic machines alone would not produce the desired result. If they are used with conventional methods of planning, they speed up the calculations, but they would not improve the methods as such. The qualitative considerations, required to correct the calculations if need be, cannot be directly entrusted to machines. At the same time those methods of optimum planning which have been clearly defined mathematically can be put into effect directly by means of machines, like any other mathematical process.

It should be mentioned that direct consideration of possible variations, except in the simplest cases, is beyond the capabilities even of electronic techniques, since the number of variations can go into billions. Furthermore, it is most important to remember that the methods of linear programming enable not only the optimum plan to be evolved, but also its indicators, which are essential for putting it into effect.

4. Properties and Applications of Ratings Variations of the Optimum Plan

Along with the finding of the plan, it is very important to correct it in accordance with any changes of the original data and to adapt it to additional plan requirements. No less essential than the plan itself are its characteristics which permit an objective evaluation and comparison of various economic factors. Such a comparison is particularly needed in the conditions of socialist society, where the final criterion of productive activity is the extent to which it satisfies the requirements of the community. From this point of view the possibility of directly comparing the various plan solutions is most valuable.

In this chapter we intend to show that the mathematical methods used to construct the optimum plan can be successfully applied to an analysis of the plan and of its indicators. In particular, the resolving multipliers (ratings) which have been discussed as a means for working out the plan, have a direct economic significance.

It would be useful to present a geometrical interpretation of the optimum plan problem. However, in order to remain within a two-dimensional drawing, we will restrict ourselves to a specific case involving only one productive factor and two kinds of product. Production processes are indicated in Table 7. A plan is required to produce an assortment of products in ratio 1 : 1. Two possible plans *A* and *B* are shown in Table 7.

TABLE 7

Technological Process	Output from Unit of Material		Share of Material machined according to each Process	
	Product I	Product II	Plan *A*	Plan *B*
1	—	22		$\frac{5}{16}$
2	8	18	$\frac{1}{2}$	
3	16	6	$\frac{1}{2}$	$\frac{11}{16}$
4	18	0		
Output from unit of material according to plan *A*	12	12		
Output from unit of material according to plan *B*	11	11		

The result of each technological process can be represented by a point in a plane, by marking the units of product I obtained from a unit of material along the abscissa, and those of product II along the ordinate. These are points I, II, III, IV in Fig. 1. Obviously any point on the line connecting a pair of these points represents the plan (programme) obtained as a result of some combination of the two respective processes. Points corresponding to all feasible plans fill the polygon I, II, III, IV. Since we are bound by the assortment requirement 1 : 1, we must look for a point on the ray corresponding to this 1 : 1 ratio, and since we wish to obtain a maximum output we take the point furthest away from the origin but still within the boundaries of this polygon. This is point α, which corresponds to plan *A*. Point β corresponds to plan *B*; again, it is within the polygon. Thus, the problem of finding the optimum plan is reduced, geometrically, to determining the extreme point of intersection of the assortment ray with the polygon formed by points corresponding to the various technological processes.

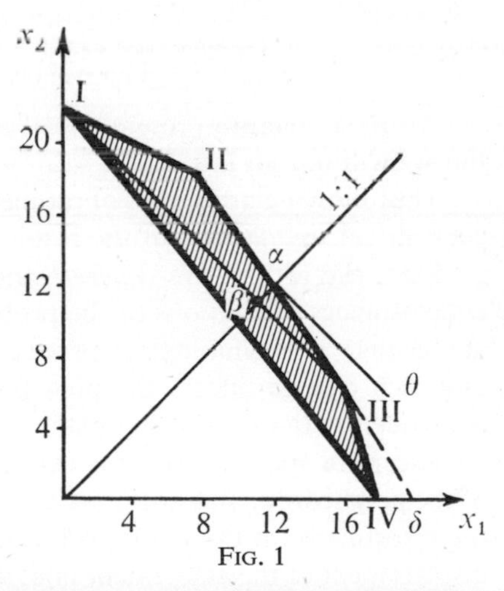

FIG. 1

This geometrical treatment of the problem does not provide a direct solution, since in the case of n different products the construction would involve n dimensions. However, this diagram (shown for only two products, but valid generally) helps one to understand a number of features and qualitative peculiarities of the problem.

Let us illustrate the geometrical significance of resolving multipliers, or ratings (Fig. 1).

We draw a supporting line $\alpha\beta$ to the polygon, which also contains the extreme point α. The equation of this line since it passes through points II (8, 18) and III (16, 6), is

$$3x_1+2x_2 = 60$$

This equation is satisfied by all points corresponding to processes 2 and 3.

Any points which correspond to other processes lie below this straight line, consequently for these points:

$$3x_1+2x_2 < 60$$

Thus it is evident that the coefficients of the equation of the straight line (II, III) are in fact the resolving multipliers (ratings) for each kind of products dealt with in this problem. This postulate has a general validity.

As resolving multipliers we may take the coefficients of the supporting plane (hyperplane) to the polyhedron representing the plans, this plane going through the extreme point—the point where the assortment ray leaves the polyhedron. Thus the equation of this plane is

$$\lambda_1 x_1+\lambda_2 x_2+\ldots+\lambda_m x_m = c$$

A similar picture presents itself in the problem of production planning, but we will not go into it.

The following properties of ratings become immediately apparent from the geometrical significance of the resolving multipliers.

First, the ratings are *concrete* and *dynamic*, that is, they depend on the circumstances (definitions of the problem), and accordingly they change with any change of technological processes, resources, and assortment. Indeed, any such change affects the plan polyhedron and the assortment ray, and consequently the supporting plane.

Except in special cases, the extreme point will be inside one of the edges of the polyhedron, and not at its boundary. Consequently, a small change of the assortment (in the basic problem, of the resources) will result in a small displacement of the assortment line; the boundary (and with it the supporting plane) will remain as before, and the resolving multipliers will not change. Other small changes (those of processes) will affect the values of multipliers a little. Thus, resolving multipliers (ratings) possess, generally speaking, a certain *stability* despite changes in the targets.

Lastly, if we replace a given point of the supporting plane by a point nearby, we may change over to the optimum plan for another composition of the assortment. If the corresponding total output is $(x_1+\Delta x_1,\ x_2+\Delta x_2)$, then

$$\lambda_1 x_1+\lambda_2 x_2 = C,\quad \lambda_1 (x_1+\Delta x_1)+\lambda_2 (x_2+\Delta x_2) = C$$

It follows:

$$\lambda_1 \Delta x_1+\lambda_2 \Delta x_2 = 0;\quad \frac{\Delta x_1}{\Delta x_2} = -\frac{\lambda_2}{\lambda_1}$$

This means that it is possible to modify the plan (at least within narrow limits) by replacing one kind of product by another in proportions defined by the ratings; this supports the *reality* of ratings (more exactly, of the ratios of equivalency as established by the ratings).

It may be noted that it is only the correlation of objectively conditioned ratings that possesses these properties. For any other correlation of ratings (shown geometrically as a line $\alpha\theta$ different from the supporting line) the replacement of one product by another in this ratio in one sense—replacement of product II by product I (in the direction $\alpha\theta$)—would be impossible and unrealistic; the reversed replacement—of product I by product II (in the direction $\theta\alpha$)—leads to a non-optimum solution.

Correlations of this kind can be obtained for the basic problem of production planning, too.

Because of the total rating for each used technological process being zero:

$$\sum_{i=1}^{m} \lambda_i x_i^s+\sum_{j=1}^{n} \mu_j z_j^s = 0$$

Multiplying these relations by p_s and adding up, we obtain for the optimum plan as a whole:

$$\sum_{s=1}^{S} p_s \sum_{i=1}^{m} \lambda_i x_i^s+\sum_{s=1}^{S} p_s \sum_{j=1}^{n} \mu_j z_j^s = \sum_{i=1}^{m} \lambda_i \sum_{s=1}^{S} p_s x_i^s+$$

$$+\sum_{j=1}^{n} \mu_j \sum_{s=1}^{S} p_s z_j^s = \sum_{i=1}^{m} \lambda_i x_i+\sum_{j=1}^{n} \mu_j z_j = 0$$

If there is another optimum plan for slightly different resources and products, so that the same ratings are valid, the equation

$$\sum_{i=1}^{m} \lambda_i (x_i+\Delta x_i)+\sum_{j=1}^{n} \mu_j (z_j+\Delta z_j) = 0$$

must also be satisfied; by subtracting the foregoing equation we find:

$$\sum_{i=1}^{n} \lambda_i \Delta x_i+\sum_{j=1}^{m} \mu_j \Delta z_j = 0 \qquad \ldots [3]$$

This relation will be called the *equation of plan variation*; it establishes the condition for equivalent replacement of some kinds of products and productive factors by others. This condition must be adhered to when changing from a given optimum plan to a modified (similar) optimum plan; it is sufficient, generally speaking, to ensure that the plan can be carried out. More specifically, this relation covers the replacement of one product by another according to ratings; this replacement has been referred to above when discussing the question of realistic ratings.

These characteristics of ratings, together with the equation of plan variation, make possible numerous applications of ratings to corrections of plan and to individual partial solutions.

Thanks to the relative stability of the ratings it is possible to neglect changes due to corrections of the plan, and to use previously established values. Further, realistic ratings together with variational correlations ensure that some products and factors can be replaced by others. Of course this statement refers to relatively small modifications which do not fundamentally change the situation (and ratings). Such is usually the case when questions of economics and planning have to be decided, when new jobs have to be incorporated in the plan, or when some tasks have to be replaced by others. If decisions have been taken or the tasks have been revised so as to change the situation drastically, then they cannot be considered as mere variations of the plan, to be analysed on the basis of previous ratings; rather, they demand a complete revision of plan and ratings.

Among questions relating to plan variation we may mention the following points to which ratings are applicable.

1. *Modification of plan target.* Let us assume that the resources of productive factors on which the plan was originally based have been changed (in either sense). Plan targets for some kinds of products have also been modified. Can these targets be reached under changed conditions within the same period of time? To answer this question it is sufficient to evaluate on the basis of existing ratings, the new volume of resources and also the new volume of output. We shall then know what percentage in excess, or short, of target can be expected. Alternatively, if the resource vector is $(z_1+\Delta z_1, \ldots, z_n+\Delta z_n)$ while the planned output is $(x_1+\Delta x_1, \ldots, x_m+\Delta x_m)$, then the required answer is given by the sum

$$\sum_{i=1}^{m} \lambda_i \Delta x_i + \sum_{j=1}^{n} \mu_j \Delta z_j$$

Indeed, if this sum is less than 0, the plan can be exceeded (on the basis of accepted technological processes and norms). Of course the modifications are assumed to be so insignificant that the ratings are not affected.

2. *Evaluation of a new technological process.* A new technological process (or method of organising production) has to be considered, which has not been taken into account when the plan was being prepared. Is this process suitable under prevailing conditions? To answer this question it is sufficient to compare, by means of existing ratings, the totals of factors to be consumed

and outputs to be expected, If the result is positive, application of the new process will increase the output, otherwise it will not. In other words, if the vector of expenditure for this process is $(\bar{z}_1, \ldots, \bar{z}_n)$ and the output vector is $(\bar{x}_1, \ldots, \bar{x}_n)$, then the new process is suitable on condition that

$$\sum_{i=1}^{m} \lambda_i \bar{x}_i + \sum_{j=1}^{n} \mu_j \bar{z}_j > 0$$

If the processes are indivisible, i.e. they must be used to a given extent, this condition is essential for this process to be useful, but generally speaking it is insufficient.

3. *Advantage of a change of product.* The question of replacing one assortment of products by another can be decided by a comparison of ratings of the original assortment with those of the new. Thus, if an assortment $(x_1', \ldots, x_m')$ can be replaced by $(x_1'', \ldots, x_m'')$, then this replacement is advantageous on condition that

$$\sum_{i=1}^{m} \lambda_i x_i'' < \sum_{i=1}^{m} \lambda_i x_i'$$

When applying the methods of optimum planning to practical problems it is often advisable to consider some special forms of expenditure and production, in addition to those normally considered in the course of economic analysis; consequently, it is necessary to obtain ratings for these new factors. For instance, among the expendable productive factors there may be the working time of a certain machine tool (including the whole of associated expenditure), non-availability of floor space, rent[1] of some equipment over a certain period (apart from wear), and so on. As to output, apart from final products and services these may be semi-finished products, individual operations, whole ranges of products or operations and so forth. Therefore it is essential to account for those products and items of expenditure, the total of which changes from one process to another. On the other hand, cost items which remain constant in all circumstances (for instance, consumption of materials or semi-finished products 'on the side') can be completely left out of the analysis, with regard to both expenditure and output.

Accordingly ratings for some factors and products have a local character; they are intended for use exclusively within a certain production unit which is being analysed.

As an illustration we refer to some calculations concerning the machine loading problem, already considered in section 2.

(1) Productivity of machine tool 2 has been increased by 20% for all kinds of work; at the same time, target output for job I has been put up 30%. Can this task be achieved?

Since the changes are not great, previous ratings may be used.

[1] For an explanation of this term, see p. 305 of this paper.

Increase of resources: $(24 \times 0{\cdot}75 \times 3 + 48 \times 0{\cdot}25 \times 1{\cdot}5) \times 0{\cdot}20 =$
$= 72 \times 0{\cdot}20 = 14{\cdot}4$

Increase of output: $36 \times 1 \times 0{\cdot}30 = 10{\cdot}8$.

Evidently, the plan can be exceeded by

$$\frac{14{\cdot}4 - 10{\cdot}8}{36 \times 1 + 36 \times 3 + 36 \times 1{\cdot}5} = \frac{3{\cdot}6}{198} = 1{\cdot}8\%$$

(2) A new process for job II has been suggested, using machine tools 1 and 3 simultaneously (co-operation). Thereby productivity reaches 50 per unit of time. Is this process advantageous?

Expenditure: $1\mu_3 + 1\mu_2 = 72 + 54 = 126$
Output: $50\lambda_3 = 50 \times 3 = 150$
The new process is worthwhile.

The following two examples comprise expenditure of factors which affect the labour conditions.

Example 1. Table 8 lists the yields of some crops on three plots, and total expenditure expressed in units of work, for a given cultivation of the respective plot. It also states the cultivation plan for these plots.

TABLE 8

Type of soil	Area (hectares)	Crop	Yield (Cntr)	Expenditure (man-days /hectare)	Allocated area (hectares)	Harvest in Cntr/h for each crop 1	2	3	Expenditure (man-days)
I	100	1							
		2							
		3							
II	200	1							
		2							
		3							
III	300 (and over)	1							
		2							
		3							
Total	600					5,000			

In the course of analysis of the cultivation plan we note that there are three kinds of products and three kinds of expenditure factors: labour and utilisation of soil I and II. We do not consider soil III, since there remains a surplus of it. Taking the expenditure of one man-day as a unit, we can work out the ratings for 1 cwt of each crop λ_1, λ_2, λ_3 and for soil of type I and II, μ_1 and μ_2. On the basis of ratings of processes used in the plan we obtain progressively:

$25\lambda_3 - 7 - \mu_3 = 0$	$\lambda_3 = 0{\cdot}280$
$15\lambda_2 - 8 - \mu_3 = 0$	$\lambda_2 = 0{\cdot}533$
$20\lambda_2 - 8 - \mu_2 = 0$	$\mu_2 = 2{\cdot}67$
$20\lambda_1 - 10 - \mu_2 = 0$	$\lambda_1 = 0{\cdot}633$
$30\lambda_1 - 10 - \mu_1 = 0$	$\mu_1 = 9{\cdot}00$

With reference to the obtained ratings it is easy to see that the sum of ratings for non-used processes is < 0; hence this plan is an optimum.

Here we have obtained a definite rating for the utilisation of the best soils (the rating is equal to labour saving achieved by cultivating one hectare under prevailing conditions). This indicates the need for introduction of a special kind of expenditure connected with utilisation or productive factors (in this case, available areas of best soils) which economise on labour, provided we have them in sufficient quantity. Naturally, only on this condition shall we arrive at a plan which makes the best use of these factors, and also at the correct relative ratings of output.

As a matter of fact, in order to obtain the correct ratings and the best solutions demanded by the plan, it is necessary to take account of differential rent which should be evaluated by objective methods for any given set of conditions.

In order to show the importance of rentals as far as cultivation of land is concerned, let us assume that the yield of crop 1 can be increased by 2 cwt by a more thorough cultivation of soil I, which however requires 10% more labour effort. Is this worthwhile? By comparing the increase of expenditure with the higher output we find that it is, since:

$$2 \times 0{\cdot}633 - 1 > 0$$

In this calculation by using the output rating we took account of expenditure of the labour-saving factor. If the direct expenditure of labour alone is considered, it would appear that the productivity of labour on this plot would be reduced: for, although 10% more labour will be needed, production will be increased by $\frac{2}{30} = 6{\cdot}7\%$ only. It follows that the use of conventional indicators can be misleading in this case, and can prevent an intensive soil cultivation.

Example 2. Let us consider the machine loading problem (Table 3) under modified conditions: during the same period less output is required—32 units of each job, and the expenditure must be reduced to a minimum. Expenditure for each machine tool is 30 roubles per unit of time (for all kinds of jobs).

Using the ratings determined previously (p. 287), we find that machine tools 1 and 2 are cheaper to run than machine tool 3, since 72 units can be produced instead of 54, for the same expenditure. Consequently in the rational plan of Table 9 these machine tools have been utilised to the full.

TABLE 9

Jobs	I		II		III	
Machine Tools	Output norm	Time fraction	Output norm	Time fraction	Output norm	Time fraction
1	72	0·44	22	—	48	0·56
2	64	—	24	0·89	48	0·11
3	48	—	18	0·59	32	—
Total Output	32		32		32	

Further, as machine tool 3 has not been fully loaded, the expenditure for increase or reduction of output is determined by the working conditions of this tool; it amounts to $30 : 54 = 0{\cdot}555$ roubles per unit. Since the use of machine tools 1 and 2 allows for additional production of $72-54 = 18$ units per time unit, the saving is $18 \times 0{\cdot}555 = 10$ roubles per day, which justifies their use. This value should be used for evaluation of expenditure with regard to this factor (use of tools 1 and 2 for this particular type of work). Indeed, if this kind of expenditure is taken into account, all processes used by the optimum plan are equally justified; for instance, for job II carried out on tools 2 and 3 the expenditure per unit is, respectively

$$(30+10) : 24 = 1{\cdot}67 \quad (= 3 \times 0{\cdot}555)$$
$$30 : 18 = 1{\cdot}67$$

If indirect expenditure is included in the output rating, as in the above example, it means that suitable 'payment' for the necessary equipment should be taken into account, as it is for hired or rented equipment. The amount of rent (rental rating) should be commensurate with the economy expected from the use of this equipment. In this example this rating for machine tools 1 and 2 is 10 roubles per unit of time.

However, if we calculate the factory cost of work of a given range of equipment without taking into account the rental cost, the absolute values of output ratings will be different. Nevertheless, we must retain the relative ratings (distribution of costs). Absolute rating of an assumed unit will be in this case $3 \times 30 : (72+72+54) = 90 : 198 = 0{\cdot}45$ roubles, and the expenditure rating per unit of work will be respectively 1·3 and 1·5 assumed units (0·45 roubles, 1·35 roubles, 0·67 roubles).

It would seem that rating of expenditure could be approached from a different angle, namely in the usual way from the actual average expenditure per unit of work of a given kind. However, such an approach would in this case produce wrong and misleading results. For instance, should job II be transferred from machine tool 3 to machine tool 1, the productivity would go up and the expenditure would go down. Yet the preceding calculations prove that such a transfer would not be worthwhile in the circumstances, because it would lead away from the optimum. A calculation based on actual expenditure is misleading, because it takes into account only the specific expenditures of this particular area. More important is the total expenditure on the whole complex of jobs; its evaluation would show that job II cannot be transferred to machine tool 1 simply because this tool is already fully loaded, so that a part of this load would have to be transferred to machine tool 3. In consequence any gain will be more than wiped out by the loss. Objectively defined ratings reflect this position, as they take account of the rental cost and for this reason lead to correct conclusions. They reflect the expenditure of the whole complex, which is most important under conditions of a socialist economy.

We are of the opinion that a consideration of this important cost heading (rent of equipment) by means of rental rating is not only unavoidable for an analysis of the optimum plan, but it is also most valuable as a means for correct utilisation and distribution of equipment in short supply, for stimulation of measures and arrangements to cope with this problem, and lastly for a correct valuation of products manufactured by means of such equipment.

5. Use of Ratings in the Computation of Statistical and Economic Indicators

We have shown that ratings of output and of productive factors which have been found in the course of constructing an optimum plan and which are determined by the plan, can themselves be used afterwards for corrections and for ensuring that the plan remains an optimum.

Let us consider the possibility of using these ratings for another purpose, for example, for indicators relating to statistics and economics of production areas and undertakings.

It is well known that successful administration of production depends to a large extent on the correct valuation of the results achieved by the enterprise. It is important that this valuation should guide the activity in the right direction, that it should encourage adherence to the optimum plan and that it should ensure decisions which are correct from the point of view of the nation's economy.

In the model examined above the production unit includes a series of processes forming part of the overall plan and the corresponding resources of productive factors; it is supposed to produce a certain output.

The planned summary rating (algebraic sum) of output and expenditure of the production unit (according to calculated ratings) should equal 0, but actually this sum may be positive if expenditure has been reduced or the output has exceeded the planned target; alternatively, it can be negative if the target has not been reached. This sum may be considered to be the indicator of how successful the work of the enterprise has been.

Endeavours to improve this indicator will result in a reduction of expenditure, increase of output, and introduction of more advanced technology. Application of methods rejected in the course of developing an overall optimum plan will prove to be unprofitable, and will affect the indicator adversely. Further, it would appear that the plan target in regard to the composition of output and the expenditure should also be taken into account, any adverse deviations being somehow made to bear a penalty.

It is essential for this indicator to include among other forms of expenditure the usage of labour-saving factors, calculated in accordance with their ratings. Otherwise the indicator will give a distorted view of the enterprise's activity.

Thus, correctly evolved work indicators stimulate the activity of the enterprise in accordance with the plan, i.e. they help to fulfil the plan and to correct it, should the conditions change. Fig. 2 illustrates the system of links; ratings as determined by the plan help to correct the plan and to ensure its remaining an optimum.

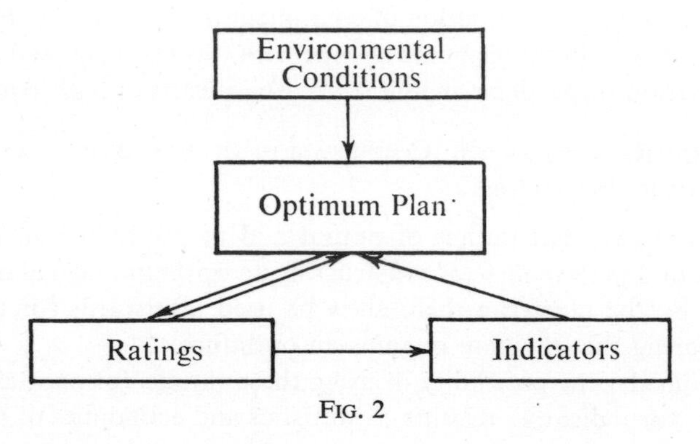

FIG. 2

Let us explain these general postulates by means of two examples which bear witness to the possibility, in principle, of using the calculating data of the optimum plan for the computation of economic indicators.

Example 1. We may be concerned with an arrangement of the annual programme for the production of equal quantities of two articles in three factories so as to load these factories fully. It is assumed that the expenditure of running the factories (except the materials) does not depend on the articles they produce, and that the expenditure of materials for an article does not depend on the choice of the factory in which it is to be made.

The data relating to monthly outputs and expenditures are listed in Table 10.

Clearly the problem of finding an optimum plan under these conditions is analogous to the machine-loading problem; it can be solved in the manner described above, for any number of factories and of products. It is equally clear that in these conditions a plan which ensures an optimum of output also ensures a minimum of expenditure. In this simple case the solution can be found easily and directly.

In this case the ratings of jobs (production of two articles) are in ratio

TABLE 10

Factory	Monthly output (units)		Monthly expenditure (less material) (roubles)	Factory cost of unit product (less material) (roubles)		Material per unit product (roubles)		Total factory cost of unit product (roubles)	
	Product 1	Product 2		Product 1	Product 2	Product 1	Product 2	Product 1	Product 2
A	4,000	2,000	44,000	11	22	6	4	17	26
B	6,000	4,000	60,000	10	15	6	4	16	19
C	5,000	5,000	40,000	8	8	6	4	14	22

2 : 3, for instance 10 and 15. (These are relative, not absolute, magnitudes of ratings for unit of production.)

If we calculate the net production,[1] i.e. the work required to finish the article, according to these ratings (10 for product 1 and 15 for product 2), it will be seen that the optimum plan (Table 11) ensures that each factory produces that article which enables the highest amount of net production to be achieved.

Thus the summary rating of net production (assuming that the ratings for individual products are correct), taken as an indicator of the volume of output produced by a factory, can stimulate a suitable spreading of programmed load according to the optimum plan. Indicators of gross production or of commodity production do not provide such a stimulus.

Further, it is useful to be able to form an opinion as to how the enterprise is running, and to decide on a production programme, by means of a structural analysis of total expenditure. Indicators of this kind can be formed in close relation to the optimum plan, if the rental rating (hire cost) is included in the total expenditure. With regard to the plant as a whole this rental cost can be treated in the same way as the planned profitability aimed at for the plant under given circumstances.

TABLE 11

Factory	Duration of work (months)		Annual production programme (thousands of units)		Monthly net production according to assumed ratings: 10 of product 1 and 15 of product 2 (thousands of assumed units)	
	Product 1	Product 2	Product 1	Product 2	Product 1	Product 2
A	12	—	48	—	**40***	30
B	6	6	36	24	**60**	**60**
C	—	12	—	60	50	**75**
Total			84	84		

* Heavily printed figures are ratings used in the optimum plan.

[1] By 'net production' we mean the labour spent on the completion of produced goods; for instance, the net production of a dress factory is not the quantity of produced garments, but the work of sewing, etc. of these garments.

To illustrate the principle of calculating such an indicator with the help of the same example of a group of factories, let us assume the price of a set of products 1 and 2 to be 40 roubles. By deducting the cost of materials the 'net production' is obtained: $40-6-4 = 30$ roubles. Since the ratings of production work on the two products are in ratio 2 : 3, the respective rating for product 1 is 12 roubles, and for product 2 it is 18 roubles. Consequently, full ratings are $6+12 = 18$ roubles and $4+18 = 22$ roubles respectively. If we calculate the profitability of the factories for the load programme of the optimum plan and then consider the extent of plant usage (rental cost) as one of planned expenditure items, then the composition of expenditure for each product will be as indicated in Table 12. For instance, the monthly rental cost for factory A will be:

$$4{,}000\times 18-4{,}000\times 11-4{,}000\times 6 = 4{,}000 \text{ roubles.}$$

TABLE 12

Factory	Monthly expenditure on production (less materials) (1,000 roubles)	monthly rental rating of equipment usage (1,000 roubles)	Expenditure on unit of product (roubles)							
			Product 1				Product 2			
			Expenditure on production	Rental of used equipment	Material cost	Total expenditure	Expenditure on production	Rental of used equipment	Material cost	Total expenditure
A	44	4	11	1	6	**18***	22	2	4	28
B	60	12	10	2	6	**18**	15	3	4	**22**
C	40	50	8	10	6	24	8	10	4	**22**

* Heavily printed figures are total expenditures as per optimum plan.

As we see, the inclusion of payment (rental rating) for the usage of equipment balances the conditions and makes this particular production profitable for all factories for which it is at all suitable. Planned profitability (taking the rental into account) is zero, but actually it can be higher. If it is taken as the principal indicator for the operation of the plant, then it will guide the management correctly in their planning and costing tasks. We mentioned a similar significance of the indicator of net production, which however permits us to answer questions unconnected with the amount of expenditure. The profitability indicator is more comprehensive, being calculated in relation to the rating of equipment usage and to ratings of output, and consequently it affords answers to questions concerned with changes of cost structure.

For instance, let us assume that the output of plant C can be increased, but only by using less productive machine tools or by ordering some components from subcontractors, so that the expenditure on making one unit of product 1 will be 11 instead of 8 roubles. Is it worthwhile to increase the output of plant C in this manner? Will it profit the national economy?

A conventional assessment of this proposal would make it appear unprofitable, since it increases the factory cost. In reality the profitability will increase, since the additional output does not involve any additional expenditure on equipment (factory cost is 12+4 = 16 roubles, whereas the selling price is 22 roubles). Increased output of product 1 from plant C is also advisable because even the increased expenditure of plant C is lower than expenditure at plant B; it follows that the suggested plan modification will reduce the total expenditure within the national economy.

Inclusion of rental rating (hire cost) of equipment provides the proper guidance for organisation of production. Conversely, its exclusion could be misleading. For instance, in the foregoing case the factory cost of product 1 at plant A would be higher than for product 2 at plant C, which is contrary to the real value of these products.

Example 2. Let us consider the application of calculating methods for the optimum plan to an assessment of indicators for transportation with a minimum of expenditure. Standard goods prices (f.o.b. departure station, f.o.b. destination station) do not offer any inducement to suppliers to choose a method of transportation which is best in the interest of national economy. A freight charge on the standard price, based on the optimum transportation plan, would help to overcome this drawback of price standardisation. It will be seen that the freight charges should be proportional to differences of transport potentials (see p. 291), to be worked out in parallel with the optimum transportation plan.

For instance, in the very simple case shown in Fig. 3, the volume of output at various plant locations is indicated in brackets and is preceded by a plus sign whereas the volume of consumption is preceded by a minus. On the basis of standard prices the best scheme for transportation is that indicated by the dotted line. However, from the point of view of national economy this scheme is not a rational one, since it includes movement of freight in the opposite direction. If freight charges (shown beneath each location) were to be introduced, the rational plan shown by unbroken lines would also be the most economical scheme for the plants in question.

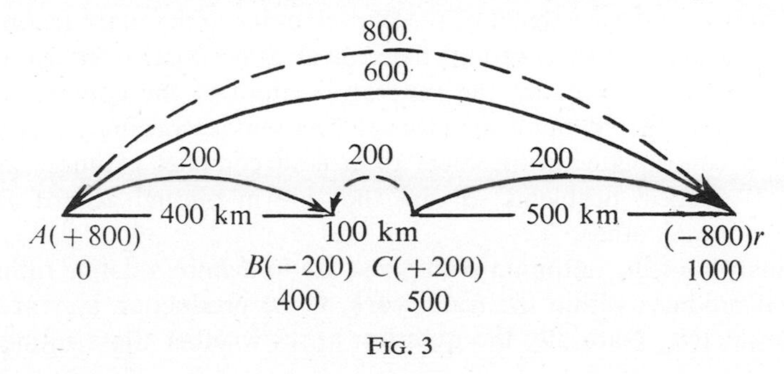

FIG. 3

Of course, these simple examples do not fully explain the whole intricate complex of questions concerning the build-up of economic indicators. However, they show clearly that the preparation of the optimum plan and of corresponding ratings is also useful for the development of a system of economic indicators, and also for an equitable distribution of costs over various goods, the production of which is in a sense interrelated.

6. Complex Production Planning

Whenever there is a complex of interrelated productive cells (enterprises), a joint production plan should be prepared to cover the whole. This question fits into the scheme of basic production planning; it is sufficient for the purpose to combine the available resources, the final targets and the production processes when calculating the programmes for individual enterprises. However, it will be frequently found that similar productive factors must be considered independently, if they are peculiar to certain enterprises and cannot be transferred to other enterprises.

As a result of this analysis we should obtain a single plan and a single system of ratings for all types of products and productive factors. Should certain goods appear in one enterprise as the final product and in another enterprise as a productive factor (material), their rating should be the same in both cases. Ratios of output ratings must be identical. Otherwise, even if the plan is an optimum for each enterprise but the ratio of ratings for any two (interchangeable) factors is different in different enterprises, the overall plan for the whole complex is bound not to be an optimum.

Further, if factors and products are interchangeable but an interchange causes some additional expenditure, their ratings may differ in different enterprises. The difference of ratings of one product in two areas must not exceed the cost of interchange and should be equal to this cost, if in fact such interchange is provided for by the optimum plan. Such questions arise, in particular, when the enterprises are in different locations and the requirement is to establish rational connexions and to determine the volumes of production.

This approach to the preparation of the optimum plan of a complex, based as it is on a single system of ratings, can be convenient also for subsequent control and adjustment of the plan in order to maintain its optimum level. By means of uniform ratings the individual productive enterprises will be able to take into account the general situation of the complex and its changes, and to face definite managerial decisions accordingly. Thus it is possible to co-ordinate the problem of overall complex planning and the individual practical problems so that they are in mutual accord and yet distinct from each other.

An analysis of the optimum plan gives rise to definite relative ratings for individual products within the framework of the production system that is being considered. Naturally the question arises whether these ratings contradict the labour theory of value, according to which even under conditions of a socialist society the value of a product should be determined in accordance with the socially necessary expenditure of labour.

An analysis of this question shows the ratings related to the optimum plan to be in full agreement with social expenditure of labour; furthermore, they can provide an important means for a quantitative analysis and calculation of this expenditure.

It ought to be said that a calculation of social expenditure of labour is by no means easy. In more complicated cases we do not have a sufficiently clear understanding of what is meant by this expression, and how it should be calculated. Thus, several suitable processes for producing certain goods may involve different expenditures of labour, although the socially necessary time spent on a unit of this product should be the same for all. Obviously the mutual interconnexion of production of different types of goods and the mutual interdependence of the required expenditure should be somehow taken into account.

It appears to us that for such a calculation the following starting propositions should be accepted: (*a*) full amounts of social expenditure should be considered; (*b*) production of goods in question should not be considered in isolation, but rather within the framework of the overall plan; (*c*) it is necessary to calculate only the rational, that is the socially necessary, expenditure; (*d*) the calculation should be based on average labour, i.e. on labour which corresponds to the average social conditions of production.

Without going into a complete calculation of social expenditure, let us consider it with reference to the production model mentioned above. We will assume that the productive unit for which a plan is being worked out is self-contained, i.e. it manufactures its products independently. (Examination of a complex undertaking can always reduce the problem to self-contained units.) In these circumstances the productive factors of the system are, firstly, the labour, and secondly, factors which increase the productivity of labour (various kinds of equipment, available natural resources, etc.).

Labour is the only source of value. Let the expenditure of physical labour be z_1, other factors $z_2, \ldots, z_n$, and quantities of manufactured products: $x_1, \ldots, x_m$ respectively.

By comparing the various kinds of products and expenditures according to their ratings found in the course of preparing the optimum plan, we find that total rating of the produced output, in assumed units, is:

$$\lambda_1 x_1 + \lambda_2 x_2 + \ldots + \lambda_m x_m$$

Since the whole output has been produced by means of z_1 units of labour (average for the given system), it follows that one assumed unit of this output demands an expenditure of $\dfrac{z_1}{\sum_{k=1}^{m} \lambda_k x_k}$ units of labour.

Accordingly, a unit of product i rated at λ_i assumed units requires an expenditure (in units of labour):

$$\bar{\lambda}_i = \frac{-z_1}{\sum_{k=1}^{m} \lambda_k x_k} \lambda_i \qquad \ldots [4]$$

(obviously, $\bar{\lambda}_i$ does not depend on the choice of assumed unit).

There are other approaches to this expression of expenditure of labour on a unit of output; these approaches explain the meaning of this expression and afford other ways to calculate it.

1. Labour rating of output represents the total expenditure of labour necessary to obtain one unit of output according to the overall plan under average conditions of labour.

Indeed, there may have taken place an increase of Δz_1 in planned labour resources. If so, in order to maintain the same average conditions, the resources of other factors must be increased proportionately:

$$\Delta z_2 = \frac{z_2}{z_1} \Delta z_1, \ldots, \Delta z_n = \frac{z_n}{z_1} \Delta z_1$$

The plan has been amended with a view to an increase of output of type i, which now will reach Δx_i (for $k \neq {}_i$ we have $\Delta x_k = 0$, that means the output of other products remains unchanged). The equation of plan variation will lead to:

$$\mu_1 \Delta z_1 + \mu_2 \frac{z_2}{z_1} \Delta z_1 + \ldots + \mu_n \frac{z_n}{z_1} \Delta z_1 + \lambda_i \Delta x_i = 0$$

Hence the expenditure of labour per unit of product, taking into account equation [4], is

$$\frac{-\Delta z_1}{\Delta x_i} = \frac{z_1}{\sum_{j=1}^{n} \mu_j z_j} \lambda_i = \frac{-z_1}{\sum_{i=1}^{m} \lambda_k x_k} \lambda_i = \bar{\lambda}_i$$

As a result we obtain the same value $\bar{\lambda}_i$ as before.

2. Product rating in respect of labour consumption may be obtained by an assessment of direct, visible expenditure of labour required to produce it, if this labour is converted into average labour, taking into account the conditions of labour.

Consider a process for manufacturing a certain product provided for in the optimum plan (or a combination of processes which satisfies the plan for a certain production unit). Assuming that this product i is the only one to be manufactured, the summary rating of this optimum process will be:

$$\mu_1 z_1^s + \ldots + \mu_n z_n^s + \lambda_i x_i^s = 0 \qquad \ldots [5]$$

Hence the direct expenditure of labour per unit of product made according to this process is:

$$\frac{-z_1^s}{x_i^s} = \frac{z_1^s}{\sum_{j=1}^{n} \mu_i z_j^s} \lambda_i$$

The value $\bar{\lambda}_i$ can be derived from this direct expenditure by multiplying it with the coefficient

$$K = \frac{\mu_1 z_1}{\sum_{j=1}^{n} \mu_j z_j} : \frac{\mu_1 z_1^s}{\sum_{j=1}^{n} \mu_j z_j^s} \qquad \ldots [6]$$

which characterises the availability of suitable labour conditions in regard to this process, as compared with average availability. Thus, K is the coefficient of converting the labour under given conditions to average labour conditions of the production unit as a whole. This coefficient is less than unity when these conditions are less favourable than the average conditions; it is greater than unity if they are more favourable.

3. The amount of social expenditure of labour per unit of product may be derived from a summation of expenditure occurring in the course of production; it should include direct and indirect expenditure, and also expenditure of factors conducive to an increase of labour productivity, according to labour rating of their efficacy expressed as average labour.

Indeed, ratings of all productive factors expressed as average labour can be obtained in the same way as output ratings:

$$\bar{\mu}_j = \frac{z_1}{\sum_{k=1}^{n} \mu_k z_k} \mu_j$$

Direct labour expenditure can also be expressed as average labour. If we base our calculation on these values, the expenditure per unit of product i (according to process s) will be found, bearing in mind equation [5], as:

$$-\frac{\sum_{j=1}^{n} \bar{\mu}_j z_j}{x_i^s} = -\frac{1}{x_i^s} \sum_{j=1}^{n} \frac{z_1}{\sum_{k=1}^{n} \mu_k z_k} \mu_j z_j^s = -\frac{\sum_{j=1}^{n} \mu_j z_j^s}{x_j^s} \frac{z_1}{\sum_{k=1}^{n} \mu_k z_k} =$$

$$= \frac{z_1}{\sum_{k=1}^{n} \mu_k z_k} \lambda_i = \frac{-z_1}{\sum_{k=1}^{m} \lambda_k x_k} \lambda_i = \bar{\lambda}_i$$

Example. With reference to the previously examined problem of machine loading with minimum expenditure (p. 303), let it be assumed that the expenditure of 30 roubles represents the pay for one day's labour. In this case one day's use of machine tool 1 and 2 will result in a saving of $\frac{1}{3}$ of a day's labour. Accordingly and in view of equation [*6*] the coefficients for conversion to average labour for the various machine tools are:

$$K_1 = K_2 = \frac{3}{3+\frac{2}{3}} : \frac{1}{1+\frac{1}{3}} = \frac{12}{11} = 1{\cdot}09; \quad K_3 = \frac{3}{3+\frac{2}{3}} : \frac{1}{1} = \frac{9}{11} = 0{\cdot}82$$

The rating for the labour-saving factor expressed as average labour (rental rating) of machine tools 1 and 2 is $\frac{1}{3} \times \frac{9}{11} = \frac{3}{11} = 0{\cdot}27$ days of average work.

Expenditures for a unit of product, and their ratings, can be easily calculated from these data. For instance, for job II done according to the optimum plan on machine tools 2 and 3 the ratings based on conversion coefficients are:

Machine tool 2: $\frac{1}{24} \times \frac{12}{11} = \frac{1}{22}$ days or $\frac{1}{22} \times 30 = 1{\cdot}35$ roubles;

Machine tool 3: $\frac{1}{18} \times \frac{9}{11} = \frac{1}{22}$ days or 1·35 roubles.

This equality of values of expenditure means that both methods are rational. A calculation of total expenditure of the complex, including indirect expenditure (rental rating), would produce the same results.

Let us stress the differences between the calculation of production ratings and complex expenditure by means of an analysis of the optimum plan on one hand, and the customary estimates of valuation on the basis of actual expenditure per unit of product (in the case of a single technological process) or average expenditure (in the case of several processes) on the other.

The main difference between the two principles is this: objective ratings take into account not only the actual expenditures of labour (somehow made compatible), but also the availability of favourable factors (environmental conditions). Average expenditures (factory costs), on the contrary, reflect only the difference in labour grades (via the wages) but neglect the labour conditions. As a result the factory cost represents only the individual expenditure of various production units, whereas objective ratings express the total expenditure of the complex; this is of decisive importance in the conditions of a unified socialist economy.

By taking account of the actual position, the realistic objective ratings permit one product to be replaced by another according to given equivalents. Consequently calculations based on objective ratings are more precise than those based on relative factory costs.

The foregoing example was used to consider the problem of assessing the social expenditure in terms of average labour of a given production unit. In its entirety this problem can be solved only for the whole society, but then a number of additional difficulties will be encountered. However, even in this case the methods of linear programming may be found to be applicable.

7. DYNAMIC MODEL.

The solution of the basic problem of production planning which has been discussed in the foregoing may be directly applied to questions of current short term planning on the basis of available productive resources.

For long term planning, the questions of investment timing and effectiveness in the course of a certain period become significantly important. Problems of this nature can also be solved by the methods of linear programming.

Let us consider the problem of planning for periods $t = 1, 2, \ldots, T$. For each period, the various products and productive factors may be considered as independent kinds of products and factors, x_{it}. Accordingly, the technological process to be used in the course of a lengthy period is characterised by two matrices of production and expenditure:

$$x^s = \| x^s_{it} \|, \quad z^s = \| z^s_{jt} \|$$
$$i = 1, 2, \ldots, m, \quad j = 1, 2, \ldots, n$$
$$t = 1, 2, \ldots, T, \quad s = 1, 2, \ldots, S$$

wherein for instance x^s_{it} signifies the output of product i during period t by means of process s.

Extreme conditions of the optimum plan may be formulated in various ways. For instance, it may be necessary to ensure a maximum output in the last period of the plan while the consumption during the preceding periods is fixed. Formally, this problem can be reduced to the basic problem of production planning by treating the products of one type produced during different periods as different products. Ratings λ_{it} and μ_{jt} of products and factors can then be defined separately for each period, so that conditions [*1*] and [*2*] are satisfied. The first condition requires that for each process s used according to plan:

$$\sum_{it} \lambda_{it} x^s_{it} + \sum_{jt} \mu_{jt} z^s_{jt} = 0$$

Consequently, for processes used in the optimum plan, the sum of results must be zero if, for expenditures connected with investments and the output over the whole plan period, their respective ratings are used. It is significant that the ratings on one hand account for dynamic movement in time and on the other hand reduce all expenditure to one single moment of time (in a sense, a certain future expenditure is replaced by an equivalent smaller expenditure at the present moment).

If the conversion coefficients, that is dynamic ratings, have been defined in the course of developing an optimum plan for the future, they may be readily used for an assessment of economic effects of the contemplated capital investment. For this purpose it is sufficient to determine the nature and composition of expenditure involved, to calculate the sum total of operational costs incurred in the course of this investment, and also to compute the volume of output produced as a result of the investment over the whole or a part of the plan period. Having obtained these data, with all the expenditure items related to certain moments of time, it is possible by means of a dynamic rating system to relate these data to one moment and one unit.

If the structure of expenditure and production associated with a certain process is expressed by two matrices $\| \bar{z}_{jt} \|$ and $\| \bar{x}_{it} \|$, it is decisive for the effect of this process that the sum

$$\sum \lambda_{it}\bar{x}_{it} + \sum \mu_{jt}\bar{z}_{jt} \geqq 0$$

is positive.

We will not go into details of the analysis of this problem nor of the special methods for solving this type of problem. Suffice it to say that methods of optimum programming, and in particular of linear programming, will be found to be applicable to problems of this kind.

8. Regarding the Field of Application of Linear Programming under the Conditions of the Socialist Economy

Before discussing the subject of this heading, a few general remarks about the methodology of our approach may be appropriate.

Experience in the use of mathematical methods in technical and natural sciences shows that a mathematical treatment does not completely solve a problem occurring in practice but merely reflects some of its more important features; in a sense it serves as a model of the problem. Consequently any conclusions reached as a result of a strictly mathematical analysis may be quite correct and precise as far as this model is concerned, but they can be applied to the actual problem only with a certain degree of accuracy, after the necessary corrections have been introduced.

But even such an approximate application of obtained results can take place only if the model has been constructed as a result of a methodologically correct and relevant analysis—if it reflects the most significant, and neglects the insignificant, features of the practical problem. However, once such a model has been constructed it would be wrong to think that it can serve only as a means for obtaining some quantitative results. Experience shows that mathematical analysis can help to discover new laws and their relationships, to forecast new effects and occurrences (e.g. the discovery of Neptune, physical phenomena connected with supersonic speeds, nuclear physics).

These remarks apply, to a certain degree, also to questions of planning and of economics. Since these questions are by their very nature quantitative, it is natural to expect them to be studied by mathematical methods.

Since the socialist society, both as a whole and in its particular production units, is capable of ensuring the best and fullest utilisation of resources for the purpose of satisfying the needs of the community, it can develop a real, realisable optimum plan. By virtue of this fact, the problem of plan construction has an extremal character, and consequently the previously discussed mathematical model, viz. the basic problem of production planning, can be used for a number of questions connected with current planning.

Of course, actual economic and planning tasks should take into account numerous circumstances which may or may not be connected with economics, and which are not included in the mathematical model. Thus, the results of an analysis of this model should be applied with a certain degree of approximation. We should constantly bear this in mind when using a mathematical approach to economic problems.

Questions of current and long-term planning arise in connexion with individual factories, productive plants and processes, whole branches, industries and districts, as well as in the overall planning problem of national economy. Mathematical schemes discussed above are applicable in one way or another to all these cases; however, these cases and the forms of application of these methods vary so significantly that it is advisable to treat each field of application separately.

A. *Production planning within a single enterprise.* To this group of questions belongs, first of all, the application of methods of linear programming to a direct improvement of technological processes. Let us recall the problem of rational cutting-up of materials.[1]

Practical use of combined 'cutting-up' technique according to linear programming methods has produced savings in the order of 2-5% for unidimensional materials and 3-10% for sheet materials. The work of V. A. Zalgaller at the Egorov carriage-building plant, and of G. Sh. Rubinstein at the Kirov plant has proved that these methods of calculation are perfectly feasible when there are up to several hundreds of different cut-off sizes.

A practical advantage of the programming method is due to ratings which help to define not only the optimum plan, but also close approximations. For this reason a number of circumstances may be considered, without significant deterioration of the optimum, which have not been considered at the time of posing the problem (technical advantage of the cutting-up process, batch size, etc.). Apart from savings achieved, this feature of the linear programming method has led to a whole series of valuable conclusions concerning the planning of jobs at preparatory shops, ordering of materials, calculation of detailed input. An improvement of the plan due to a more rational method of cutting-up has been achieved at the Leningrad steel-rolling plant.

A rational cutting-up method is of particular importance for the technology of the timber industry, where this problem is of a special nature.[2]

[1] See pp. 236-38 of this book.

[2] See L. V. Kantorovich, 'Selection of timber to ensure a maximum output of a given assortment', *Timber Industry*, 1949, Nos. 7, 8; V. A. Zalgaller, 'New approach to selection of timber for log sawing', *Proceedings of ZNIL North-West Timber*, No. 67, 1956.

Some other applications of linear programming also have a technological significance—use of composite materials, most favourable layout of airfields or construction sites, etc.

Apart from technological problems, there are other jobs within an enterprise which can derive considerable benefit from programming. Among them is the machine loading problem already discussed at some length; it can frequently be applied in practice (work allocation to different plants, distribution of road transport loads for lorries of different types, work loading of rolling mills etc.). The following tasks also may be mentioned:

1. When different machines of varying productivity are available for similar jobs, it is necessary so to load the jobs on to these machines as to use the equipment to the best effect. The use of machines having a higher efficiency may be considered as a special type of expenditure; the rental rating (hire cost) for this equipment should be determined.

2. If the plan instructions for an enterprise or a production unit are incomplete, it is advisable to consider additional tasks so as to reconcile the programme as far as possible with the available productive resources. To do this it is necessary to determine the spare capacity (in terms of time) of various groups of equipment (for instance turning lathes, milling machines etc.). For all alternative products that may be included in the programme it is essential to know the amount of each type of work required. Taking these amounts of work as different kinds of expenditure, a programme can be defined for maximum net output (or man-hours at maximum commodity production). A mathematical solution of this problem is similar to that of the mixture problem.

3. With regard to savings on various factors in short supply (electrical power, certain kinds of material) at the cost of increasing expenditure of another kind, the problem is how to achieve the required economies of this factor while keeping other expenditure at a minimum.

4. In serial production it is very important when deciding on batch size to determine the corresponding amount of work preparation. A rational selection of batch size enables a full economic effect of large quantities to be very nearly achieved while keeping the amount of work preparation relatively low. Such an analysis (taking the amount of work preparation as a kind of expenditure) was carried out 1949-1950 by a group of members of the Mathematical Institute (I. N. Sanov, G. P. Akilov, and A. A. Ivanov),[1] using data of the K. Marx Factory in Leningrad.

5. The problem of rational utilisation of work preparation jobs, given a certain volume of these jobs; selection of most effective jobs and determination of their sequence.

[1] See 'Organisation and planning of smooth working of engineering enterprises', *Mashgiz*, 1958; also C. A. Dumler, 'Linear programming and its use in production', *Vestnik Mashinostroeniya*, 1958, No. 10.

6. Planning problems related to calendar time; in particular, smooth loading over various periods under given conditions, for instance production planning of merchandise or timing of material intake. Alongside extremal problems of linear programming arise also problems of a combinational nature which relate to the so-called *theory of scheduling*.

Apart from engineering problems mentioned above, similar questions occur in other branches of our national economy (metallurgy, road transport, mechanisation of agriculture and others). It is important to point out that the application of linear programming methods permits us in all these cases not only to define an optimum plan, but also to answer other questions, such as costing on a scientific basis of various concurrently manufactured products and evolving indicators for such factors as extent of utilisation of equipment or of various grades of labour.

We may mention that in a few cases coefficients which define the extent of shortages of some factors are already in use. The method of linear programming enables these coefficients to cease being relative and to be calculated on an objective basis. Further, linear programming allows for a simultaneous assessment of shortages of a number of factors.

Lastly, we should like to draw attention to the possibility of applying the scheme of the general problem of production planning to such a concrete question as an improvement of a plan that already exists. A plan worked out in the customary manner takes into account the available resources, a definite programme, and processes to be used. Using the same data and processes, but applying the methods of linear programming, it may be possible to exceed the plan significantly.

B. *Economic planning within a branch or an economic region.* Methods of optimum programming, in particular of linear programming, can be frequently used for planning concerned with an industrial branch or an economic region. The following points may be mentioned:

1. Distribution of programmed tasks among the plants of a certain industry as a whole or within a given area, taking into account productive capacities of various types of equipment, workshop areas, costs per unit of output, and also a suitable redistribution of loads on, say, foundries, with a view to specialisation and co-operation between individual plants.

2. Allocation of various types of fuel to different enterprises, with a view to a better balance of available fuels.

3. As above, in regard to electric power.

4. Allocation of movable equipment to various plants and construction sites, with a view to using it most advantageously and fully.

5. Transport routing for various kinds of freight.

6. Combined analysis of production volumes and transport costs for a given product.

Apart from subjects of current planning enumerated above, questions of long-term planning may be investigated: capital investments, evaluation of new techniques, location of plants and transport routes—questions to be decided in connexion with the overall plan for the nation's economy. However, when formulating any individual problem it is essential to work out a scheme containing the least possible number of factors. This scheme should be based on obtainable data; as far as possible it should be self-contained, and it should be freely modifiable. The scheme's connexion with the overall plan of the national economy depends largely on requirements with regard to resources and targets. At the same time the scheme should depend as little as possible on the price system; this can be achieved by calculating the main forms of expenditure and products in terms of physical units and not of money.

It is very important to remember that a solution of these problems by means of linear programming methods not only ensures the formulation of an optimum plan, but also produces a system of ratings which enables the plan to be corrected according to changing circumstances; this results in the necessary flexibility and practical value of planning. Furthermore, once the ratings have been calculated, they can assist in the economic analysis of other questions. For instance, these ratings can play an important part in stimulating the most expedient financial interrelations in industry—additional charges to obtain an advantageous organisation of transport, rental rating for equipment to ensure its full utilisation, rental for a proper use of natural resources, etc.

C. *Questions of planning of national economy.* An improvement of planning methods for the national economy in the light of contemporary scientific achievements poses a very difficult problem. This improvement demands, apart from development of mathematical means, better and more complete technical data, statistical indicators and methods of economic analysis as such. However, the advantages that will flow from such an improvement are so important for a further upsurge of our national economy that no effort or expenditure should be spared to overcome all difficulties and to continue scientific research in this field.

Let us take a look at just one of many aspects of this vast theme, namely the possible point of application and the part to be played in the planning of our national economy by the methods of linear programming.

On the whole, the scheme of the basic problem of production planning embraces the task of current planning, and the dynamic scheme circumscribes that of long-term planning. However, apparently it would be futile to try to tackle the planning of national economy by means of either scheme, since it would involve millions of different products and billions of data.

Evidently a realistic approach would be to construct a whole system of models. A model of the national economy should be made according to the most generalised main indicators for a relatively small number of products and factors. Alongside this main model auxiliary models should be developed of industrial branches and of locally grouped enterprises; the operative plan should be analysed and every possibility of variation studied. Probably the process of plan construction should comprise a series of stages of gradually increasing accuracy and co-ordination of original data, plans, budgets and indicators, with subsequent corrections as the plan is being put into effect.

We firmly believe that in such a system the methods of optimum programming, and particularly of linear programming, will play an essential part, of course jointly with improved forms of economic analysis and statistical indicators. Undoubtedly, electronic computers will have to be used systematically in order to put this comprehensive method into effect. Apart from optimum planning, linear programming ought to be used to determine economic indicators, especially with regard to pricing.

We have considered only a few models which could be used in connexion with production planning. No doubt other models will have to be designed and investigated when the whole range of planning problems of national economy will come under review, and also when attempts will be made to use mathematical analysis for other questions of economics (composition of final output, distribution problems and so forth). We hope that our work has made some contribution to this mighty but promising task.

Methods of Establishing the Shortest Running Distances for Freights on Setting up Transportation Systems

A. L. Lur'e

The volume of goods traffic required to meet all the needs of the national economy depends to a large extent, once the location of industries has been taken into account, on the way in which the actual transport links are established between the areas and points of production and the areas and points of consumption of the various products.

One of the most important requirements which arises when rational schemes of transport links are being set up is the need to establish, all other conditions being equal, the minimum overall running distance for loads (the smallest number of ton-kilometres). Quite obviously setting up transportation systems which satisfy this requirement is by no means the same thing as devising a really rational transport plan which takes into account every factor relevant to the general economy and general transport situation. Nevertheless, the ability to solve this comparatively elementary problem does make other more complicated problems connected with the rationalisation of transport easier to solve.[1]

The methods of calculation proposed below may be applied also in cases where it is possible to utilise data relating to transport costs over separate sections of railway track. For this purpose the costs of conveying a unit of load over the relevant sections must be entered in the diagrams and tables appearing in this article in place of distances between stations.

The methods suggested for establishing systems of load-flow may also be used without modification for establishing systems for routing empty waggons. If this is done, points which have a surplus of empty waggons will take on the

[1] Suggestions on 'How to obtain minimum total mileage' when setting up transportation systems were first put forward by the Soviet economist Tolstoi (see the symposium *Planning of Transportation*, Moscow, 1930; also A. N. Tolstoi, *Methods of eliminating irrational transportation in constructing operational plans*, Moscow, 1941, and Z. N. Pariiskaya, A. N. Tolstoi and A. B. Mots, *Planning Goods Traffic*, Moscow, 1947).

function of dispatch points, and points which have a deficit of these will take on the function of arrival points. Thus the methods of calculation outlined in this article will also offer guidance to reducing the running distances of empty waggons, which is such an important saving in transport.

1. The Graphic Method

Rule 1. If the railway lines which connect the dispatch and arrival points of any homogeneous load by the shortest routes do not form closed circuits, it is a simple matter to establish a system of transportation which will secure minimal overall running distances by a purely graphic method without recourse to calculating distances. It is necessary only to make certain that

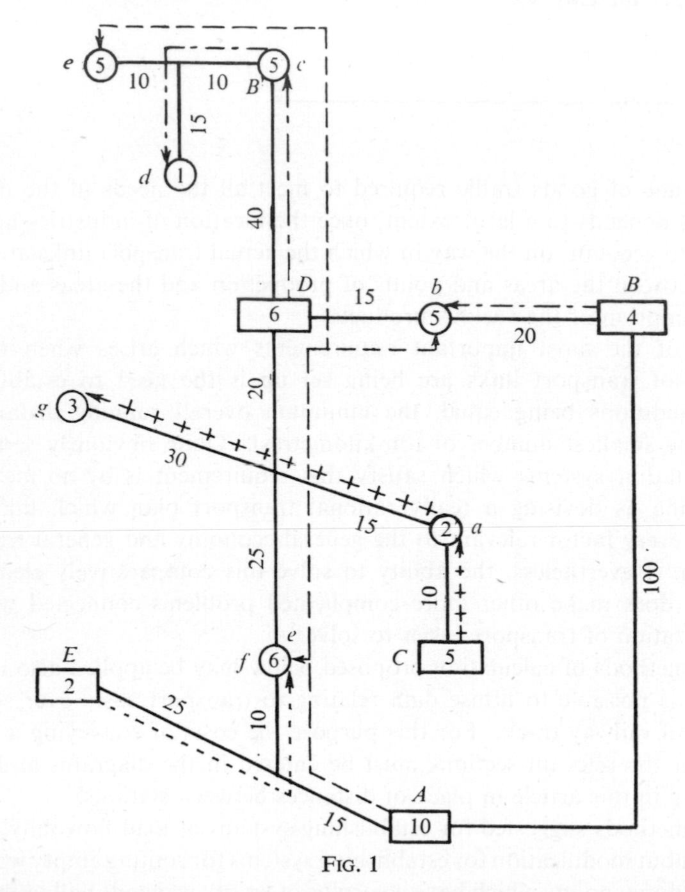

Fig. 1

there are no cross hauls (i.e. the same goods do not travel in opposite directions) when the dispatch and arrival points are being connected. The quantity of goods dispatched from and arriving at each point is presumed to be known.

A case of this sort is shown in Fig. 1. The figures inside the rectangles denote the number of units of load (in thousands of tons, trucks etc.) being dispatched, and the figures inside the circles denote the number of units received. Distances between points are also shown in the drawing. The line *AB*, which forms part of the closed circuit *ABDA*, need not be taken into consideration because the shortest routes from any dispatch point to any arrival point do not pass through it.

It is easy to see that the system in Fig. 1 shown by the various dotted lines which connect the dispatch points *A*, *B*, *C*, *D* and *E* to the arrival points *a*, *b*, *c*, *d*, *e*, *f* and *g* results in the same overall running distances as any other system would, provided that no cross hauls were permitted, and that these distances are minimal in the given conditions. In fact, if we were to link, say, point *g* to *A* instead of *C*, and dispatch the three units of load now surplus at *C* to *e*, while proportionately reducing the loads dispatched from *A* to *e*, there would be no change in the overall running distance. As far as the point of intersection of lines *AD* and *Cg* each unit of load travels the same route as before; beyond that point, three units of load from *A* now travel to *g* instead of *e* as formerly, but at the same time three units from *C*, previously routed to *g*, now go to *e*. Losses exactly counterbalance gains. We should arrive at the same result if we changed, either completely or in part, the pattern of connexions between *c*, *d* and *e* and *A* and *D*, and satisfied part of the demand at *b* or *e* with the two units now surplus at *E*, and so on.

An examination of all these cases confirms the accuracy of our original formulation, and also permits us to draw the following conclusion:

Rule 2. If the travel routes of loads from any one of several dispatch points (e.g. *A*, *C* or *E*) to any one of several destinations (e.g. *b*, *c*, *d*, *e* or *g*) pass through at least one common point, the overall running distance does not depend on precisely which dispatch point is connected to which destination point.

2. Closed Circuits and the Rule of Continuous Lines

If the railway lines linking dispatch and arrival points by the shortest routes form a closed circuit or several closed circuits (let us call such circuits 'circles'), the purely graphic method for setting up connexions becomes inadequate, and must be supplemented by calculations of the distances involved.

Let us examine Fig. 2. Let point *A* be connected to *b*, *B* to *a* and *C* to *a* and *c*. A system of connexions such as the one shown in the Fig. 2 by a line of dashes does not permit cross hauls yet nonetheless leads to excessive running distances. One may be convinced of this either by comparing the overall totals of ton- or truck-kilometres on this layout with the results obtained by using other systems of connexions, or, less laboriously, by employing the following arguments.

It follows from Rule 2 that if, still employing the same railway lines *Ab* and *Ba*, we dispatch loads from *A* to *a* and from *B* to *b* the overall running distance will be the same as with the previous routing (the travel routes of loads from *A* and *B* to *a* and *b* pass through a common point *J*). But if we connect *B* to *b* it is obvious that loads from *B* must be sent not by the roundabout route *BJb* but by the direct route *Bb*.

Thus it clearly emerges that although it was never intended to carry traffic from *B* to *b* via *J*, the original system of connexions does in fact lead to

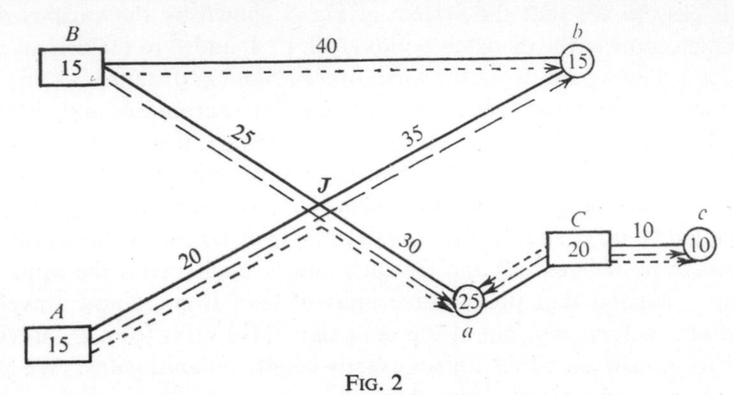

FIG. 2

exactly the same excessive mileage being covered as with any obviously irrational plan. The correct routing is shown by a dotted line.

In order to formulate a general rule based on this example we shall introduce here the following definition: we shall say that two points are joined in any given direction by a *continuous line* of load-flow if consignments encountered at any intermediate point are travelling in the same direction. Thus in the original system of connexions point *B* was joined by a continuous line of load-flow both to *a* and to *b* (along the route *BJb*), but had no continuous communication with point *c*, since although consignments were to be met with on section *aC* the direction of their travel did not coincide with the direction of load-flow on *Ba* and *Cc*. The example we have chosen illustrates the 'rule of continuous lines' which follows.

Rule 3. If two points on a network are joined by a continuous line of load-flow which is not the shortest route (in our example points *B* and *b*), a system of connexions incorporating such a line will not yield the shortest overall running distances.

In particular it follows from this that if two points are joined by continuous lines of load-flow in two directions, excess mileage will almost always occur. It is exceptional, in fact, for both routes to be equal in length, and as soon as one ceases to be the 'shortest route' the system of connexions will no longer yield the shortest overall running distances in accordance with Rule 3.

Numbers of defects in projected systems of transportation or routing of empty waggons[1] are the result of ignorance of the scientific methods of estab-

[1] Of course, in some cases this rule may be deliberately broken in the interests of some local factor, e.g. limits imposed by carrying capacity. If Rule 3 is broken, however (and

lishing connexions. The 'rule of continuous lines' often enables them to be picked out at a glance.

In the majority of cases where closed circuits are involved neither the absence of cross hauls nor the observance of the conditions following from Rule 3 are sufficient to ensure that the shortest overall running distances will be obtained. For example, the transportation system shown in Fig. 3 by a line of dashes does not break any of the general rules, but a comparison with the dotted line system shows that the latter produces shorter running distances.

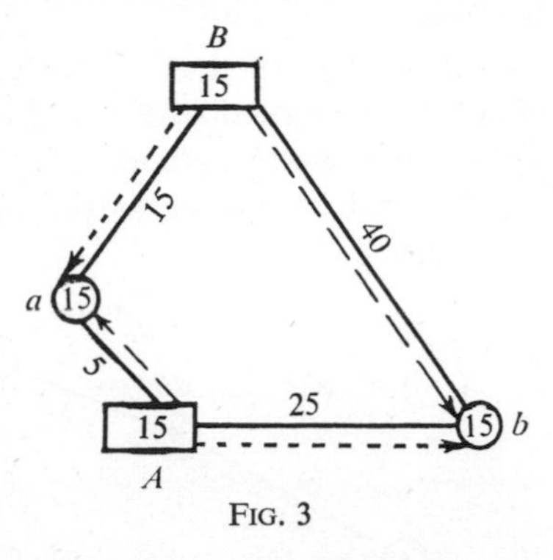

FIG. 3

Where the number of dispatch and arrival points is considerable a direct comparison of all possible alternatives to establish the shortest overall running distance is a process extremely laborious to apply in practice and may even be impossible if the number of alternatives is exceptionally great. A special method is needed, therefore, which will make it possible to arrive at the most efficient system of connexions by combining graphic representation with relatively simple calculations. This will remove the need to establish total running distances for each alternative. Such a graphico-analytical method is the method of *circle differences.*[1]

3. The Circle Differences Method

If an analysis is made of the systems of connexions shown in Fig. 3 it is easy to see that selection of the most efficient alternative may be made without recourse to calculations of total ton- or truck-kilometres. It is sufficient to compare 'gains' (+) and 'losses' (−), and these we obtain by changing the direction of travel of any unit of load in relation to the original version of the system. Any conclusion which is true for one unit of load (tons or trucks) will also be true for all subsequent values.

By re-routing a unit of load from *A* to *b* instead of *a* as in the original version (shown by the line of dashes) we 'gain' 5 kilometres from *A* to *a*, which the unit in question no longer has to cover, and 'lose' 25 kilometres, which is the distance this unit must now be sent. But as point *b* will now be receiving a unit of load from *A*, the unit previously sent from *B* to *b* becomes superfluous, and this can (and must) be sent to *a* in exchange for the unit which has changed direction. To do this will result in a 'gain' of 40 kilometres (*Bb*) and a 'loss' of 15 kilometres (*Ba*). Adding, we obtain

indeed if any increase at all is made in the overall running distances), it should be for a definite reason.

[1] Tolstoi applies the term 'graphico-analytical' to the method outlined by us in Section 1.

$+5-25+40-15 = +5$. The gain exceeds the loss by 5 kilometres, and therefore our modification of the system has been advantageous.

In this way we have been able to show that the system represented by the dotted line is the preferable one simply by comparing the distances between *A*, *B*, *a* and *b*, without having had to calculate the total running distances involved.

Calculation of the differences between 'losses' and 'gains' obtained by changing the direction of travel of a unit of load also forms the basis of the 'circle differences' method.[1]

We shall demonstrate the application of this method with an actual example (see Fig. 4).

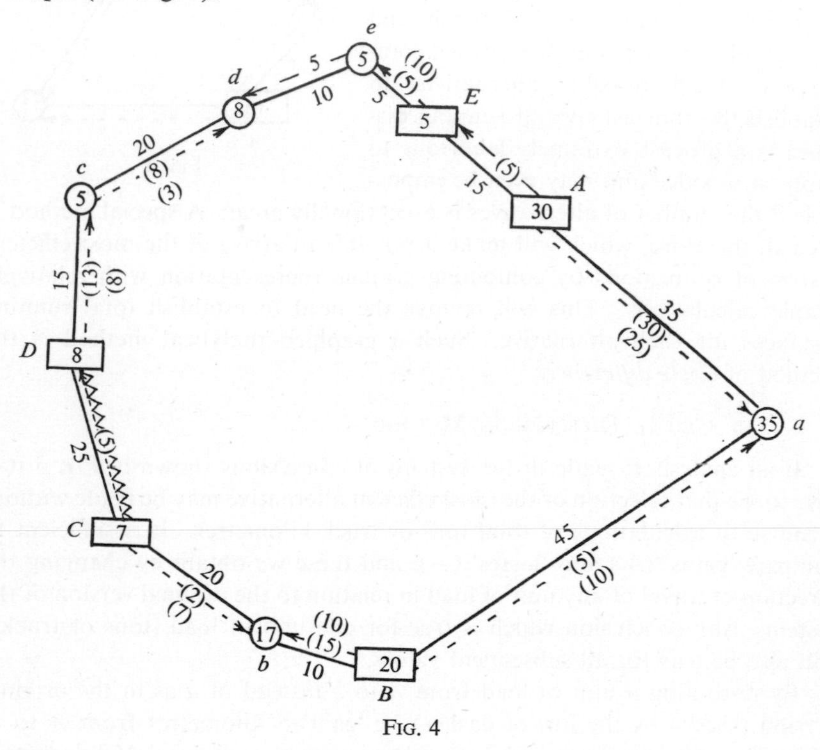

FIG. 4

The work of setting up an efficient system of connexions is begun by connecting dispatch points and arrival points in an arbitrary fashion, taking care only that the elementary rules (concerning convergent routes and continuous lines) are not infringed. It is best to begin with the largest dispatch or arrival point, e.g. point *a*. This we connect to the nearest dispatch points,

[1] Both in its original form, as described in the work of Tolstoi, and in the version outlined below. This same comparison of 'losses' and 'gains' also forms the basis of the methods of Kantorovich and Gavurin (see the symposium *Problems of raising transport efficiency*, USSR Academy of Sciences, 1949) as well as of a number of methods of resolving 'the transportation problem', in foreign literature.

routing 30 units of load for *a* from *A* and 5 from *B*. The remaining 15 units available at *B* must evidently be sent to *b*, otherwise we shall find ourselves with converging load-flows. Continuing to connect all the dispatch and arrival points one after the other in such a way as to prevent load-flows converging, we arrive at the system indicated in Fig. 4 by the dotted lines.[1]

This system leaves certain details unsettled. It does not show whether part of the traffic is sent from *B* to *d*, or whether *d*'s demands are entirely satisfied by *D* and *c*'s by *C*. Such precision, however, is not needed for our purposes, because Rule 2 shows that these factors would have no effect on the total running distances anyway.[2]

Does the system we have obtained yield the best results by guaranteeing the smallest amount of ton-kilometre work? If not, how may it be modified in order to do so?

Let us agree to term any change in the system of connexions an *anti-clockwise advance* if it has the effect of reversing the direction of loads originally travelling in a clockwise direction. Any change of the opposite sort we shall term a *clockwise advance*. It is easily seen that the 'advance' of any unit of load is inevitably accompanied by changes in the numbers of consignments on all sections of the circle.

For example, suppose we re-route to *b* a unit of load originally travelling from *B* to *a* (clockwise advance). It is obvious that this will make available at *C* a unit of load which was previously sent to *b*. This will have to be sent in a clockwise direction until it reaches the first point receiving consignments from the opposite direction, i.e. to *e*. The unit which *e* used to receive from *E* will now have to be sent to *a*, i.e. to the consumption point from which we began the 'advance'. On all the sections over which in the original version of the system loads were travelling in a direction opposite to the advance (in this case an anti-clockwise direction) the load-flow will be reduced by one unit, and on all the remaining sections of the circle it will be increased by one unit.

The example of advancement we have chosen leads us to the following conclusion. The general 'gain' derived from advancing a unit of load (the saving in ton- or truck-kilometres) is equal to the length of the sections over which loads were travelling in the direction opposite to the advance in the original system of connexions, while the 'loss' is equal to the length of the remaining portions of the circle, i.e. to the length of those sections over which loads were travelling in the same direction as the advance, and of those sections over which no loads were travelling at all (*'free' sections*).

[1] Besides distances, figures showing traffic density are also entered on the diagram in brackets interrupting the dotted lines (e.g. 30 on section *Aa*, 5 on *Ba*, etc.). The significance of the line of dashes and zigzag line will be explained below.

[2] Once the general outline of the system is established, the suitability of connexions which are not going to have any bearing on the overall running distance can be decided on other considerations, such as the principle of concentrating connexions, which facilitates a wide application of dispatch routing.

If the sections over which loads travel in a clockwise direction are longer than those over which they travel in the opposite direction (as in our example), we call the clockwise direction *predominant*. In the converse case the anti-clockwise direction will be predominant.

From all that has been said above it is possible to deduce the following rule for connecting dispatch and arrival points which are situated on the same closed circuit ('circle'):

Rule 4. If the load travel routes are on a closed circuit, and the difference between the length of the sections carrying loads in one direction and the length of the sections carrying loads in the opposite direction is less than the length of the 'free' sections; or, in other words, if the length of the sections carrying loads in the predominant direction is less than the length of the rest of the circle, then the corresponding system of connexions will yield the shortest overall running distance. If this condition is not present, an advance must be made in the direction opposite to the predominant direction.

In our example the length of the sections carrying loads in a clockwise direction is equal to 105 kilometres; in the opposite direction, 70 kilometres; and not carrying loads at all, 25 kilometres. Since 105 is greater than 70+25 it follows that it is expedient to make an advance in an anti-clockwise direction.

But if it is expedient to advance one unit of load in an anti-clockwise direction, it seems reasonable by the same token to move two or more. How many units, then, should we advance? Evidently the expediency of advancing units will not be called in doubt while the original balance of losses and gains continues to hold good.

The losses and gains in our example will be the same for units 2, 3, 4 and 5; but by the time unit 6 is reached the balance of pluses and minuses will have altered, since all the loads which had been travelling previously from point *C* in a clockwise direction (5 units) will now prove to be travelling in the opposite direction, and section *CD* will have become free.

A general rule to establish the quantity of loads which should be advanced may be stated in the following terms:

Rule 5. The number of units of load which should be advanced on the basis of Rule 4 is equal to the lowest density of traffic on any section carrying traffic in the predominant direction of the original system.

This 'limiting' section may be at once identified as *CD* in our drawing.

Once the direction and extent of the advance needed are ascertained, it only remains to put it into effect, i.e. to plot on the scheme the new system of connexions resulting from the relevant modifications of the original system. The solution of this problem presents no difficulties. One can begin at any dispatch or arrival point. Let us take point *a*, say. If we advance 5 units in an anti-clockwise direction, this will means that we must send 10 units from *B* to *a* instead of 5.[1] It follows that out of the 30 units previously received

[1] The new density figures are set out in Fig. 4 beside the old.

by a from A, 5 are now travelling in an anti-clockwise direction to the nearest point which had been receiving loads in the predominant direction (opposite to the advance), i.e. to point d. The release of 5 units, which had previously been coming to d from the direction of C (whether directly from C or D is immaterial), makes it possible to send 5 units from C to b in exchange for the ones which we sent from B to a instead of b.

The new transportation system is represented in Fig. 4 in the following manner: sections which were free in the original version but which are now carrying traffic, are denoted by a line of dashes; dotted lines are retained for sections over which traffic has not changed direction, and the new indices of density are marked; and for sections where it has been possible to reduce traffic the dotted lines are cancelled by a zigzag line.

When checking the new system of connexions, we obtain the following results: the length of sections carrying loads in a clockwise direction is 80 kilometres, and in the reverse direction 95 kilometres, while the length of free sections comes to 25 kilometres. The system we have obtained guarantees minimum overall running distances in accordance with Rule 4.

It is possible to simplify the testing of the new system. For this purpose one must take double the length of the free sections resulting from the advance, and compare this figure with the result calculated for the original version, since this is exactly the amount by which the difference between the sections of the predominant direction and the remainder of the circle will have changed.

In our example this section is CD. Twice its length is equal to 50 kilometres, and the difference between the length of the sections carrying traffic in the predominant direction and the remainder of the circle was $105-70-25 = 10$ kilometres. It is clear that this difference will cease to be positive in the new system of connexions (since 50 is greater than 10) and that the condition of Rule 4 will be satisfied as a consequence.

If a test of the second version of the plan showed the necessity for a new advance, it would be necessary to construct a third version, and once again to test its suitability by means of the same simple calculation. If we adopt this procedure we shall eventually arrive at a system of connexions which will ensure that the shortest overall running distance is obtained, wherever the dispatch and arrival points happen to be situated on the closed circuit.

4. General Application of the Graphico-Analytical Method

The method of circle differences permits a system to be constructed which will link dispatch and arrival points in such a way as to ensure that minimal total running distances are obtained whatever the layout and the situation of the dispatch and arrival points.

The normal procedure for establishing such a system is as follows. First we take those sections of the transport network for which the system of connexions can be set up by making use of the graphic method (Rules 1 and 2). Once these have been disposed of we can set about establishing preliminary links between the dispatch and arrival points which lie on closed circuits (circles).

These preliminary links can be established by rule of thumb; travel lines must not be permitted to converge, of course, and the rule of continuous line must be observed. Then all the closed circuits must be tested and corrected one after the other by the circle differences method. In the course of this it may happen that changes made at a later stage impair the efficiency of systems of connexions adopted for other circuits which have already been

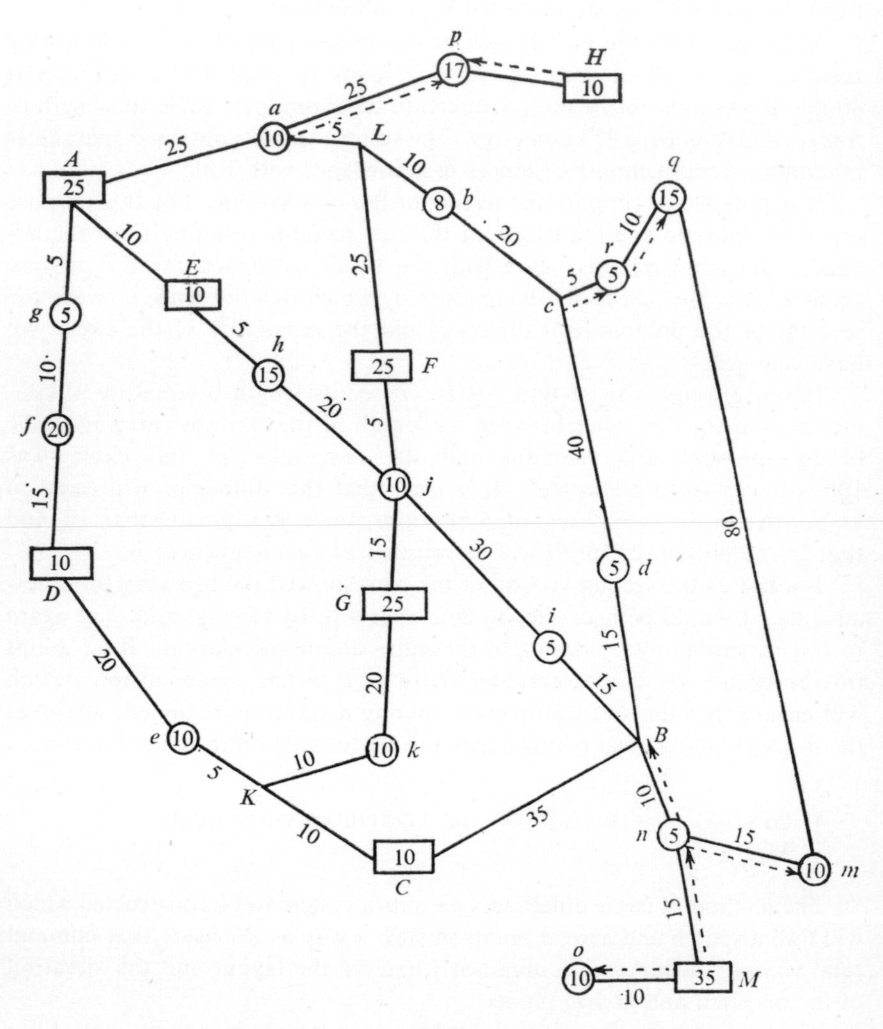

FIG. 5

tested and corrected. In this event, these systems will have to be re-tested. We proceed in this way until every circle satisfies the conditions of Rule 4.

Let us take an example to show the successive steps needed in the normal application of the methods described above in setting up a system of connexions (see Fig. 5).

We note first of all that the extreme right-hand line *mq* does not form part of a closed circuit because the shortest routes for goods from any dispatch to any arrival point do not pass through it. Therefore we apply the graphic method, not only to stations *p* and *H*, but also to *r* and *q*, and to points *o*, *M*, *n* and *m*. Consequently we can plot the load-flows shown in the drawing by dotted lines, without any calculations.

For example, it is obviously necessary to dispatch from *M* 10 units of load to *o*, 5 to *n*, and 10 to *m*. The remaining 10 units at *M* will be dispatched to other points, and these will have to pass through *B* (we have already established that there would be no point in using the section *mq* with the present arrangement of dispatch and arrival points). The distance loads must run from *M* to *B* does not depend on what stations beyond *B* are connected

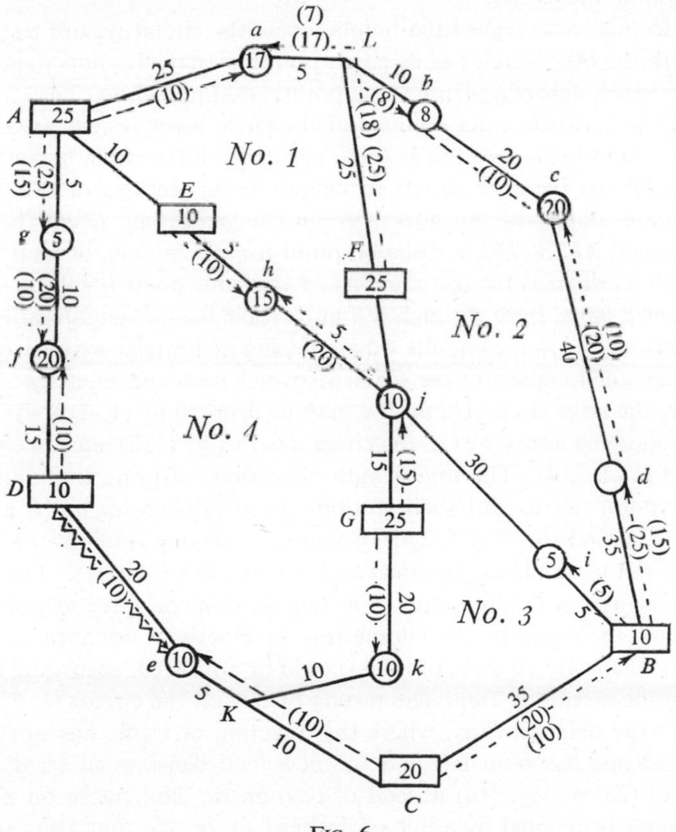

FIG. 6

to *M*. In all subsequent calculations, therefore, we may ignore line *MB* and regard the junction *B* as the source of 10 units of load.

Similarly point *c* will be regarded henceforth as a junction receiving the 20 units of load which are in practice intended for *r* and *q*, and point *a* as an arrival point for 17 units, since apart from the 10 units needed to satisfy *a*'s own requirements, 7 units for *p* must also inevitably pass through this point. Thus we can substitute junctions for those parts of the network to which the graphic method is applicable.

Subsequent steps in developing the system of connexions are shown in Fig. 6. *B*, *c* and *a* are shown as dispatch or arrival points for calculated quantities of load (10, 20 and 17 units respectively) in accordance with our substitution of these junctions for the three groups of stations *o*, *M*, *n* and *m*, *r* and *q*, and *p* and *H* respectively. Those stations of the network which did not form parts of closed circuits have been omitted entirely.

We make a first draft of the system at random. Let us say, for example, that, having begun with the major dispatch points *A*, *F* and *G*, we have arrived at the system represented in the diagram by a dotted line We set about testing the circles.

To do this let us regard the points where the circuit we are testing intersects with the other circles as dispatch points or arrival points depending on whether loads, departing from these points or approaching them from other parts of the network, enter sections of the circle being tested, or whether on the other hand loads arriving at these points from the circle being tested are either unloaded there or depart to neighbouring sections of other circuits. Thus, for example, in the given system of connexions *L* will be, for the 'large' circuit *ALcBCDA*, a dispatch point for the 25 units of load travelling to it from *F*, whereas for the circle *ALjA* the same point *L* will be a point of arrival for 8 units, since through it 8 units leave for the neighbouring section *Lb*. We can refer to the circuits we are testing in a briefer manner by putting in brackets the numbers of the segments which each encompasses. Thus, for example, the large circle *ALcBCDA* may be denoted by (1, 2, 3, 4), the circle *ALjA* mentioned above by (1), the circle *ALcBjA* by (1, 2), etc. We begin our test with (1, 2, 3, 4). The total length of sections carrying traffic in a clockwise direction (let us call such sections *positive*) adds up to 10 kilometres (section *Lb*), and the total length of sections carrying traffic in the opposite direction (let us call these *negative*) adds up to 130 kilometres. The length of the free sections is 75 kilometres. The length of the negative sections exceeds the rest of the circle by 45 kilometres. A clockwise advance is therefore necessary (Rule 4). 10 units of load should be advanced, according to Rule 5 (the limiting section is *De*). The results of this on the circuit (1, 2, 3, 4) are shown in the diagram thus: where the direction of traffic has not changed, the dotted line has been left and the new load densities inserted, e.g. (15) instead of (25) on *Ag*, (10) instead of (20) on *cd*, etc.; traffic on previously free sections is denoted by a line of dashes (*Aa*, *bc*, *Ce*, and *Df*); and where traffic has ceased (on section *De*) the dotted line is cancelled by a zigzag line.

Testing the new system we obtain the following lengths: positive sections, 85 kilometres; negative sections, 110 kilometres; free sections (only *De* in fact), 20 kilometres. Since 110 is greater than 85+20, a further advance is necessary.

If we advance another 7 units of load in the same direction (the limiting section is now *La*) we obtain a system of connexions which differs from the second version in having traffic (7 units) on *eD* and none on *La*. This system is shown by dotted lines in Fig. 7.

On being tested a third time the circle (1, 2, 3, 4) is seen to satisfy Rule 4, since twice the length of the now free section *La* (10 kilometres) is greater than the difference found in the previous test (5 kilometres).

The system shown by dotted lines in the Fig. 7 can be arrived at by an even shorter method, and for this it is necessary to modify Rule 5 in such a way as to ensure that no more than one advance is needed on any closed circuit to obtain a system of connexions which will satisfy Rule 4. Such a modification of Rule 5 is quite feasible. As we have seen, the difference

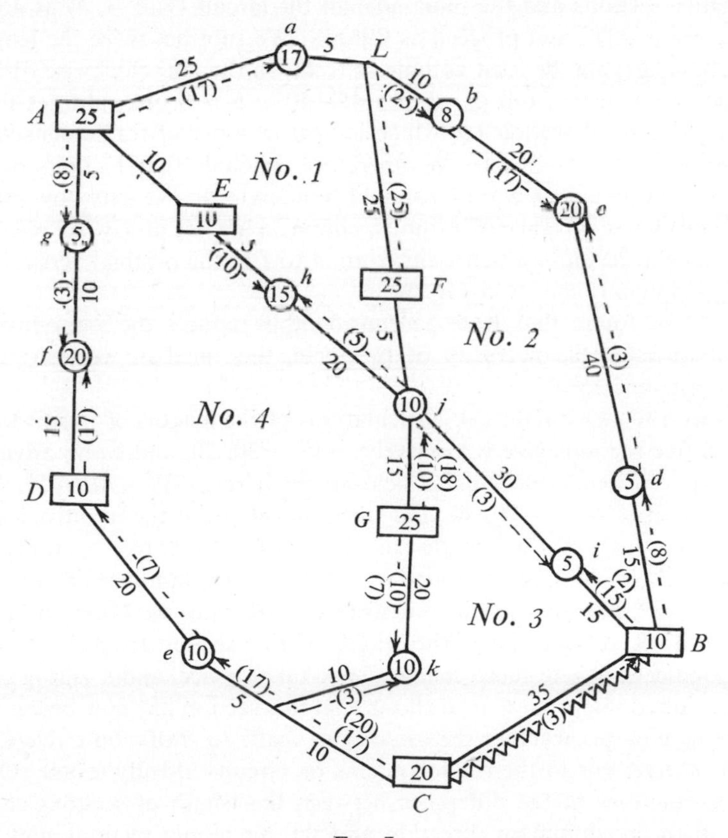

FIG. 7

between the length of the sections carrying traffic in the predominant direction and the rest of the circuit, which shows a gain when a unit of load is advanced, is reduced every time one of the sections carrying traffic in the predominant direction (i.e. the section where traffic is least dense) becomes free, and reduced, moreover, by twice the length of that section. We shall therefore find it useful to proceed in accordance with this rule:

Rule 5a. To establish how many units of load should be advanced, twice the length of the section carrying the least traffic in the predominant direction must be subtracted from the difference between the length of the sections carrying traffic in the predominant direction and the rest of the circuit. If this difference is greater than zero, we subtract from it twice the length of the section carrying the next least volume of traffic in the predominant direction, and we proceed in this way until our subtraction results in a difference less than zero. The number of units of load which should be advanced is equal to the density of traffic on the last section which we have to treat in this way.

Making use of this rule, we calculate the difference between the lengths of negative sections and the remainder of the circuit (1, 2, 3, 4) as 45 kilometres (see p. 334), and proceed as follows: We subtract twice the length of the section carrying the least volume of traffic in the anti-clockwise direction (i.e. *De*, see Fig. 6) from 45. Since $45-40 = 5 > 0$, we subtract from 5 twice the length of section *La*, which is next in order of traffic density, and we obtain $5-10 = -5 < 0$. We therefore conclude that 17 units of load, equal to the traffic density on *La* should be advanced. We may now put into effect a clockwise advance of 17 units, commencing, let us say, by re-routing to *a* 17 of the 20 units which went from *A* to *f* in the original version. The resulting system is shown in Fig. 7.

It will be found that Rule 5a considerably reduces the work involved, since it obviates the necessity of producing intermediate versions of the system of connexions.

Let us now test circuit (1). Calculations of the lengths of positive, negative and free sections give respectively $+45$, -30, 20, and so no advance is necessary. We reach the same conclusion for circle (2): $+70$, -55, 35. A test of (3) gives $+25$, -70, 40, and since the length of the negative sections exceeds the sum of the lengths of the positive and free sections by 5 $(70-40-25)$, a clockwise advance is called for. The number of units to be advanced is 3, namely the traffic density on *CB*, since we obtain a negative quantity if we subtract twice the length of this section from 5. A line of dashes indicates where these changes have taken place, and a zigzag cancelling the dotted line from *C* to *B* shows that this section has now become free.

Let us now see whether the alterations made to traffic on circle (3) call for any corrections to the traffic systems on circuits already tested. On any circle an increase in the difference between the length of sections carrying traffic in the predominant direction and the remaining sections may cause traffic to appear on sections which were previously free, or may transform negative sections into positive or positive into negative. The appearance of a new free section, however, cannot lead to an increase in the difference with which we are concerned, and for this reason the unoccupied section which our alterations to circuit (3) have produced on the large circle (1, 2, 3, 4) does not require further test calculations.

The advance which we have made on circle (3), therefore, necessitates a second test only of circuit (2), which has a common section *ji* with circuit (3). (Circuit (4) has not been tested at all as yet.) This new test of circuit (2) gives us $+70$, -85, 5, and therefore a clockwise advance is necessary. If we advance 3 units (the limiting sections are *ji* and *cd*), we arrive at a new version of the system of connexions. This is shown in Fig. 8 by the dotted lines.

Traffic has appeared on section *jF*, and sections *ji* and *dc* have become free. Twice the length of sections *ji* and *dc* is greater than 5. It follows that it is not necessary to advance more than 3 units. But this has produced a change in the situation or circuit (2), since traffic has now appeared on section *jF*, and this requires a second test of circle (1). The result of this test

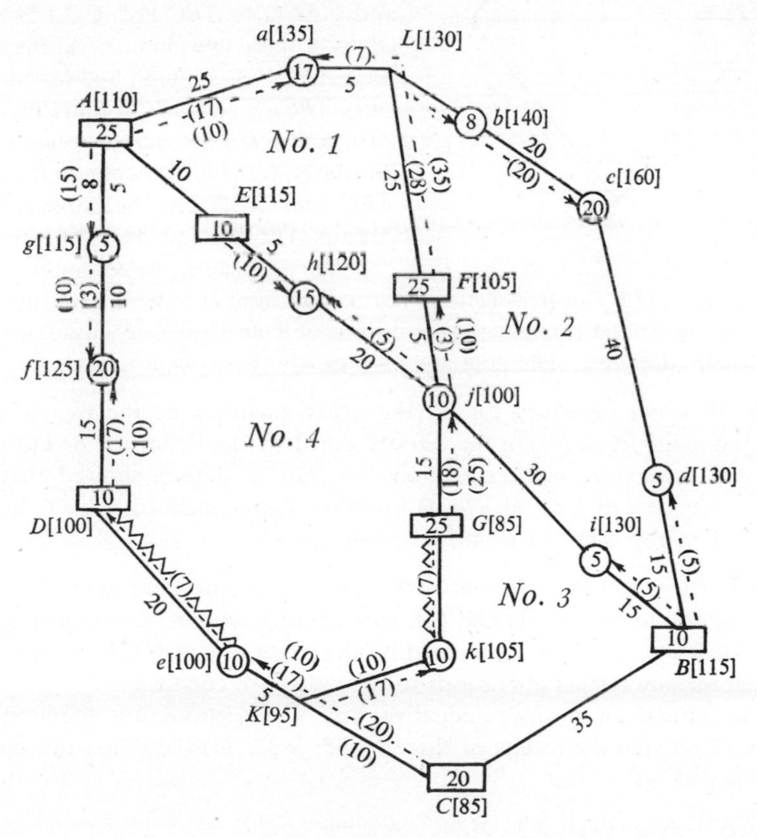

FIG. 8

will be obvious. The length of the negative sections will be increased at the expense of the free sections by only 5 kilometres, and therefore the relationship between the length of the sections carrying traffic in the predominant direction (in this case positive) and the rest of the circle will remain undisturbed; circle (1) will continue to satisfy the conditions of Rule 4. In this way we have examined all the consequences of our modifications of circuit (3).

Continuing the test of the circuits, we note that no change is required on circle (4), since the relevant calculations show +65, −60, 10. Will it be necessary to re-connect the points which are situated on circle (1, 2)? A simple rule enables us to decide this question without resorting to further calculations. Before formulating this rule let us agree to call those sections which form part of two circuits their *common line*, and the remaining sections of the same circuits their edges.

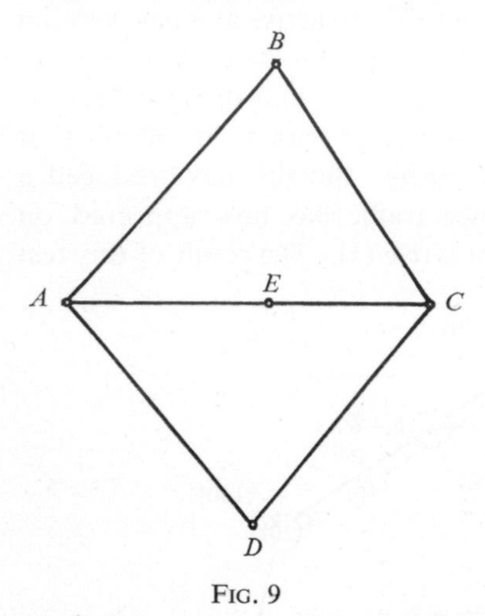

FIG. 9

For example, line *AEC* in Fig. 9 is a common line for circuits *ABCEA* and *AECDA*; *ABC* and *CDA* are the edges of these two circuits. At the same time *ABC* is a common line for the circuits *ABCEA* and *ABCDA* and the lines *AEC* and *CDA* are their external parts. Similarly, *CDA* is the common line, and *ABC* and *AEC* are the edges of the circuits *ABCDA* and *AECDA*.

Rule 6. If on a line common to two circuits (e.g. *AEC*) no free sections occur, and both the circuits (in our case *ABCEA* and *AECDA*) satisfy the conditions of Rule 4, then any circuit formed from their edges (e.g. *ABCDA*) will also satisfy these conditions.

NOTE. It is not necessary for all the areas encircled by the two original circuits to lie within the circle formed by their edges. For example, if there were no free sections on *ABC* and tests showed that the circuits *ABCEA* and *ABCDA* met the requirements of Rule 4, testing the circle *AECDA* would be superfluous.

Now let us return to Fig. 8. After the changes we have made *jFL*, the line common to circuits (1) and (2), has no free sections. Consequently, by virtue of Rule 6 circle (1, 2), formed by the edges of circles (1) and (2), does not call for any further alterations to the system of connexions.[1]

Calculations of positive, negative and free sections are required for circuit (2, 3), and the results of these (+95, −35, 75) show that this circuit satisfies Rule 4.

[1] If we check circle (1, 2) by the method outlined earlier we see that Rule 6 is correct for this case, for we obtain +80, −20, 85.

No calculations are required for circuit (3, 4) because this circuit consists of the edges of (3) and (4) which have already been tested, and because there are no free sections on their common line *Kj*.

A test of circle (1, 4) shows that an anti-clockwise advance is necessary (the figures here are +85, −70, 5). The number of units to be advanced is indicated here by sections *Gk* and *eD*, with a traffic density of 7 units. We show the consequences of this advance of 7 units of load by cancelling the dotted lines running from *e* to *D* and from *G* to *k* by zigzag lines, and showing by a line of dashes where traffic has appeared on section *La*.

The appearance of traffic on *La* calls for a second test of circuits (1, 2, 3, 4) and (1). For (1, 2, 3, 4) it is sufficient to establish that the total length of negative section (which has increased by 5 kilometres) is now 25 kilometres, and therefore clearly less than the rest of the circle. We obtain the same result for circle (1). It follows that no changes are needed in the system connecting the points on these two circuits.

There remain to be tested now the circuits (1, 2, 3), (2, 3, 4), (3, 4, 1) and (4, 1, 2). Calculations are needed only in the case of circuit (3, 4, 1), and the results of these (+55, −65, 85) show that this circuit answers the requirements of Rule 4. Rule 6 shows that no changes are required in the system connecting the points situated on the remaining circuits. To save reiterating the same argument for every circuit, let us take circle (2, 3, 4) as a representative example. This circle is made up of the edges of circuits (1, 2, 3, 4) and (1) (i.e. of *LcBCKDA* and *LjA*), and their common line *AaL* has no free sections on it. It follows from this that (2, 3, 4) does satisfy the conditions of Rule 4.

We have now tested and corrected all the circuits shown in Figs. 6, 7 and 8. The dotted lines in Fig. 8 which are not cancelled by zigzag lines show the system guaranteeing the shortest overall running distance in its final form.[1]

5. The Use of Potentials in Testing Transportation Systems

The volume of work involved in the application of the graphico-analytical method quickly grows with the increase in the number of closed circuits which need to be tested and corrected by the calculation of circuit differences. Moreover, where the layout of the transportation network is very complicated the possibility of overlooking one or two circuits is not to be excluded. It is therefore recommended that transportation systems set up by means of the methods described above be submitted to a final check by the calculation of potentials.[2]

[1] In practice all the work may be done on one diagram by successively deleting lines showing load-flow on sections which become free and adding lines on sections where our modifications have caused traffic to appear.

[2] See L. V. Kantorovich and M. K. Gavurin, op. cit. In our opinion it is not always desirable to calculate potentials while actually setting up transportation systems and to enter them on the diagram for each intermediate version. More work may be involved in setting up a traffic plan than in using the circuit differences method.

Let us briefly explain the concept of potentials. Let each point on a network $i, k, l \dots$ ($i, k, l \dots$ may be either dispatch or arrival points, or junctions) be allotted a value P ($P_i, P_k, P_l \dots$).

If the traffic system ensures the shortest overall running distance for loads, the values of P may be selected in such a way as to satisfy two requirements:

I. If on section *ik* traffic is travelling from i to k, the difference $P_k - P_i$ must be positive, and equal to the length of the section *ik*.

II. If section *ik* is free, the absolute value of the difference $P_k - P_i$ must not be greater than the length of section *ik*.

Values of P satisfying these requirements are called *potentials*. The possibility of constructing a system of such potentials where any traffic plan is being considered is not only a necessary but also a sufficient condition of the establishment of the shortest overall running distances for loads.[1]

Still using our previous example we shall demonstrate the use of potentials in testing the adequacy of networks. Let us determine the potentials for the final version of the traffic plan shown in Fig. 8. To one of the points on the network, to j let us say, we attribute an arbitrary potential of 100.[2] We obtain the potentials of the neighbouring points linked to j by traffic routes either by adding the lengths of the relevant sections to 100 if the traffic passes over them away from j, or by subtracting these lengths if the traffic is moving in the opposite direction. This procedure ensures that requirement I (above) is observed, and gives as a result a potential of 105 for F, 120 for h, and 85 for G (see the numbers in square brackets in Fig. 8). By adding the distance from F to L to the potential of F we obtain the potential of thc junction L (130), and it is now a simple matter to assign potentials to a (135) and (b) (140). If we continue our calculations in this fashion we shall obtain potentials for all the points on the network which are linked to j by traffic routes.

For stations B, i and d, and stations C, K, k and e, which are not linked by traffic routes to any points on the remainder of the network, we can obtain potentials in the following way. To determine the potentials of the group of stations B, i and d we commence with the station which is nearest to points which have potentials already, in this case i. It is obvious that i's potential may not be greater than 130 (100, the potential of j, plus 30, the length of section ji) or less than $100-30 = 70$, otherwise requirement II will not be observed. If we try out a potential of 130, we obtain 115 ($130-15$) for B and 130 ($+115+15$) for d. As may be seen from Fig. 8, a potential of 130 satisfies requirement II, since $160-130 = 30 < 40$.

[1] The relevant theorem was proved by Kantorovich in 1942 (see *Reports of the USSR Academy of Sciences*, Vol. 37, Nos. 7-8, pp. 227-9, 1942). It is easy to show that the possibility of constructing systems of potentials is equivalent to satisfying the requirements of Rule 4.

[2] It is convenient to take a positive number large enough to ensure that only positive numbers are obtained in the successive calculations.

If requirement II had not been satisfied with respect to section *cd*, we should either have had to try out different potentials for *i* within the range of values permissible (70 to 130) until we hit upon one which did satisfy requirement II, or, if that proved impossible, recognise that the system we had constructed was not the 'best', and that it would itself have to be changed. For example, if the potential of point *c* had been 80 instead of 160, the difference (130 − 80 = 50) would have been greater than the length of the section (40). In this case it would have been possible to reduce *i*'s potential by 10, which would also have meant the reduction of *d*'s potential by 10 (120 instead of 130), which would *ipso facto* have ensured that requirement II was met. But if *c*'s potential had been less than 30 or greater than 170, no amount of adjustment could have brought about a simultaneous observation of requirement II with respect to both sections *ij* and *cd*. The plan would have had to be rejected as not securing minimal overall running distances.[1]

Let us assign potentials to the group of stations *C*, *K*, *k* and *e*. Let us attribute 105 (85+20) to *k*; we obtain thereby the following potentials: *K* 95, *e* 100, *C* 85. It is easy to see that no adjustment of these figures is necessary, since requirement II is satisfied for both sections *BC* and *De*. At this point we may conclude our calculations of potentials. It follows from the nature of these calculations that requirement I is satisfied, and a comparison by means of Fig. 8 of the length of any free section with its two terminal points will show that requirement II is also satisfied. If the system we were testing did not secure the miminum overall running distance for loads, the simultaneous satisfaction of both requirement I and II would not have been possible.

6. Analytical (Tabular) Methods for Establishing the Shortest Running Distances for Loads when Setting up Transportation Systems

A. N. Tolstoi has suggested a remarkably simple and convenient method of drawing up traffic plans which will secure the shortest overall running distance for loads in cases where only two dispatch points are involved: the method of *successive differences*.[2] This method has great practical importance, since quite complicated transportation systems may frequently be reduced, either wholly or in part, to problems involving two dispatch points or two arrival points, particularly if junctions are substituted for groups of stations. Let us demonstrate this method.

[1] For greater detail on the construction of potentials see L. V. Kantorovich and M. K. Gavurin, op. cit.

[2] For this method see also T. S. Khachaturov, 'Fundamentals of railway transport economics, pt. 1', *Transzheldorizdat*, 1946, pp. 363-6; Y. I. Koldomasov, 'Fundamentals of transportation planning on railways', *Transzheldorizdat*, 1949, chap. 6; E. D. Khanukov, 'Transport and the location of production', *Transzheldorizdat*, 1955, chap. 9; S. K. Danilov, ed., 'Transport economics', *Transzheldorizdat*, 1957, chap. 7.

Let *A* dispatch 70 units of load, and *B* 80. The arrival points *a, b, c, d, e* and *f* require respectively 10, 20, 30, 15, 35 and 40 units of load. Table 1 shows the distances between these points and *A* and *B*. Whatever the layout of the railway track on which these points are situated, the connexions to be made between *A* and *B* and *a, b, c, d, e, f* may be ascertained in the following way:

TABLE 1

Dispatch points	Distances between dispatch and arrival points					
	a	*b*	*c*	*d*	*e*	*f*
A	30	20	40	10	50	15
B	50	30	20	25	5	10
Gain' (+), 'loss' (−) on being connected to *A*	+20	+10	−20	+15	−45	−5

For each arrival point *a, b, c, d, e* and *f* we subtract its distance from *A* from its distance from *B*. The differences will indicate the 'gains' (+) and 'losses' (−) which we should obtain for each unit of load if we connected these arrival points to *A* in preference to *B*. Let us arrange the arrival points in the order in which they should be connected to *A* to obtain maximum advantage, and then join them to *A* one after another until all the loads dispatched from *A* (70 units) are accounted for. This order is: *a, d, b, f, c, e*. Taking into consideration the consumption requirements of each point we are now brought to our final conclusions: *a, d* and *b* must be entirely supplied from *A*; *f* must receive 25 units from *A* and 15 from *B*; the remaining arrival points (*c* and *e*) must be connected to *B*.

The method of successive differences is a purely analytical or tabular method. Its application does not involve plotting load-flows on a diagram of the track layout, and the only initial data needed are the distances between the dispatch and arrival points. When dispatch and arrival points are situated in a way that would involve the examination of a number of circles by the graphico-analytical method the method of successive differences offers a considerable simplification.

The question will suggest itself whether this purely analytical method may be applied more generally to situations where there are more than two dispatch or arrival points. The method put forward by L. V. Kantorovich for the solution of a number of technological, organisational and planning problems with the help of *resolving multipliers* or *ratings* makes it possible to give an affirmative answer. We have already met a specific instance of the use of ratings in the solution of the problem of drawing up a traffic plan by means of potentials. It is possible to draw up a plan which will guarantee the shortest overall running distances by constructing a number of consecutive alternative plans in the form of 'chess tables' which are tested and corrected by exactly the same calculations of potentials as we described above.[1]

[1] Very close to this method of drawing up a transportation plan and solving this problem are the various modifications of the *simplex method* put forward in foreign literature.

In this article, however, we put forward another means of solving these problems by a tabular method which derives immediately from the process using *resolving multipliers* evolved by Kantorovich in 1939. With this method of establishing the 'best' system of transportation there is no need to multiply the quantities which stand in the place of the *resolving multipliers* (as we shall see below, they are simply added to the distances between dispatch and arrival points), and for this reason we shall in future call these quantities *resolving addends*.[1]

The essence of the resolving addends method may be expressed as follows. Let us renumber all the dispatch and arrival points, and let us denote the numbers of the dispatch stations by the letter i, and the numbers of the arrival stations by the letter k. If n is the number of dispatch points and m the number of arrival points, then i will represent the values 1, 2, . . . , n, and k the values 1, 2, . . . , m. The distances between dispatch and arrival points may be denoted as l_{ik}, i.e. l_{11} will be the distance from dispatch station to arrival station 1, l_{12} the distance from the same dispatch station to arrival station 2, etc.

Is it then possible to arrive at the least total ton-kilometre work by connecting each unloading point (k) to the dispatch station (i) to which the distance (l_{ik}) is shortest? This simple solution of the problem will not work. The consumption requirements of a number of stations k would remain unsatisfied, and no use would be made of loads at a number of points i because as a rule the volume of loading and unloading at the dispatch and arrival stations nearest to each other would not match.

The idea of the method proposed here is to select values for $\lambda_1, \lambda_2, \ldots, \lambda_n$ in such a way that if we connect up our points according to the shortest distance principle (each destination to the nearest dispatch point), but instead of actual distances use some assumed distances (arrived at by adding to the actual distances l_{ik} the corresponding numbers λ_i, i.e. taking $l_{11}+\lambda_1$ instead of l_{11}, $l_{12}+\lambda_1$ instead of l_{12}, $l_{21}+\lambda_2$ instead of l_{21}, etc.), then the requirements of each destination will be fully met by the dispatch points to which it is connected.

[1] If we apply the connotations adopted by Kantorovich (see pp. 228-9) of the present work) we can express the conditions of our problem as follows:

(1) $h_{ik} > 0$ (2) $\sum_{k=1}^{m} h_{ik} = 1 \quad (i = 1, 2, \ldots, n)$

(3) $\sum_{i=1}^{n} \alpha_i h_{ik} = z_k$ (4) $\sum_{1}^{n} \alpha_i = \sum_{1}^{m} z_k.$

It is necessary with α_i and z_k given to find h_{ik} which secures the minimum value of:

$$\sum_{i=1}^{n} \sum_{k=1}^{m} c_{ik} \alpha_i h_{ik}$$

(c_{ik} are given). Because the values of α_i are independent of k there is no need to carry out multiplication to arrive at a solution of this problem.

If values could be found for $\lambda_1, \lambda_2, \ldots, \lambda_n$ which would satisfy this condition (let us call them *resolving addends*), the problem of establishing the shortest overall running distance would be solved. Connexions made over the shortest assumed distances $(l_{ik}+\lambda_i)$ would be the most efficient, i.e., they would ensure minimal ton-kilometre work.

Indeed, if we denote the number of loads to be sent from i to k by x_{ik} $(k = 1, 2, \ldots, m)$, the overall running distance, if we reckon with actual distances, may be expressed as $\sum_1^n \sum_1^m l_{ik}x_{ik}$, and if we reckon with assumed distances, as

$$\sum_1^n \sum_1^m (l_{ik}+\lambda_i)\, x_{ik}$$

It is easy to see that if we connect the arrival and dispatch points over the shortest assumed distances (in this case we take the values of x_{ik} which do not correspond to the shortest assumed distances as equal to zero) the following inequality occurs:

$$\sum_{i=1}^n \sum_{k=1}^m (l_{ik}+\lambda_i)\, x_{ik} \leqq \sum_{i=1}^n \sum_{k=1}^m (l_{ik}+\lambda_i)\, x'_{ik} \qquad \ldots \quad [1]$$

where x'_{ik} is the quantity of loads sent from i to k on any other version of the system of connexions. Since, whatever the version of the plan used, all the loads at every dispatch point must be distributed, it follows that

$$\sum_{k=1}^m x_{ik} = \sum_{k=1}^m x'_{ik} = \alpha_i \quad (i = 1, 2 \ldots n) \qquad \ldots \quad [2]$$

where α is the quantity of loads at the dispatch points. It follows further that the sums

$$\sum_{i=1}^n \sum_{k=1}^m \lambda_i x_{ik} = \sum_{i=1}^n \lambda_i \sum_{k=1}^m x_{ik}$$

and $\qquad \ldots \quad [2]$

$$\sum_{i=1}^n \sum_{k=1}^m \lambda_i x'_{ik} = \sum_{i=1}^n \lambda_i \sum_{k=1}^m x'_{ik}$$

are equal, since each is equal to $\sum_1^n \lambda_i \alpha_i$. If we subtract these sums from the left and right sides of the inequality (1), we obtain:

$$\sum_{i=1}^n \sum_{k=1}^m l_{ik}x_{ik} \leqq \sum_{i=1}^n \sum_{k=1}^m l_{ik}x'_{ik} \qquad \ldots \quad [3]$$

In other words, when arrival points are connected to dispatch points over the shortest assumed distances (x_{ik}), the overall running distance cannot be greater than it would be in any other alternative plan (x'_{ik}).[1]

We have thus been able to reduce the problem of establishing the shortest overall running distance for loads when drawing up a transportation plan linking dispatch points and destinations to the problem of determining the values of the resolving addends ($\lambda_1, \lambda_2, \ldots, \lambda_n$)[2] and of drawing up a plan based on the shortest assumed distances. The resolving addends, and the system of connexions giving the shortest running distances, may be found by means of successive approximations.

7. Calculating Procedure for the Method of Resolving Addends

Let us take an example. The conditions are set out in Table 2.[3]

TABLE 2

$d_1 = 5$

Dispatch points	Arrival points						'Surplus' or 'deficit' of loads (+, -)
	a 4	*b* 30	*c* 16	*d* 27	*e* 18	*f* 5	
A 15	**10** (4)	75	80	50	52	40	+11
B 20	100	**22** (20)	**16**	48	70	**29**	-31
C 25	25	27	31	90	66	45	+25
D 40	44	26	38	**37** (27)	33 (13)	50	- 5
Differences in distances		5	15	13	19	11	

In this table letters denote dispatch points (*A*, *B*, *C* and *D*) and arrival points (*a*, *b*, *c*, *d*, *e* and *f*). The figures beside these letters denote the quantity of loads dispatched or received, and the figures in the respective columns

[1] The existence of resolving addends is not only a sufficient but also a necessary condition for ensuring that the transportation plan meets the requirements for producing minimal overall running distances for loads. This proposition can be considered as a consequence of the potentials theorem. It is, in fact, easy to see that the resolving addends and shortest assumed distances are the respective potentials of the dispatch and arrival points of loads.

[2] Dispatch and arrival points have an exactly analogous role in setting up networks. Where there are fewer arrival points than dispatch points it is more convenient to find resolving addends for the arrival points instead of the dispatch points: $\lambda', \lambda'_2, \ldots, \lambda'_m$. In this case the assumed distances will be expressed by the values $l_{ik} + \lambda'_i$ and not $l_{ik} + \lambda_i$ as in the text. Similar changes will be made in all subsequent considerations.

[3] The example shown and the form of table used were worked out in 1948 by A. M. Dubinsky, at that time a student at the Moscow Institute of Railway Transport Engineers, and put forward by him at a students' scientific conference.

indicate the distances between the dispatch and arrival points (e.g. from *A* to *a* is 10 kilometres, from *A* to *b* 75, etc.).

Let us first examine what would be the result of connecting each arrival point to the nearest dispatch point. In that case we should have to connect *a* to *A*; *b*, *c* and *f* to *B*; and *d* and *e* to *D*, and the distances (the smallest number in each column) would be as shown in Table 2 in heavy type. With this network *A* would meet in full the requirements of *a*, but 11 units of load out of the 15 at *A*'s disposal would not be utilised.

A similar 'surplus' would occur at *C*, which is not the 'nearest dispatch point' for any arrival point at all. None of *C*'s 25 units would be utilised. We shall call such stations *surplus points*. At the same time the 20 units available at *B* would prove insufficient to meet all the requirements of the points connected to it (*b*, *c* and *f*), since $30+16+5 = 51$; 31 units would be 'lacking'. Another 'deficit' would be revealed at *D*, which with only 40 units to dispose of is connected to *d* and *e* which together require 45 units. Stations in this position we shall call *deficit points*.

The 'surpluses' (+) and 'deficits' (−) obtained are set out in the last column of Table 2. The totals of the positive and negative figures must balance.

To obtain a clearer picture of the transportation possibilities between the various stations with the present scheme, we have set out in Table 2 figures in brackets to show the number of loads which may be received by each destination from its respective source. To some extent these figures are arbitrary. For instance, if we reduced the supply from *B* to *b* shown here, we could route some of the loads at *B* to other points connected to this station, such as *c* or *f*. Such changes would make no difference to our argument, however, since the amounts of 'surplus' or 'deficit' would remain the same.

The next part of our procedure is to calculate the differences between (*a*) the distances between deficit dispatch stations and the arrival points connected to them, and (*b*) the distances between these same arrival points and the surplus stations nearest them. To the deficit station *B* are connected points *b*, *c* and *f*. We can find the distances between these arrival points and their nearest surplus stations in the relevant vertical columns: 27, 31 and 40. The differences in distance which concern us are $27-22 = 5$, $31-16 = 15$ and $40-29 = 11$. Similarly for *d* and *e*, which are connected to another deficit station, *D*, we obtain $50-37 = 13$ and $52-33 = 19$. These differences are set out in the last row of Table 2.

Let us represent the smallest of these differences by d_1 and enter it in the top right-hand corner of Table 2. This difference we may take as a first approximation to our resolving addend for *B* and *D* (which are 'deficit stations'), that is to say, we shall use this number to obtain a first variant of our 'assumed distances'. To do this we increase all the distances between *B* and *D* and the destination points (all the figures in the rows *B* and *D*) by d_1 ($= 5$ in our example). The results obtained are shown in Table 3.

TABLE 3

$d_2 = 8$

Dispatch points	Arrival points: a 4	b 30	c 16	d 27	e 18	f 5	'Surplus' or 'deficit' of loads (+, −)
A 15	**10** (4)	75	80	50	52	40	+11
B 20	105	**27** (5)	**21** (15)	53	75	**34**	− 6
C 25	25	27 (25)	31	90	66	45	− 0
D 40	49	31	48	**42** (27)	**38** (13)	55	− 5
Differences in distances		48	59	8	14	6	

Making use this time of the distances shown in Table 3, we once again connect each destination point to its nearest dispatch point (as in Table 2 the relevant figures are printed in heavy type) and assess the quantity of supplies which the dispatch stations can now send to each destination (the figures in brackets), always bearing in mind the need to make the best use of the loads available at the dispatch stations and to satisfy as far as possible the requirements of the arrival points. The changes in the distances make it possible to reduce the amounts 'surplus' and 'deficit'. Now only 6 units are 'lacking' from the destinations connected to *B* instead of 35, and there is no longer any 'surplus' of loads at *C*.

The question arises how we should regard *C* henceforth: is it a 'surplus' or a 'deficit' point? The goods available at this station are now utilised in full, as in the case of deficit stations; at the same time the requirements of point *b* connected to it are also fully satisfied, as in the case of destinations connected to surplus stations. To cover cases like these we shall adhere to the following rule. If the requirements of the destination points connected to a given dispatch point are satisfied in full, but if even one of these points is being simultaneously supplied from another station which is a deficit point, then the dispatch station we are considering must also be regarded as a deficit point. In the converse case a station which is able to satisfy all the requirements of the destinations connected to it must still be regarded as a surplus point, even if in fact the 'surplus' at its disposal is equal to zero.

From this it follows that *C* is a deficit point, since *B* participates in the supply to *b*. We therefore prefix the '0' in the last column of the Table, row *C*, with the minus sign.

We now proceed as we did with Table 2, finding the differences between (*a*) the distances between deficit dispatch stations and the arrival points connected to them, and (*b*) the distances between these arrival points and their nearest surplus stations. By referring to the columns under the arrival points which are connected to deficit stations, we obtain the figures shown in the bottom row of Table 3. The smallest difference is 6.

However, if we increase all the distances between arrival points and deficit stations by 6 (in the same way as we increased them by 5 when we made the transition from Table 2 to Table 3) it soon becomes evident that in the new network there will be no change in the classification of dispatch points as surplus and deficit stations. The only change, in fact, will be that alongside *B* the surplus station *A* will also have to be connected to *f* because the distance between *f* and *A* and *f* and *B* will become the same. This will ensure that *f*'s requirements are satisfied, but *A* will still remain a surplus station and *B* and *C* deficit stations. To make the transition to the next variant of the network in such cases as these it is best to use the second smallest difference (i.e. the second smallest figure in the last row of the relevant table) instead of the smallest or, if this fails to alter the balance of surplus and deficit stations, the third smallest, and so on.

In Table 3 the smallest figure after 6 is 8 (the difference between the distances *d* to *D* and *d* to *A*), and so we enter $d_2 = 8$ in the top right-hand corner of the Table. By adding 8 to the figures in the rows of the deficit stations we obtain our new assumed distances, and these are set out in Table 4. Just as with Tables 2 and 3 we now set up a new network, calculate the load 'surpluses' and 'deficits', and enter the differences in the distances which concern us in the bottom row of the table.

TABLE 4

$d_3 = 4$

Dispatch points	*a* 4	*b* 30	*c* 16	*d* 27	*e* 18	*f* 5	'Surplus' or 'deficit' of loads (+, −)
	Arrival points						
A 15	**10** (4)	45	80	**50** (6)	52	**40** (5)	+0
B 20	113	**35** (5)	**29** (15)	61	83	42	−1
C 25	33	**35** (25)	39	98	74	53	−0
D 40	57	39	51	**50** (21)	**46** (18)	63	+1
Differences in distances		4	22				

We note that $d_3 = 4$, and then set up the next variant of the network exactly the same way as when making the transitions from Table 2 to Table 3 and Table 3 to Table 4. As is shown by Table 5, the new assumed distances are now such as to permit the full supply of every arrival point from its 'nearest' dispatch points. Table 5, therefore, offers the final solution to this particular problem.[1] *A* supplies *a*, *d* and *f* (4, 6 and 5 units), *B* supplies *b* and *c* (4 and 16), *C* sends all its loads to *b*, and *D* has a share in the supply of *b* (1), *d* (21) and *e* (18).

TABLE 5

	Arrival points						'Surplus' or 'deficit' of loads (+, −)
Dispatch points	*a* 4	*b* 30	*c* 16	*d* 27	*e* 18	*f* 5	
A 15	**10** (4)	75	80	**50** (6)	52	**40** (5)	0
B 20	117	**39** (4)	**33** (16)	65	87	46	0
C 25	37	**39** (25)	43	102	78	57	0
D 40	57	**39** (1)	51	**50** (21)	**46** (18)	63	0

It will be readily observed that the distances in each row of Table 5 differ from the corresponding figures in the same row of Table 2 by the same amount. These amounts are: row *A*, 0 (the figures are the same in both tables); row *B*, 17 $(d_1+d_2+d_3)$; row *C*, 12 (d_1+d_3); and row *D*, 13 (d_1+d_2). In each case they are also the same as the resolving addends $(\lambda_A, \lambda_B, \lambda_C, \lambda_D)$ which were discussed in Section 6. As we can see, for the purposes of setting up a transportation system there is no point in working out their ultimate values because our network has already emerged at an earlier stage of our calculations. The actual process of establishing the system requires only the auxiliary numbers $d_1, d_2, d_3, \ldots, d_n$. The method just outlined for establishing networks, however, is based on the fact that there exist systems of numbers which will satisfy the definition of resolving addends and that transportation schemes based on these systems will minimise overall running distances.

It is advisable to calculate resolving addends for the purpose of checking

[1] In this example three 'steps' are needed in the transition from the original to the final version of the plan. It is possible to show that the number of 'steps' needed to solve the problem is finite. This may be proved as follows. Let the squares of any table of assumed distances from arrival points to their nearest dispatch points correspond exactly to the same squares of a second table. These tables we shall call 'equivalent' (the same versions of the system of connexions correspond to them). It is easy to see that the gradual transition according to the rules stated above from one table of assumed distances to another cannot produce 'equivalent' tables. It is similarly easy to show that the number of 'non-equivalent' tables distinguished from each other by the assumed distances set out in the corresponding squares is finite. Hence it follows that a finite number of 'steps' must lead to a solution of the problem. It must be borne in mind that when ordinary practical problems are being tackled instead of specially selected examples, the number of 'steps' will as a rule remain below $n+m$ and, in fact, only in exceptional cases exceed half that sum $\left(\frac{n+m}{2}\right)$.

TABLE 6*

Arrival points	a 4				b 30				c 16				d 27				e 18				f 5				$d_1=5$	$d_2=8$	$d_3=4$
Dispatch points																									'Surplus' or 'deficit' of loads (+, −)		
A 15	**10** (4)	**10** (4)	**10** (4)	**10** (4)	75	75	75	75	80	80	80	80	50	50	**50** (6)	**50** (6)	52	52	52	52	40	40	**40** (5)	**40** (5)	+11	+11	+0 0
B 20	105	105	113	117	**22** (20)	**27** (5)	**35** (5)	**39** (4)	**16**	**21** (15)	**29** (15)	**33** (16)	48	53	61	65	70	75	33	87	**29**	**34**	42	46	−31	−6	−1 0
C 25	25	25	33	37	27	**27** (25)	**35** (25)	**39** (25)	31	31	39	43	90	90	98	102	66	66	74	78	45	45	53	57	+25	−0	−0 0
D 40	44	49	57	57	26	31	39	**39** (1)	38	43	51	51	**37** (27)	**42** (27)	**50** (21)	**50** (21)	**33** (13)	**38** (13)	**46** (18)	**46** (18)	50	55	63	63	−5	−5	+1 0
					5				15				13				19				11						
Differences in distances						18				59				8				11				6					
							4				22																

* At each stage in the calculations only the last figures set out on the right are to be taken into consideration. All the rest may be deleted.

transportation systems which have been established by the method just described. All that need be done is to check (as we did above) that the figures in each row in the final table have indeed increased by the same amount (the resolving addend) when compared with the figures in the corresponding rows in the original table, and that the system does satisfy the principle of the shortest assumed distances.

For each successive approximation to our ideal network we made use of a separate table. We did this for clarity of exposition: in practice, so long as the number of stations is not too great, all the calculations may be set out in one large working table. Table 6 shows how such a table would look for the example we selected.

If we take as starting data the distances between stations and the quantities of goods dispatched from and unloaded at separate points in accordance with the network shown in Fig. 6, the final appearance of the working table after the application of the method of resolving addends will be as shown by Table 7. The network derived from this table is, as may have been anticipated, identical with the one produced by the use of the circuit differences method (see Fig. 8).

8. Comparison of the Features of Different Methods of Setting up Transportation Systems

The possibility of successfully solving problems connected with transportation systems by purely analytical methods by no means invalidates the graphic or graphico-analytical methods. The graphic method (see Section 1) remains, of course, the simplest and most convenient in all cases where closed circuits are not involved. The first step in making connexions between dispatch and arrival points when railway or inland waterway traffic is being planned should therefore always be to plot the load data on a diagram of the layout of the track (or waterways) and to apply the graphic method to every section possible.

It is only when the load-flows which are discernible as efficient by a direct examination of the diagram have been drawn in and relevant junctions substituted for groups of stations (see Section 4) that the question of making use of the graphico-analytical or resolving addends methods arises. (Other methods have not been examined in this paper.) To assess the relative merits and defects of the two latter methods is a more complicated problem, and the selection of one rather than the other must depend on the actual conditions of the problem involved.

The comparative laboriousness of the two methods varies in accordance with the number of stations to be linked up and the number of closed circuits formed by the routes linking the dispatch and arrival points. The resolving addends method grows rapidly more laborious with an increase in the number of dispatch and arrival points, but is not directly affected by the configurations of the transport network. On the other hand the amount of work

TABLE 7

Arrival points / Dispatch points	*a* 17				*b* 8				*c* 20				*d* 5				*e* 10				*f* 20				*g* 5			
A 25	**25** (17)	**45** (17)	50 (10)	50 (10)	40	60	65	65	60	80	85	85	95	115	120	120	50	70	75	75	**15** (8)	**35** (8)	**40** (10)	**40** (10)	5	25	30 (5)	30 (5)
B 10	80	100	100	100	75	95	95	95	**55**	**75**	**75**	**75**	**15** (5)	**35** (5)	**35** (5)	**35** (5)	50	70	70	70	85	105	105	105	85	105	105	105
C 20	90	90	90	90	95	95	95	95	90	90	90	90	50	50	50	50	**15** (10)	**15** (10)	**15** (10)	**15** (10)	50	50	50	50	60	60	60	60
D 10	55	75	80	80	70	90	95	95	90	110	115	115	85	105	110	110	20	40	45	45	**15** (10)	**35** (10)	**40** (10)	**40** (10)	25	45	50	50
E 10	35	55	60	65	50	70	75	80	70	90	95	100	85	105	110	115	60	80	85	90	25	45	50	55	15	35	40	45
F 25	30	50	**50**	**50**	**35** (8)	**55** (8)	**55** (8)	**55** (8)	**55** (7)	**75** (17)	**75** (17)	**75** (17)	65	85	85	85	55	75	75	75	55	75	75	75	45	65	65	65
G 25	50	50	**50** (7)	**50** (7)	55	**55**	**55**	**55**	75	**75** (3)	**75** (3)	**75** (3)	75	75	75	75	35	35	35	35	65	65	65	65	55	55	55	55
Difference in distances	25				20				20				35								35				50			
		5																				15				30		

TABLE 7 *continued*

Arrival points Dispatch points	*h* 15				*i* 5				*j* 10				*k* 10				d_1 20*	d_2 5	d_3 5	
A 25	15	35	40	40	65	85	90	90	35	55	60	60	65	85	90	90	−7	−7	+0	0
B 10	65	85	85	85	**15** (5)	**35** (5)	**35** (5)	**35** (5)	45	65	65	65	55	75	75	75	−13	+0	+0	0
C 20	75	75	75	75	50	50	50	50	55	55	55	55	**20** (10)	**20** (10)	**20** (10)	**20** (10)	+0	+0	+0	0
D 10	45	65	70	70	85	105	110	110	65	85	90	90	35	55	60	50	−0†	−0†	+0	0
E 10	**5** (10)	**25** (10)	**30** (10)	**35** (10)	55	75	80	85	25	45	50	55	60	80	85	90	−5	−5	−5	0
F 25	25	45	45	45	35	55	55	55	**5** (10)	25	25	25	40	60	60	60	−0†	+0	+0	0
G 25	35	35	35	**35** (5)	45	45	45	45	15	**15** (10)	**15** (10)	**15** (10)	**20**	**20**	**20**	**20**	+25	+12	+5	0
Differences in distances	30				30				10											
		10																		
			5																	

* If d_1 is taken as 10 the division of the dispatch points into surplus and deficit stations in the second variant of the plan will remain unchanged in comparison with the original version.

† Arrival point *f* (connected to *D*) is two units short. But since these two units were reckoned in *A*'s deficit (and *f* is also connected to *A*) *D*'s deficit is taken as nil to avoid a double reckoning. Alternatively *A*'s deficit could be reckoned as 5 instead of 7 (attributing only the under-supplying of *G* to *A*) and the figures for *D* entered on the graph as −2 instead of −0. The only essential is to avoid double counting. Similarly the shortage at *c* (13 units) could be ascribed to a deficit either at *B* (as in Table 9) or at *F*, the two stations responsible for supplying *c*; or, finally, it could be split up between both (e.g. 7 units at *B* and 6 at *F*).

involved with the graphico-analytical method depends mainly on the number of 'circles' which must be checked, and only to a small extent on the number of stations involved.

Thus, for example, constructing a network for the example dealt with in Section 3 (see Fig. 4) with the aid of the circuit differences method involves almost no work at all; whereas the use of this method to solve the problem posed in Section 4 (see Figs. 5, 6, 7 and 8) would necessitate a vast expenditure of labour, since here we would be dealing with thirteen closed circuits instead of only one. However, the expenditure of labour would differ but slightly, if either of these problems were solved by the resolving addends method (5 dispatch and 5 arrival points as against 7 and 11). In many cases it may be best to combine different methods, including the resolving addends and circuit differences methods. It is possible, for example, where there is a large number of dispatch and arrival points, to consider the loading and unloading at minor stations as functions of neighbouring major stations, and having thus reduced the number of stations to be examined, to apply the resolving addends method, and then to plot the results obtained on the diagram and to check doubtful points with the aid of the graphico-analytical method.

Where it is desired to establish minimum transport costs instead of running distances, expressed either in money or natural units (roubles, truck-hours, tons of fuel, etc.) it is important not to overlook one limitation of the graphico-analytical method. It can be used only if the transport costs from A to C via B are equal to the sum of the transport costs from A to B and from B to C.

This proviso does not prevent the setting up of systems to minimise expenditure envisaged on the basis of actual or planned transportation costs on separate sections. This may be done simply by substituting costs for distances in the diagram and using these costs when calculating circuit differences or potentials. This method of calculation need hardly be changed even where the costs of running laden trucks and empty ones are to be kept apart. In this case two figures ('forward' and 'return') must be entered for each section, and slight modifications will have to be made to the rule formulated above.

Situations may arise, however, where the proviso as to the balance of costs on adjacent sections cannot be observed. This is the case, for example, where a plan is required to minimise transport costs arising from the system of freight rates. The combined costs from A to B and from B to C will not, as a rule, be equal to that from A to C (on account of freight reductions for distance and the existence of special rates). In cases like these the graphico-analytical method is not applicable (nor is the purely graphical method), whereas calculations in accordance with the resolving addends method may still be made exactly as outlined above. The resolving addends method can thus be applied more widely than the graphico-analytical method.

Definite conclusions as to the merits and demerits (especially the laboriousness) of the various methods of drawing up transportation plans to minimise running distances and costs must await the accumulation of practical experience. It should be observed, however, that the application of any of the methods described in this paper on a massive scale to an entire transport network with a great number of widely scattered dispatch and arrival stations will involve a formidable amount of labour and time, and for this reason it is advisable to make use of the latest computer techniques. If fast modern computers are used, any transportation system can be set up without any difficulty in a minimum of time.

The methods described here have already given practical proof of their efficacy. For example, the Institute of Complex Transportation Problems of the Academy of Sciences used the resolving addends method to draw up a plan for the most efficient road haulage of sand in Moscow. The orders for sand issued by the construction enterprise Mosstroisbyt during a ten-day period in June 1958 were used as starting data. To establish the most efficient plan distances had to be calculated from each of the eight wharves where sand was picked up to each of 209 building sites. All calculations were carried out with the help of the *Strela* electronic digital computer in one hour thirty-five minutes (including fifty minutes spent on preparation of input data).

Comparison of the optimum plan obtained with the lorry journeys which would have been necessary under the old system of ordering showed a reduction of 189,000 ton-kilometres, i.e. a saving of 11·4%. Approximate calculations show that the introduction of the optimum plan in Moscow would mean a saving of more than two million roubles a year, solely for the transportation of sand.

A Short Annotated Bibliography of Linear Programming and Related Problems

Prepared by A. A. KORBUT

Numbers in square brackets refer to items so numbered in the Bibliography

In 1939 L. V. Kantorovich examined a wide range of problems of organisation and planning of production; this problem consisted in selecting the optimal one among a large number of different variants [6]. This led him to consider the mathematical problems of the extremum where the variables are subject to linear relations and constraints. In this work the author suggested a very general and efficient method of solution of similar problems—the method of solution multipliers.

It was shown here that it is theoretically possible and desirable to apply mathematical methods in such types of techno-economic problems as that of assignment of machine-time to different jobs or of land to different types of cultivation, the planning of transportation, the processing of complex raw materials, in particular, the rational cutting of industrial materials, etc. This work of Kantorovich largely determined the content and the further development of a new branch of applied mathematics that came later to be known as linear programming.

In their subsequent works Soviet authors further developed the methods of linear programming. Thus the article by L. V. Kantorovich and M. K. Gavurin [14] gave the general method of solution of the transportation problem—the method of 'potentials' which is a variant of the method of solution multipliers.[1] In his note [7] Kantorovich investigated more general extremal problems and, in particular, showed the possibility of applying methods of linear programming to systems of non-homogeneous equations and to the problem of finding best approximations to functions (cf. [20]). Generalisation of the transportation problem and its application to the solution of the Monge problem (on the equalisation of areas) are given in the works [8] and [9].

In a book [15] devoted to problems of the rational cutting of industrial materials both the theoretical and the practical sides of the question are analysed. Similar problems relating to the wood-processing industry are examined in [10] and [34].

He also formulated [11] the so-called general (or basic) problem of production planning; the problems of linear programming mentioned above

[1] The statement of the transportation problem is to be found in the non-mathematical works of A. N. Tolstoi ([29] and [30]); however, no rigorous mathematical solution is given.

appear as special cases of this general problem. Generalisation of these problems to an infinite-dimensional space is given in the works [16] and [17].

G. Sh. Rubinshtein [22, 24 and 25] applied in his own way the method of solution multipliers in studying the geometrical problem of the extremal point of intersection of the axis and the polyhedron. Researches into other mathematical methods of capital importance for the theory of linear programming (the theory of convex sets, systems of linear inequalities, etc.) were carried on by many Soviet mathematicians including A. D. Aleksandrov, S. N. Chernikov, A. G. Shkol'nik and others [1, 2, 3, 21, 23, 27 and 28].

Not only the theory but also the computational aspect of linear programming was elaborated in detail by Soviet mathematicians. One can mention here the method of successive improvement of an existing plan (see [15] Ch. I, para. 8), the method of correction of multipliers [6], the method of upper and lower limits for the multipliers [15], the method of potentials for the transportation problem [14].

There is also accumulated experience in the practical application of linear programming. An example is the fruitful introduction of methods of rational cutting (of materials) in some Leningrad factories (the Egorov factory at Kirov) or the experience of the Chelyabinsk sovnarkhoz (see [4 and 5]). One would expect that the systematic use of linear programming methods in a socialist economy would yield enormous over-all economic benefits due to the better use of existing resources and possibilities.

From 1947 to 1949 intensive work on linear programming began in the USA. Organised at first to respond to military needs, it soon acquired a wider scope. In particular, the results found diverse application in such fields as planning at the shop and the factory level, intra-firm planning and planning of trade.

Serious researches were made abroad on the theory of linear programming; the fundamental dual problems were investigated ([91 and 98]); the equivalence between the basic problems of linear programming and the theory of matrix games was demonstrated ([61, 91 and 147]); many problems in the theory of linear inequalities and of convex sets were worked out in detail ([89, 97 and 123]).

Significant work was done abroad in establishing the purely numerical methods of solving linear programming problems. The first description of the Simplex Method, most frequently in use abroad, is due to G. Dantzig and was published in 1951 [59]. There is a considerable literature on the exposition and modifications of this method. (See, for example, [60, 120, 147, 149 and 150].) A very simple exposition, designed exclusively for practical workers, is contained in the books [99 and 135]. The Generalised Simplex Method which enables one to avoid cases of degeneracy is described in the article [66]. A method of avoiding the possibility of degeneracy was also proposed by Charnes [50 and 54]. One of the possible cases of degeneracy in the Simplex Method is cycling, i.e. the repetition of one and the same basis at different steps of the (iteration-)process. This was analysed by Beale [42].

Among other methods which received some currency abroad, we note the dual-simplex method of Lemke [116] and a similar method of leading variables of Beale [41], the relaxation method of Motzkin [124], the projection method of Tompkins [144] and the double-description method for matrix games proposed by Motzkin, Raiffa, Thompson and Thrall [125]. (See also [74].)

All these above methods of the foreign authors dealt with the solution of only one of the pair of dual problems. Only in 1956 did Dantzig, Ford and Fulkerson work out a method for the simultaneous solution of the primal and the dual problem of linear programming. This method is, in essence, identical with Kantorovich's method of correcting multipliers; however, the problems of finding a first approximation and the problems of degeneracy are examined in greater detail. An original method of logarithmic potential was put forward by Frisch [88].

Various generalisations of the programming problem, mainly by way of introducing more complicated maximising or minimising function, were considered by many authors. Thus Gass and Saaty [95 and 96] investigated the case where this function depends on the parameter; Charnes and Lemke [55], Beale [43] and others developed the algorithm for minimising a convex function with linear constraints on the variables; minimisation of a quadratic function was examined in [38 and 85]. Problems of non-linear programming are dealt with in the works [120 and 146].

Linear programming under uncertain or stochastic (probabilistic) conditions is studied in [57, 62 and 134].

An interesting generalisation, from the mathematical point of view, of the basic dual problems of linear programming in the continuous case, was given by Duffin [76].

Electronic computers should become a powerful means of solving linear programming problems where a large amount of calculation is necessary. The method and technique of computer-based calculation have been examined in [71, 103 and 104]. Experience gathered in solving linear programming problems with computers that are in continuous operation is described in [35].

It is very difficult in a short note to illustrate at length the various practical applications of linear programming. We might first recall the transportation problem, which owing to its relatively simple structure has been studied in great detail. The first statement of the transportation problem in foreign literature was in 1941 by Hitchcock [102]. This was investigated by Koopmans in [108] and by Koopmans and Reiter in [111] (hence the transportation problem is very often known abroad as the Hitchcock-Koopmans problem). The solution of the transportation problem by the Simplex method is given by Dantzig [60]. Flood in [81] describes a variant of the Simplex method for the solution of the transportation problem, which is essentially similar to the method of potentials. For other methods of solution of the transportation problem see the articles [51, 126 and 133]. The capacity-constrained transportation problem is investigated in [69 and 83].

The assignment problem, equivalent to the transportation problem, is studied in [77 and 126]. A simple combinatorial algorithm for its solution (known as the 'Hungarian method') was given by Kuhn in [112]. Closely connected again are the caterer problem [105 and 132] and the travelling salesman problem [70 and 82].

In the work [53] linear programming is applied to oil-refining industry (the problem of the optimal mixture of different kinds of petrol is examined).

Different variants of the warehousing and of the stock-management problems leads to linear programming. For this consult, for example, the work [52].

Linear programming is widely applied in the so-called 'theory of the firm'. The monograph [72] and also one chapter in the book [74] are devoted to this question.

A general survey of the various applications of linear programming in a capitalist economy is to be found in the articles [39, 89 and 143]. Use of linear programming for military purposes is the theme of the article [106].

The survey article [143] which looks into the general questions of the economic setting of linear programming (and also of the theory of games and input-output analysis) deserves to be specially noted. To this article is appended a wide-ranging bibliography containing 100 titles.

There already exists a whole series of monographs on linear programming.[1] We may mention first of all the book by Charnes, Cooper and Henderson [54] which, in spite of its small size, contains much valuable material. Linear programming is treated at some length in the books [47, 72 and 75]. An elementary exposition of linear programming, suitable for a wide circle of practical workers (although from a mathematical point of view not wholly satisfactory) is given in the book [135]. In addition one should note the supreme craftsmanship of Gass in [94]. Valuable sources of material, purely theoretical as well as applied, are the symposia on linear programming [37 and 131]. Note especially the collection [110] which is the first mature publication on linear programming and remains to this day one of the most valuable texts in this subject. Apart from this we refer to the collection [115], containing 18 articles on the theory of linear programming and its application to economic models.

Of bibliographies on linear programming we refer to that by Virginia Rohde [138] (266 titles) and the supplementary bibliography by Wagner [148] (193 titles). The fullest bibliography is the one by Gass and Vera Riley [136]. Part of the literature on the methods of solution of linear programming problems is cited in the articles of Hoffman [103] and Wagner [150].

Another line of application of mathematical methods in economics—the

[1] Introductions to linear algebra and N-dimensional geometry, necessary for a reading of the works on linear programming, can be found, for example, in S. E. Shilov's book [26].

input-output analysis [117]—was formulated somewhat earlier than linear programming. The domain of its application is quite narrow and is limited to problems not related to the finding of extremal solutions (the study of inter-sectoral, inter-regional relationships, the analysis of balance schemes, etc.).

Of the general works and textbooks on the application of mathematics to economic researches note the monograph [36], giving a full chart of the basic directions of research abroad and the more important applications.

The theory of games as a self-contained mathematical discipline can claim a history of about three decades (early works are Borel [48] 1927 and von Neumann [127] 1928). However, its systematic development began only in 1944 with the publication of the fundamental monograph of von Neumann and Morgenstern [130]. At present this theory has a number of branches, each of which has been deeply studied; in particular, intensive work was done during recent years on the numerical methods of solving the fundamental problem in the theory of matrix games. These methods of solution are dealt with, for example, in the works [46, 49, 92, 125, 129 and 137].

Extremely valuable sources on the theory of games are the collections of articles [75, 113, and 114], containing also the basic results in the theory of games and a bibliography.

Systematic research in the theory of games began somewhat later in our country. As an example, the interesting works of N. N. Vorob'ev [31, 32 and 33] may be cited.

An original method of solving extremal problems, now known as dynamic programming, was elaborated by Bellman. The majority of published results in dynamic programming is covered by the monograph [45].

The queueing theory and the theory of large-scale sample surveys—an important adjunct to the theory of probability—are usually associated with the works of A. Ya. Khinchin [18]. For foreign sources we refer to the article [139].

Various combinatorial problems, not contained within the framework of linear programming, are studied in theory of scheduling. The survey article [44], containing general bibliographical materials, can be recommended for gaining an acquaintance with this theory.

A new synthetic branch of applied mathematics has come into being comparatively recently. This is known as operations research which makes extensive use of probabilistic and statistical methods, linear programming, scheduling theory and the theory of games. In Russian there is the item [19]; apart from this we refer the reader to a complete textbook [56]. The detailed annotated bibliography on operations research [40] contains over 3,000 titles.

Russian Literature

1. Chernikov, S. N. 1953. Systems of linear inequalities. *UMN 8*, No. 2, 7-73.
2. 1956. Positive and negative solutions to systems of linear inequalities. *Matematicheskii sbornik 38*, No. 4, 479-508.
3. 1957. Homogeneous linear inequalities. *UMN 12*, No. 2, 185-192.
4. Dumler, S. A. 1958. Linear programming and its application to production. *Vestnik mashinostroeniya*, No. 10, 70-74.
5. 1957. The generalised method for calculating production cycles and stoppages. In *Voprosy ekonomimiki i organizatsii proizvodstva*, Chelyab. P.T.I.
6. Kantorovich, L. V. 1939. Mathematical methods of organisation and planning of production. Izd. LGU (2nd Ed. 1959, in present volume).
7. 1940. On an efficient method of solving some classes of extremal problems. *DAN SSSR, 28*, No. 3, 212-215.
8. 1942. On the translocation of masses. *DAN SSSR, 37*, Nos. 7-8, 227-229.
9. 1948. On a problem of Monge. *UMN 3*, No. 2, 225-226.
10. 1949. Choice of sawing schedule to maximise output of saw-products with a given assortment. *Lesnaya promyshlennost'*, No. 7, 15-17; No. 8, 17-19.
11. 1951. On the methods of analysis of several extremal problems of production planning. *DAN SSSR, 115*, No. 3, 441-444.
12. 1958. Possibilities of applying mathematical methods in problems of production planning. In *Organisation and Planning of Uninterrupted Operation of Machine-building Enterprises*, Mashgiz, 338-353.
13. 1959. *Economic Calculus of the Best Utilisation of Resources*. Izd., AN SSSR.
14. Kantorovich, L. V. and Gavurin, M. K. 1949. Application of mathematical methods in problems of analysis of freight capacity. In *Problems of Raising the Operational Efficiency of Transport*. Izd. AN SSSR, 110-138.
15. Kantorovich, L. V. and Zalgaller, V. K. 1951. *Calculation of the Rational Cutting Of Industrial Materials*. Lenizdat.
16. Kantorovich, L. V. and Rubinshtein, G. Sh. 1957. On a functional space and some extremal problems. *DAN SSSR, 115*, No. 6, 1058-1061.
17. 1958. On a space containing fully additive functions. *Vestnik LGU, 7*, No. 2, 52-59.
18. Khinchin, A. Ya. 1955. *Mathematical Methods of the Theory of Large-scale Sample Surveys*. Izd. AN SSSR.
19. Morz, F. M. and Kimbell, V. I. 1956. Methods of Operations Research. In *Sovietskoe Radio*, Moscow.
20. Remez, E. Ya. 1957. *General Numerical Methods of Chebyshev Approximation*. Izd AN SSSR, Kiev.
21. Rubinshtein, G. Sh. 1954. General solution to a system of linear inequalities. *UMN, 9*, No. 2, 171-177.
22. 1955. Problem of the extremal point of intersection of the axis with the polyhedron and its application to the study of a finite system of linear inequalities. *DAN SSSR, 100*, No. 4, 627-630.
23. 1955. On a method of investigating convex sets. *DAN SSSR, 102*, No. 3, 451-454.
24. 1955. Problem of the extremal point of intersection of the axis with the polydehron and some of its properties. *UMN, 10*, No. 4, 206-207.
25. 1957. Generalisation of the problem of the extremal point of intersection of the axis with the convex polyhedron. *DAN SSSR, 113*, No. 5, 987-990.
26. Shilov, G. E. 1956. *Introduction to the Theory of Linear Spaces*. Gostekhizdat.
27. Shkol'nik, A. G. 1940. On systems of linear inequalities. *Uchenye Zapiski Fiziko-Mathematicheskogo Fakulteta MGPI, 1*, 235-250.

28. —— 1951. Linear Inequalities. *Ibid. 16*, 127-174.
29. Tolstoi, A. N. 1939. Methods of eliminating irrational transportation in planning. *Sotsialisticheskii Transport*, No. 9, 28-51.
30. —— 1941. *Methods of Eliminating Irrational Transportation in the Construction of Operational Plans*. Transzheldorizdat.
31. Vorob'ev, N. N. 1957. Reduction of games strategies to a generalised form. *DAN SSSR, 115*, No. 5, 855-857.
32. —— 1958. State of equilibrium in a bimatrix game. *Teor. ver. i ee prim., 3*, No. 3, 318-331.
33. —— 1959. On coalition games. *DAN SSSR, 124*, No. 2, 253-256.
34. Zalgaller, V. A. 1956. New methods of construction of the sawing schedule for wood-cutting. Izd TsNII tresta *Sevzaples*, Leningrad.

Non-Russian Literature

35. Ablow, C. M. and Brigham, G. 1955. An analog solution of programming problems. *Operat. Res. 3*, 388-394.
36. Allen, R. G. D. 1957. *Mathematical Economics*, London.
37. Antosiewicz, H. A., ed. 1955. Proceedings of the Second Symposium in Linear Programming, Washington.
38. Barankin, E. W. and Dorfman, R. 1958. On quadratic programming. *Univ. of California Publications in Statistics. 2*, No. 13, 285-318.
39. Batchelor, J. H. [37] A commercial use of linear programming, 103-116.
40. —— 1959. *Bibliography on Operations Research*, 2nd ed. St. Louis.
41. Beale, E. M. L. 1954. An alternative method for linear programming. *Proc. Cambridge Philos. Soc. 50*, No. 4, 513-523.
42. —— 1955. Cycling in the dual Simplex algorithm. *Naval. Res. Logist. Quart. 2*, 269-275.
43. —— 1955. On minimising a convex function subject to linear inequalities. *Journ. Roy. Stat. Soc. 17*, 173-183.
44. Bellman, R. 1955. Mathematical aspects of scheduling theory *J. Soc. Industr. Appl. Math. 4*, No. 3, 168-205.
45. —— 1957. *Dynamic Programming*. Princeton.
46. Bohnenblust, H. F., Karlin, S. and Shapley, L. S. [113]. Solutions of discrete two-person games, 51-72.
47. Boles, J. N. 1955. Linear programming and farm management analysis. *J. Farm Econ. 37*, No. 1, 1-24.
48. Borel, E. 1927. Sur les systèmes de formes linéaires à déterminant symétrique gauche et la théorie générale du jeu. *C.R. Acad. Sci. Paris 184*, 52-54.
49. Brown G. W. [110]. Iterative solution of games by fictitious play. 374-376.
50. Charnes, A. 1952. Optimality and degeneracy in linear programming. *Econometrica, 20*, No. 2, 160-170.
51. Charnes, A. and Cooper, W. W. 1955. The stepping-stone method of explaining linear programming conditions in transportation problems. *Manag. Sci. 1*, 49-69.
52. —— 1955. Generalisations of the warehousing model. *Operat. Res. Quart. 6*, 131-172.
53. Charnes, A., Cooper, W. W. and Mellon, D. 1952. Blending aviation gasolines—a study in programming interdependent activities in an integrated oil company. *Econometrica 20*, No. 2, 139-159.
54. Charnes, A., Cooper, W. W. and Henderson, A. 1953. *An Introduction to Linear Programming*. New York.
55. Charnes, A. and Lemke, C. E. 1954. The minimisation of nonlinear separable convex functionals. *Naval. Res. Logist. Quart. 1*, No. 4, 301-312.

56. CHURCHMAN, C. W., ACKOFF, R. L. and ARNOFF, E. L. 1957. *Introduction to Operations Research*, New York.
57. DANSKIN, J. M. [37]. Linear programming in the face of uncertainty: example of a failure, 39-53.
58. 1955. Mathematical treatment of a stockpiling problem. *Naval Res. Logist. Quart*, *2*, 99-109.
59. DANTZIG, G. B. [110]. Maximisation of a linear function of variables subject to linear inequalities, 339-347.
60. [110]. Application of the Simplex method to a transportation problem, 359-373.
61. [110]. A proof of the equivalence of the programming problem and the game problem, 330-335.
62. 1954-55. Linear programming under uncertainty. *Manag. Sci. 1*, 197-206.
63. [37]. Developments in linear programming, 667-685.
64. 1956. Recent advances in linear programming. *Manag. Sci. 2*, No. 2, 131-144.
65. DANTZIG, G. B. and JOHNSON, S. [37]. A production-smoothing problem, 151-176.
66. DANTZIG, G. B., ORDEN, A. and WOLF, PH. 1955. The generalised Simplex method for minimixing a linear form under linear inequality restraints. *Pacific J. Math. 5*, No. 2, 183-195.
67. DANTZIG, G. B., FORD, U. R. and FILKERSON, D. R. [115]. A primal-dual algorithm for linear programs, 171-181.
68. DANTZIG, G. B. and FULKERSON, D. R. 1954. Minimising the number of tankers to meet a fixed schedule. *Naval Res. Logist. Quart. 1*, 217-222.
69. DANTZIG, G. B. and FULKERSON, D. R. 1955. Computation of maximal flows in networks. *Naval Res. Logist. Quart. 2*, 277-283.
70. DANTZIG, G. B., FULKERSON, D. R. and JOHNSON, S. 1954. Solution of a large-scale travelling salesman problem. *Operat. Res. 2*, 393-410.
71. DAVIS, C. 1955. Linear programming and computers I, II; *Computers and Automation*, *4*, No. 7, 10-17, No. 8, 10-16.
72. DORFMAN, R. 1951. *Application of Linear Programming to the Theory of the Firm.* Berkeley.
73. 1953. Mathematical or linear programming. *Amer. Econ. Review*, *43*, 797-825.
74. DORFMAN, R., SAMUELSON, P. A. and SOLOW, R. 1958. *Linear Programming and Economic Analysis.* New York.
75. DRESHER, M., TUCKER, A. W. and WOLFE, P. 1957. Contributions to the Theory of Games, Vol. III. *Ann. of Math. Studies*, No. 39. Princeton.
76. DUFFIN, R. J. [115]. Infinite programs, 157-170.
77. EISEMANN, K. 1955. Linear programming. *Quart. Appl. Math. 13*, No. 3, 209-232.
78. KY FAN. [115]. On systems of linear inequalities, 99-156.
79. FERGUSON, R. O. and DANTZIG, G. B. 1956. The allocation of aircraft to routes—an example of linear programming under uncertain demand. *Manag. Sci. 3*, No. 1, 45-73.
80. FISCHER, W. D. and SCHRUBEN, S. W. 1953. Linear programming applied to feedmixing under different price conditions. *Journ. of Farm Econ. 35*, 471-483.
81. FLOOD, M. M. 1953. On the Hitchcock distribution problem. *Pacific J. Math. 3*, No. 2, 369-386.
82. 1956. The travelling salesman problem. *Operat. Res. 4*, No. 1, 61-75.
83. FORD, L. R. and FULKERSON, D. R. 1957. A simple algorithm for finding maximal network flows and an application to the Hitchcock problem. *Canad. J. Math. 9*, 210-218.
84. FOULKES, J. [37]. Linear programming and structural design. 117-184.
85. FRANK, M. and WOLFE, P. 1956. An algorithm for quadratic programming. *Naval Res. Logist. Quart. 3*, No. 1-2, 95-110.

86. French, C. E., Snodgrass, M. M. and Snyder, J. C. 1958. Application of operations research in farm operations and agricultural marketing. *Operat. Res. 6*, No. 5, 766-775.

87. Freund, R. J. 1956. The introduction of risk into a programming model. *Econometrica, 24*, No. 3, 253-263.

88. Frisch, R. 1956. La résolution des problèmes de programme linéaire par le méthode du potentiel logarithmique. *Cahiers du séminaire d'économétrie* No. *4*, 7-23.

89. Gale, D. [110]. Convex polyhedral cones and linear inequalities, 287-297.

90. [115]. The closed linear model of production, 285-303.

91. Gale, D., Kuhn, H. W. and Tucker, A. W. [110]. Linear programming and the theory of games, 317-329.

92. Gale, D. and Sherman, S. [113]. Solutions of finite two-person games, 37-49.

93. Gass, S. I. [37]. A first feasible solution to the linear programming problem, 495-508.

94. 1958. *Linear Programming*, New York.

95. Gass, S. I. and Saaty, T. L. 1954. The parametric objective function. *Operat. Res. 2*, No. 3, 316-319.

96. Gass, S. I. and Saaty, T. L. 1955. Parametric objective function (Part 2)—generalisation. *Operat. Res. 3*, No. 3, 395-401.

97. Gerstenhaber, M. [110]. Theory of convex polyhedral cones, 298-316.

98. Goldman, A. J. and Tucker, A. W. [115]. The theory of linear programming, 53-97.

99. Greenwald, D. U. 1957. *Linear Programming. An Explanation of the Simplex Algorithm.* New York.

100. Gunther, P. 1955. Use of linear programming in capital budgeting. *Operat. Res. 3*, No. 2, 219-224.

101. Heller, I. [37]. On the travelling salesman problem, 643-665.

102. Hitchcock, F. L. 1941. Distribution of a product from several sources to numerous localities. *J. Math. Phys. 20*, 224-230.

103. Hoffman, A. J. [37]. How to solve a linear programming problem, 397-424.

104. Hoffman, A. J., Mannos, M., Sokolowsky, D. and Wiegmann, N. A. 1953. Computational experience in solving linear programs. *J. Soc. Industr., Appl. Math. 1*, No. 1, 17-33.

105. Jacobs, W. W. 1954. The caterer problem. *Naval Res. Logist. Quart. 1*, 154-165.

106. [37]. Military applications of linear programming, 1-27.

107. Kemeny, J. G., Morgenstern, O. and Thomson, G. U. 1956. A generalisation of the von Neumann model of an expanding economy. *Econometrica, 24*, No. 2, 115-135.

108. Koopmans, T. C. 1940. Optimum utilisation of the transportation systems. *Econometrica, 17*, supplement, 136-146.

109. [110]. Analysis of production as an efficient combination of activities, 33-97.

110. (ed.) 1951. *Activity Analysis of Production and Allocation.* New York.

111. Koopmans, T. C. and Reiter, S. [110]. A model of transportation, 223-249.

112. Kuhn, H. W. 1955. The Hungarian method for solving the assignment problem. *Naval Res. Logist. Quart. 2*, 83-97.

113. Kuhn, H. W. and Tucker, A. W. (ed.) 1950. Contributions to the Theory of Games, Vol. I. *Ann. of Math. Studies*, No. *24*. Princeton.

114. Kuhn, H. W. and Tucker, A. W. (ed.) 1953. Contributions to the Theory of Games, Vol. II, *Ann. of Math. Studies*, No. *28*, Princeton.

115. Kuhn, H. W. and Tucker, A. W. (ed.) 1956. Linear inequalities and related systems. *Ann. of Math. Studies*, No. *38*, Princeton.

116. Lemke, G. E. 1954. The dual method of solving the linear programming problem. *Naval Res. Logist. Quart. 1*, No. 1, 36-47.

117. Leontief, W. W. 1953. *Studies in the Structure of the American Economy.* New York/Oxford. Moscow, 1958.

118. McKinsey, J. C. C. 1954. *Introduction to the Theory of Games.* New York.
119. Manne, A. S. 1957. On the solution of discrete programming problems. *Econometrica, 25,* No. 1, 84-110.
120. Marcovitz, H. [37]. Concepts and computing procedures for certain x_{ij} programming problems. 509-565.
121. 1956. The optimisation of a quadratic function subject to linear restraints. *Naval Res. Logist. Quart. 3,* 111-134.
122. Morgenstern, O. (ed.) 1954. *Economic Activity Analysis.* New York.
123. Motzkin, T. S. 1936. *Beiträge zur Theorie der linearen Ungleichungen.* Jerusalem.
124. [131]. New techniques for linear inequalities and optimisation, 15-27.
125. Motzkin, T. S., Raiffa, H., Thompson, G. U. and Thrall, R. M. [114]. The double description method. 51-73.
126. Munkres, J. 1957. Algorithms for the assignment and transportation problems. *J. Soc. Industr. Appl. Math. 5,* No. 11, 32-38.
127. von Neumann, J. 1928. Zur Theorie der Gesellschaftsspiele. *Math. Ann. 100,* 295-320.
128. 1937. Über ein ökonomisches Gleichungsystem und eine Verallgeneimerung des brouwerschen Fixpunktsatzes. *Ergebnisse eines mathematischen Kolloquiums,* No. 8, 73-83. (Eng. transl. A model of general economic equilibrium.) *Rev. Econ. Studies, 13,* No. (1945-6), 1-9.
129. 1945. A numerical method to determine optimum strategy. *Naval Res. Logist. Quart. 1,* No. 2, 109-115.
130. von Neumann, J. and Morgenstern, O. 1953. *Theory of Games and Economic Behaviour.* 3rd ed. Princeton.
131. Orden, A. and Goldstein, L. (ed.) 1952. Symposium on Linear Inequalities and Programming. Washington.
132. Prager, W. 1956. On the caterer problem. *Manag. Sci. 3,* No. 1, 15-23.
133. 1957. Numerical solution of the generalised transportation problem. *Naval Res. Logist. Quart. 4,* No. 3, 253-261.
134. Radner, R. [37]. The linear team: an example of linear programming under uncertainty, 381-396.
135. Reinfeld, N. V. and Fogel, W. R. 1958. *Mathematical Programming.* New York.
136. Riley, V. and Gass, S. I. 1958. *Bibliography on Linear Programming and Related Techniques.* Baltimore.
137. Robinson, Julia 1951. An iterative method of solving a game. *Ann. of Math. 54,* 296-301.
138. Rohde, F. Virginia 1957. Bibliography on linear programming. *Operat. Res. 5,* No. 1, 45-62.
139. Saaty, T. L. 1957. Résumé of useful formulas in queueing theory. *Operat. Res. 5* No. 2, 161-200.
140. Salveson, M. E. [37]. The assembly line balancing problem, 55-101.
141. Smith, L. W. 1956. Current status of the industrial use of linear programming. *Manag. Sci.* No. *2,* 156-158.
142. Tintner, G. [37]. Stochastic linear programming with applications to agricultural economics, 197-228.
143. 1957. Game theory, linear programming and input-output analysis. *Z. Nationalökon., 17,* No. 1, 1-38.
144. Tompkins, C. B. [37]. Projection methods in calculation, 425-448.
145. Tucker, A. W. [37]. Linear inequalities and convex polyhedral sets, 569-602.
146. 1957. Linear and non-linear programming. *Operat. Res. 5,* No. 2, 244-257.
147. Vajda, S. 1957. *The Theory of Games and linear programming.* London.
148. Wagner, H. M. 1957. A supplementary bibliography on linear programming. *Operat. Res. 5,* No. 4, 555-563.

149. 1958. The Simplex Methods for beginners. *Operat. Res. 6*, No. 2, 190-199.
150. 1958. A practical guide to the dual theorem. *Operat. Res. 6*, No. 3, 364-384.
151. WALD, A. 1933-34. Über die eindeutige positive Lösbarkeit der neuen Produktionsgleichungen. *Ergebnisse eines mathematischen Kolloquiums*, No. 6, 12-20.
152. 1934-35. Über die Produktionsgleichungen der ökonomischen Wertlehre. *Ergebnisse eines mathematischen Kolloquiums*, No. 7, 1-6.

Postscript

V. S. Nemchinov

As this book is a symposium on a problem which has not been adequately covered in the Soviet literature during the last two or three decades, some of the propositions in it may not have been quite correctly understood and appreciated by a number of readers. Some clarification and critical commentary seems essential and must, in our opinion, help towards a more thorough understanding of the problems connected with introducing mathematical methods into economics.

1. The Input-Output Balance

The contribution entitled *Some Observations on Input-Output Analysis* (pp. 191-223), by Professor Oskar Lange, one of Poland's most distinguished economists, is an interesting attempt to deal with a mathematical model of an input and output balance. This type of statistical-economic construction appeared for the first time in 1923-4, when it formed an integral part of the Soviet Union's *Balance of the National Economy* for that year.

The Soviet constructions were well known to the American economist V. Leontief. Greatly influenced by the Soviet economic thinking of the 1920's, he worked out a method in his research on the United States economy over the period 1919-29, which became known in western economic literature as input-output analysis. Leontief's treatment of the gross social product is similar to ours. He includes in the aggregate social product not only deductions for amortisation but also material input in the form of used-up objects of labour or, in western economic terminology, 'intermediate products'. Such an approach differs from the western economists' conception of the social product as exceeding the national income only by the sum of the amortisation deductions.

The concepts of surplus labour and surplus product, however, are alien to Leontief, as to all bourgeois economists. The importance of Lange's work is that, transforming the expanded reproduction systems developed by Leontief, he proceeds from the Marxist concept of aggregate social product to that of material input (c), the wage fund of workers in the material sphere of production (v) and the surplus product fund (m). In analysing accumulation and demand he pays special attention to that part of the surplus product fund which is to be accumulated—capital investment. The mathematical treatment of expanded reproduction systems in Lange's work is, therefore, based on Marxist propositions. Therein lies its value.

This interesting work nevertheless calls for certain critical comments.

In passing from a two-variable model (the sphere of capital goods production and the sphere of consumers' goods production) to a multi-variable, multi-sectoral model Lange does not preserve the division of social production into two basic parts. It therefore proves impossible to compare material input in the sphere of consumers' goods production (c_2) with newly created value in the sphere of capital goods production (v_1+m_1). As Lenin pointed out, the ratio of these qualities must be important not only under the conditions of socialism but also under those of communism. This ratio determines the expanded reproduction potential. The implication is that the input-output table, as one of the main summary tables in the balance sheet of the national economy, certainly cannot be regarded as the characteristic of a dynamic model of expanded reproduction. To perform such a function it must be transformed into a balance sheet of expanded reproduction. An attempt at such a transformation has been described in my paper at the beginning of this collection (pp. 1-32). Only then can the conditions of expanded reproduction be economically analysed.

Lange has not sufficiently allowed for the economic conditions of the expanded-reproduction process and attributes excessive importance to the technological interconnexions and the technical coefficients. He consequently reaches the wrong conclusion that under socialism the price-wage-surplus product ratios are entirely determined by the technological conditions of production (p. 215).

In fact, however, the conditions governing the utilisation of labour are determined not only by the technological conditions involved but mainly by the relations of production (social-economic relations). Under capitalism, surplus value depends on the relationship between class forces. In socialist society the surplus product depends on the 'initial situation' of the national economy, that is, not so much on the ratio between the financial and material elements of reproduction of the social product as on—and this is the main factor—the economic feedbacks of social labour input and particularly, on the quality of socialist productive relations.

We hope that so distinguished an economist as Oskar Lange will in his future scientific investigations work out more exact methods of constructing an expanded reproduction balance sheet along Marxist lines, which will take into account both the role of the basic social subdivisions, on the one hand and, on the other, the social conditions of labour utilisation and the relations of production.

2. Differential Outlays of Labour, Rent and Objectively Determined Valuations

Novozhilov's paper on *Cost-Benefit Comparisons in a Socialist Economy* (pages 34 to 189) introduces the concept of differential outlays. These are due to scarcities in the means of production, insufficiency of the best natural conditions and the fact that capital investment is as a rule restricted to a definite limit. Differential outlays are thus connected with restrictions on favourable labour conditions.

Since it is impossible for the entire output of any one product or group of products to be produced exclusively under the most advantageous labour conditions, society uses a variety of labour utilisation methods simultaneously, the level of productivity being quite different in each case. From this point of view the labour utilisation methods applied in getting coal for power purposes are different in the Donbas, Kuzbas, Moscow, Pechora and Kansk-Achinsk basins. The same can be said of wheat production in the Northern Caucasus and the Ukraine or in the virgin lands in Kazakhstan and Western Siberia. Each method of labour utilisation differs from the rest, as regards level of social productivity, if the total labour input is taken into account.

The use of less favourable labour conditions, which is imposed by the relative shortage of the best conditions as compared with the socially necessary volume of production, means that under the best conditions differential outlays of labour are not equal to actual labour input but are higher than it by the amount of feedback outlays. This is because production under the most favourable conditions increases the amount of socially necessary labour needed to produce other products under less favourable conditions.

There are mathematical methods of determining differential labour outlays. One such method, that of 'resolving multipliers' has been described by Kantorovich (pp. 225-80). In his second paper (pp. 281-322) he adduces figures on the yield and expenditure of labour on three plots sown with three different agricultural crops (Table 8, p. 302). The best size of plot in terms of agricultural labour conditions is limited; so under optimum planning the best (first) plot is used for the highest-yield crop, while the third crop is sown mainly in the third (worst) plot. The plan requirements are met by the total yield of each crop and the aggregate labour input corresponds to the actual labour resources.

Let us denote the labour required to produce one centner of the product by λ_i (where i is the number of the crop) and the normative effect of the labour conditions in the different plots by μ_j (where j is the number of the plot). This effect, like the labour spent in producing the crop, is expressed in units of labour. Then, following Kantorovich's method, we can write the following five equations from the figures given in Table 8:

$$25\lambda_3-\mu_3 = 7; \quad 15\lambda_2-\mu_3 = 8; \quad 20\lambda_2-\mu_2 = 8;$$
$$20\lambda_2-\mu_2 = 10; \quad 30\lambda_1-\mu_1 = 10$$

The coefficients with λ_i are the yield in centners of a given (*i*th) crop on a given (*j*th) plot.

The labour expenditure in labour units per hectare appears on the right hand side of the equation: consequently, the whole equation is expressed in labour units. We find the insufficient, sixth, equation where the normative effect of the labour conditions is zero ($\mu_3 = 0$), that is in plot II, which has too large an area. By solving these equations we obtain the labour required to produce crops 3 and 2 (λ_3 and λ_2), equal to the actual labour costs on the worst plot (0·28 and 0·533 labour units). The differential labour outlay for crop 1 on plot I (the best), however, is higher than the mean actual expenditure (λ_1 being 0·633 of a labour unit, against an actual labour costs of 0·333 of a labour unit in all).

The differential labour outlay under the most advantageous conditions is in this case almost double the actual labour input. The difference equals the sum of the increased input of other products, produced under less favourable conditions, which society must produce in order to obtain the required (planned) volume of production.

From the equations given above we also obtain:

$$\mu_1 = 9 \text{ labour units}; \ \mu_2 = 2{\cdot}67 \text{ labour units and } \mu_3 = 0$$

These quantities express the ground rent originating from different labour conditions. It must be remembered that under socialist conditions there is not only a differential ground rent but also a differential mining rent and a differential building rent. Differential labour outlay arises also when machines of different productivity are used to manufacture different articles because the total production of those articles cannot be effected by machines giving maximum productivity and maximum economy of social labour.

Kantorovich's paper gives a method of determining the hire valuation of equipment, which is a particular kind of rental valuation.

Differential ground rent and mining rent are distribution, not production categories. They merely describe parts of the surplus product which have been isolated in the process of redistributing the national income. These estimates can in no sense be regarded as elements of social costs, as Kantorovich wrongly treats them. Moreover, rental valuations for equipment play an even more modest role: not only can they not be considered as a component part of social labour cost; they are not even an expression of differential labour outlays. Rental valuations are merely constant elements in a specific economic calculation in which allowance is made for the limitations and scarcity of particular types of equipment. They are used in solving problems relating to the proper use of resources. The criterion here is of an internal, not a national, economic nature. The use of rental valuations in drawing up production programmes enables an enterprise to reduce its production costs. Kantorovich is therefore wrong in putting rental valuations for equipment on the same level of importance as differential ground and mining rents.

The term 'differential outlays', extensively used by Novozhilov in his paper, is insufficiently precise: 'differential labour costs' would, in our opinion, be better.

Differential outlays of fuel, raw materials and electrical power are essentially differential outlays of past social labour. Differential outlay of equipment work time (for example, machine-hours) is differential outlay of labour not only because it indicates differences in the expenditure of human labour (machine-hours indicate man-hours if the number of machines manned by the workers is taken into account) but also because so-called capital costs of labour are embodied in the equipment. Capital costs of labour and of the means of labour should in general be distinguished from the operational costs of labour in current production.

This more accurate terminology obviates the erroneous conception based on regarding production costs as the input of production factors. This notion is upheld by bourgeois political economy, which maintains that the value factor is not only labour but also capital and land.

Feedback inputs of raw materials, fuel and the means of production in general are of scientific interest only because they express labour input, albeit in other ('conventional') units. It must never be forgotten that the amount of differential input is in the last analysis invariably expressed in labour units (units of social labour).

The main danger in using mathematical methods in economics is that the qualitative nature of the economic phenomena under study may be forgotten. As Lenin said, attacking idealist theories in physics and mathematics, the role of mathematics is distorted, whether in natural or in social sciences, when substance disappears and only equations remain. The comment is particularly worth keeping in mind when one is applying mathematical methods to economic phenomena. In particular, some readers acquainted with Kantorovich's treatment of objectively determined valuations in some parts of his paper (pp. 286-8, 300 and elsewhere) may imagine that these valuations spontaneously leap, so to say, out of the equations instead of being formed objectively in the course of real economic activity. We must forewarn the reader against this dangerous pitfall.

In applying Kantorovich's resolving multiplier method to the solution of economic problems one must never allow 'substance' to disappear or forget the labour nature of the social production process.

The method of objectively determined valuations (resolving multipliers) proposed by Kantorovich has a definite, fairly narrow but important sphere of application. These valuations are characteristics (indices) expressing deficiency, limitation and scarcity of available resources; they are applicable to the economic calculations involved in discovering how best to use resources so as to ensure maximum fulfilment of a production programme. Kantorovich often tends to foist a universal character on the method and there he is gravely at fault.

Nor can we ignore his narrow conception of the optimum conditions for a national economic plan. Here the main prerequisite is not that the objectively determined valuations of output and input should match; the decisive factor is that certain ratios should match—the ratio between the growth-rate of social labour productivity and the national income, the ratio between consumption and accumulation, the ratio between the growth-rates of Departments I and II of social production and so forth. Kantorovich allows himself the mistake of leaving aside these decisive aspects and is content with the condition for the existence of consistent, objectively determined valuations in the system of optimal plans.

3. National Economic Cost and the Price of Production

Novozhilov, in his paper on *Cost-Benefit Comparisons in a Socialist Economy*, puts forward a new and very important concept, 'national economic cost'. This is a transformed form of value, peculiar to socialist conditions, which expresses differential labour input in terms of cost.

Although national economic cost outwardly resembles 'production price', there are very important intrinsic differences between these two forms of transformed value. These differences call for special emphasis, since it has been widely asserted in recent Soviet economic literature that the production price retains its theoretical and practical importance even under socialist conditions. This is the view, in particular, of I. S. Malyshev, L. A. Vaag, V. D. Belkin, Z. V. Atlas, V. A. Sobol', M. V. Kolganov and others. The proposition that available fixed and working capital (in their value expression) contribute to the formation of 'production prices', through a single mean profit norm related to the value of these funds, is common to all these authors, who see in the insistent real-life demands, that not only current prime cost (enterprise costs) but also specific capital input be taken into account, a reason for necessarily retaining 'production prices' under socialist conditions too.

The significance of national economic cost, however, is that it takes into account not only these real-life requirements but at the same time also all the peculiar features of transformation of value under socialism.

National economic cost is a more perfect form of transformed value than is production price. In capitalist society the latter spontaneously takes into account differential and capital costs of labour, through the competitive mechanism. National economic cost, on the other hand, is consciously determined by society, by taking into account the objective operation of economic laws.

National economic cost has two features in common with 'production prices':

(*a*) the objective social process of the formation of both the socially necessary and the differential labour outlays in the course of expanded reproduction;

(*b*) the solution by society of extremal problems arising in the process of material production.

The nature of these extremal problems, however, is completely different: in 'production prices' the problem solved is that of maximum profit, average profit being regarded as the minimum; in national economic cost it is that of achieving maximum economy of social labour (minimum expenditure of social labour).

The part played by differential and capital costs of labour is not the same in national economic cost as in 'production prices'. The economic efficiency norms of capital inputs as well as the rent indices of the economic efficiency of favourable labour conditions, enter into national economic cost but are no longer forms of national income redistribution among particular enterprises.

Production price regulates the production of material values and the distribution of capital investment. National economic cost does not fulfil these functions. The individual enterprise bases its operations on national economic (full) costs, because these must be the basis of its delivery prices; it therefore takes into account the national criteria of economic efficiency in planning its own activity and bases its internal economy on the principles of economic accounting.

Differentiated indices of the economic efficiency of capital investment enter into national economic cost but are by nature different from the average profit norm in 'production prices'. Economic efficiency norms differentiated by branches of production can be regarded as differentiated norms of the rent payments centrally and compulsorily deducted on behalf of society in relation to the entire fixed capital apportioned to the given enterprise. The total contribution of each enterprise must in this case be assessed in advance, on the basis of the amount of fixed capital the enterprise has, so that any increase in commodity production per unit value of fixed capital may be accompanied by a reduction in cost per unit of commodity production.

In prices of production the average profit norm expresses the minimum input, on the part of the enterprise, needed in order to compensate the owner, since profit is regarded as payment for the use of capital. The profit norm characterises the mean ratio between the whole surplus product and the value of the fixed and working capital.

In the formula for national economic cost, on the other hand, the coefficient of economic efficiency of capital investment merely ensures that the enterprise returns to society the social labour expended in maintaining continuity of expanded reproduction. It does not reflect that part of the surplus product spent in maintaining the non-productive sphere, nor does it take into account any future increase in capital costs of labour. Moreover, the coefficient of economic efficiency can be differentiated with respect to the most important branches of production, whereas the profit norm is an average for the whole national economy.

These are the main differences between production price and national economic cost.

While in the main we share Novozhilov's conception of national economic cost, or, to use a better term, national economic outlays, there are a few critical remarks and points of detail to be made.

Novozhilov assumes that the overall national economic cost calculated for society as a whole in terms of the final products of the national economy, including the entire production vertical, differs from the social value of those products. He even believes that national economic cost takes differential labour outlays into account better than does social value. Nevertheless, in a socialist society the sum of national economic costs of final products of the national economy must be equal to the sum of their social values. National economic cost begins to diverge from social value only when we stop considering the national economy as a whole and start looking at conditions in particular districts or particular enterprises.

The structure of social value differs from that of national economic cost as regards the procedure for separating the value of the surplus product. Social value takes into account the surplus product created in proportion to the input of human labour. National economic cost takes into account the surplus product redistributed proportionally to differential labour outlays (corresponding to the capital-investment economic efficiency factor and the labour-efficacy of favourable conditions of social labour utilisation). The aggregate redistributed surplus product is equal to the aggregate surplus product created by labour. For the national economy as a whole, therefore, social value is a constant both in its primary and in its transformed form.

Engels wrote that society must know how much labour each article of consumption requires for its production. To determine the social value one must know the socially necessary cost of labour, in terms of man-hours and of money wages, and also the valuation of the national income created per unit of labour.

In determining the social cost of a unit of any given article of consumption allowance is made for labour input over the entire production vertical, from the labour expended in producing the raw materials and the intermediate products to the labour expended in the final production of the unit. Labour input on the tools of labour is counted to the final production in proportion to the value contributed by them.

Additional capital costs of labour over the year, necessary to society in order that the flow of expanded reproduction may be uninterrupted during the production of the article in question, must also be counted to the final product (increments to resources in the form of working capital funds, the creation of new means of labour such as machinery and machine tools, equipment, buildings and installations).

In determining national economic cost as a converted form of value, allowance for labour input for operational purposes and the the form of capital must be supplemented by allowance for differential labour outlays connected with the simultaneous and joint social use of favourable natural conditions of labour utilisation.

The following, then, are the components of national economic cost (outlays): human labour input embodied in articles and tools of labour, current human labour input, additional capital costs of labour entailed in expanded reproduction, additional differential outlays of labour entailed by the various natural conditions of labour utilisation. National economic cost (outlays) therefore differs from social value in that it distinguishes in the surplus product those parts of it set aside in the redistribution process, namely capital investment efficiency and differential rent.

Under capitalism all these categories find expression as elements of production price: transferred value, wages, returns on capital, and absolute and differential rent.

The first two of these elements, transferred value and wages, are formally common to national economic cost and the price of production. As regards the surplus product, however, national economic costs includes, not merely formally but also in reality, other redistribution categories, in the form of the economic efficiency of capital investments and the assessment of additional differential labour outlays under favourable natural conditions of labour utilisation.

Modern mathematical techniques and electronic computers enable us to determine both the social value and the national economic cost (national economic outlays) of all consumers' goods. Economists, planners, statisticians and mathematicians should now concentrate on producing the necessary initial statistical and normative data and working out algorithms for calculating value and national economic cost with modern electronic devices.

Our developing economic planning system must be provided with scientific methods of determining social value and full economic cost, which are the initial data for establishing a scientifically sound system of plan prices (retail prices for consumers' goods and delivery prices for industry and agriculture).